R86√8 432

D1545814

Experimental Approach to Electrochemistry

N. J. Selley M.A., B.Sc.

Senior Lecturer, Kingston Polytechnic (Gipsy Hill Centre)

A HALSTED PRESS BOOK

John Wiley & Sons
New York

© N. J. Selley 1977

Published in the U.S.A.
by Halsted Press, a Division
of John Wiley & Sons, Inc.
New York

First published 1977
by Edward Arnold (Publishers) Ltd., London

Library of Congress Cataloging in Publication Data

Selley, Nicholas J.

   Experimental approach to electrochemistry.

   "A Halsted Press book."
   Bibliography: p.
   Includes index.
   1. Electrochemistry. I. Title.

QD553.S37 1977   541'.37   77-7914

ISBN 0-470-99204-2

To H. G. Andrew

Printed in Great Britain

Preface

This book treats a well-established subject in a new way. The content matter corresponds approximately to the basic electrochemistry component of an ordinary degree course in chemistry, but the style of treatment will be seen to be more expansive and less mathematical than the usual student text. (No more than O-level maths is presupposed.)

The first two chapters are devoted to a closer look at topics first met with at O-level, with the intention of revealing aspects which the now more mature reader will appreciate. It is hoped that this critical approach to elementary material will be of particular interest to (present or prospective) science teachers.

After what may serve as a revision of earlier work, the book proceeds (in Chapters 3 to 6) to examine the concepts and principles shown on the diagram overleaf. The aim is full understanding rather than rapid coverage, and the practical work and exercises are designed to assist in this. The practical work does not require elaborate or expensive apparatus, and it should be possible to carry out most of it in a very modestly equipped laboratory. The book may be used either with an organized course or for private study, and in the latter case the student will benefit from the fuller 'Answers', which include indications as to the method of working the exercises.

Chapters 7 and 8 continue with an account of some analytical and technical applications of electrochemistry. The intention here is to illustrate the principles and point to the variety of their practical applications, not to give full working instructions for the techniques.

An unusual feature of the book is that the last chapter is entirely devoted to suggestions for individual research or further study projects, over a range of levels of difficulty corresponding to the rest of the book (and in some cases a little beyond). I hope that this chapter will assist lecturers who wish to develop courses based in the laboratory rather than the lecture theatre, and I believe that electrochemistry—a comparatively safe, clean and manageable subject—is a suitable area for experiments along these lines. In schools, too, there may be teachers who reject the view that the need to 'cover the syllabus' (of, say, two or three A-levels) precludes a more searching study of any one topic. They may find that this book enables their students to work individually for a couple of months, each at his

iv *Preface*

own pace, pursuing the study to the point where it becomes a real intellectual challenge.

My thanks are due to the following, for their kind assistance and advice: H. G. Andrew, Esq., Professors J. O'M. Bockris, D. J. G. Ives and A. J. B. Robertson, and Dr T. J. Stone. I am also grateful to the copyright holders for permission to reproduce certain illustrations (as acknowledged in the respective captions).

1976   N. J. Selley

Contents

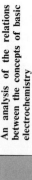

An analysis of the relations between the concepts of basic electrochemistry

On this diagram the concepts have been placed at the level where full understanding becomes possible. Many of the concepts can be *used* in routine situations at a much lower level. This applies particularly to the two equations which lie across the boundary between central and upper sections.

The boundaries are arbitrary, and correspond roughly to years of a three-year course. The lower section contains ideas first met in 'O' level and mastered by lower VI; the central area contains ideas which are normally dealt with in some depth for 'A' level; while the upper areas show concepts which, though closely associated with or even fundamental to the others on the diagram, are generally regarded as college or university level.

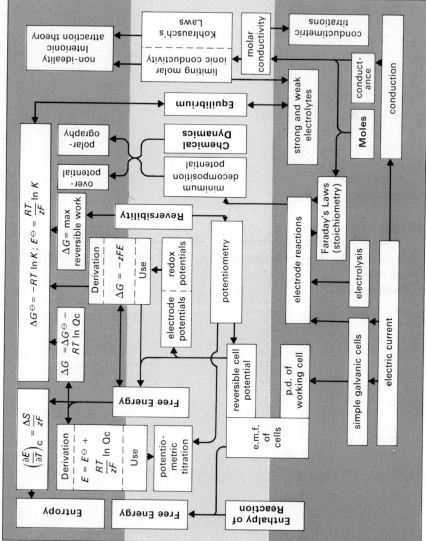

1

Some Basic Facts

1.1 Conduction

Most simple systems which conduct electricity obey Ohm's Law, though electrolytes with direct current may need a 'minimum decomposition potential' (§4.2) of up to 2 volts before significant current passes. Ohm's Law states that the current I is proportional to the potential difference E across any conductor, so:

$$E = IR \quad \text{or} \quad I = EG$$

where the constants of proportionality are called the resistance R and the conductance G. If E is measured in volts and I in amperes, R will have the unit volts per ampere, named the ohm and given the symbol Ω. Since conductance is the reciprocal of resistance, G will have the unit Ω^{-1}, at one time called the mho. Electricians, but not often chemists, refer to the reciprocal ohm as the siemens.

The resistance of a particular body is usually proportional to the length l of the path of the current, and inversely proportional to the cross-sectional area a. Therefore in order to eliminate the geometry of the particular sample, and to obtain the *resistivity* of the substance, the resistance is multiplied by (area/length). The common unit of resistivity is Ω cm.

Similarly, *conductivity* κ (kappa) is obtained by the relationship

$$\kappa = \frac{l}{a} G \quad \text{or} \quad I = \kappa E \frac{a}{l}$$

Conductivities of various substances may be compared, roughly, by means of a circuit consisting of a 6 V supply, an ammeter, a pair of copper plates, and a variable resistor (rheostat) of about 20 Ω, adjusted to give full-scale deflection on the meter when the copper plates are in contact. The 'ohms' range of any multi-range meter will serve the same purpose. For solids, similarly sized samples are pressed between the plates; and for liquids, the plates are immersed to some standard depth. More careful methods of measurement will be discussed in Chapter 3.

In the case of metallic (electronic) conductors and semiconductors, no chemical change results from the passage of the electric current, but when a current passes through an electrolyte there is invariably chemical reaction at the electrodes (for alternating current see §3.3). The electrodes are the points of contact where the

1

Table 1.1   Results of Conductivity Tests

		Examples
(i) Very good conductors	All metals (solid* or molten)	Fe, Pb, Na, Hg
(ii) Good conductors	Some compounds (electrolytes) when molten, but not solid.	NaOH, $PbBr_2$
	Some aqueous solutions of salts, acids and bases (electrolytic solutions)	NaOH, H_2SO_4, $CuCl_2$
	Graphite	C(gr)
(iii) Poor conductors	A few solid compounds (solid electrolytes)	AgCl
	Solutions of weak (slightly dissociated) electrolytes	CH_3COOH(aq), NH_3(aq)
(iv) Very poor conductors†	A few pure liquids (slightly ionized)	pure H_2SO_4, H_2O
(v) Non-conductors	Non-metal elements (solid or liquid)	S, Br_2, C (diamond)
	Molecular compounds (non-electrolytes)	CCl_4, C_6H_6, PCl_5
	Some aqueous solutions (non-electrolytes)	$C_{12}H_{22}O_{11}$, $CO(NH_2)_2$
		sucrose urea

Gases conduct only at low pressures and with high potential differences.

---

* *Powdered* metals may appear to conduct badly because of poor contact between particles.

† These very weak electrolytes show a misleadingly high conductivity unless specially purified.

current enters or leaves the electrolyte, that is, where there is a change from electronic to electrolytic conduction.

An interesting difference between metallic and electrolytic conductors is the effect of temperature on conductance. The conductance of metals decreases with rise in temperature, though the effect is not very pronounced; but the conductance of electrolytes increases markedly with increasing temperature—it may increase by a factor of five from 10°C to 80°C. (Graphite is anomolous in that it is an electronic conductor which increases its conductance on heating: carbon filament lamps exploit this property.)

The explanation of this difference is that since the conduction in electrolytes is due to the movement of ions (electrically charged atoms or molecules), there is considerable friction or viscosity within the electrolyte; so an increase in temperature, and freer movement of the particles, reduces this friction. In metals, however, conduction is due to the movement of electrons, which may be pictured as small and fast-moving compared to atoms; a rise in temperature causes an increase in the space between the atoms, which hinders the electron flow.

1.2 Ionic theory

X-ray crystallography shows that solids consist of regular crystal lattices, but while some solids have the same unit (the molecule) at all lattice points, others (the 'ionic' solids) have two (or more) different types of unit. In the ionic crystal, any one ion is surrounded by several (often 6) oppositely-charged ions, all equally distant. No ion is connected to any other particular ion: there are no ion-pairs such as Na–Cl or Ca–SO_4 in the solid (though they are predominant in the vapour).

Molecular solids melt and boil at relatively low temperatures, showing that although the bonds within molecules are strong, the forces between molecules are weak. In contrast, ionic solids melt at high temperatures, showing the strong forces between the particles—forces which are interpreted as attractions between oppositely-charged ions.

The modern theory of electrolyte solutions is due to Arrhenius, who announced it in 1883 although it was not generally accepted until 20 years later. The theory is that all solutions of 'strong' electrolytes consist entirely of ions, now known to be 'hydrated' by association with a number of solvent molecules.[1] Thus aqueous sodium chloride solution is $Na^+(aq) + Cl^-(aq)$, with no NaCl molecules; and aqueous H_2SO_4 is almost entirely $H^+(aq)$, $HSO_4^-(aq)$ and $SO_4^{2-}(aq)$.

Chemists in 1890 found this hard to accept because they did not understand the important difference between ions and atoms. Since sodium and chlorine combine so vigorously to form sodium chloride, it was difficult to believe that merely dissolving the salt in water could separate the sodium and chlorine. They were happier with an earlier theory of dynamic equilibrium between dissolved molecules and a *small proportion* of ions, since this would not require so much 'energy of ionization'.

---

[1] The manner and extent of hydration of aqueous ions are not properly understood, and only recently have techniques such as the effect of high pressure on conductivity begun to provide answers. There is little doubt, though, that the hydration arises from electrostatic attraction between the ion and either the partly negative O or the positive H atoms of appropriately oriented H_2O molecules. The energy of hydration (and hence the number of molecules held) is a function of the charge density on the ion (which increases with smaller size and higher charge).

Fortunately van't Hoff had provided evidence of a non-electrochemical kind: his vapour pressure measurements on aqueous solutions only made sense if the electrolyte solutions contained a number of particles twice or three times as great as that of these supposed 'molecules' of the electrolytes. The depression of the vapour pressure of 1 dm³ of water by 1 mole of $CaCl_2$ approached a value three times as great as that caused by 1 mole of the non-electrolyte urea; that is, the van't Hoff factor *i* was approximately 3.

However, conductivity and vapour pressure measurements on solutions of some acids and bases showed that they existed largely as molecules with only a small proportion of 'dissociation' into ions. These were the 'weak electrolytes',[2] for example ethanoic (acetic) acid, hydrocyanic (prussic) acid, or ammonia solution.

The ionic theory for strong electrolytes gained further support from the X-ray crystallography results mentioned at the start of this section. If salts are fully ionized in the solid state, it was argued, then no energy will be required to ionize them when they dissolve. This point is not so sound as it seemed at the time, and the objections are (i) the dissolution of a salt in water *is* accompanied by an energy change, which is sometimes so great an absorption of energy as to make the salt insoluble: (ii) some electrolyte solutions are formed by the dissolution of *molecular* solids or liquids (e.g. H_2SO_4, $AlCl_3$), yet these processes are often exothermic, despite the supposed 'energy of ionization'. The misunderstanding lay in supposing that the energy of ionization would be simply that for the splitting of the molecule into fragments, with the breaking of bonds; but in fact this energy is more or less regained when the anhydrous ions combine with water to give hydrated ions. This is shown in Fig. 1.1, which displays diagramatically the energy (enthalpy) changes which would accompany a *hypothetical* route from solute to solution via free gaseous anhydrous ions. It is not suggested that these free ions are actually formed as intermediates in the process of dissolution, but such an analysis helps to explain differences in the solubilities of different electrolytes.

The ionic theory readily explains the conductance of electricity through the bulk of the molten or dissolved electrolytes, since in these states the ions are free to move, and those with positive charge (the cations) will move towards the negative electrode, while the negative ions (anions) drift towards the positive electrode. But what happens when the ions reach the electrode is another matter; there must be a change from electrolytic to electronic conductance. Therefore there must be a discharge or creation of ions and an absorption or release of electrons. Fig. 1.2 shows the movement and discharge of ions during the electrolysis of ZnI_2 solution.

Practical work

A simple but convincing demonstration of the movement of ions (electrophoresis) is given by the electrolysis of copper(II) dichromate(VI) solution in a U-tube, with dilute sulphuric acid in the two limbs (Fig. 1.3). As the current passes, a blue colour

---

[2] Note that since 'weak' and 'strong' are used to indicate partial and complete dissociation, these words should not be used to mean 'dilute' and 'concentrated'.

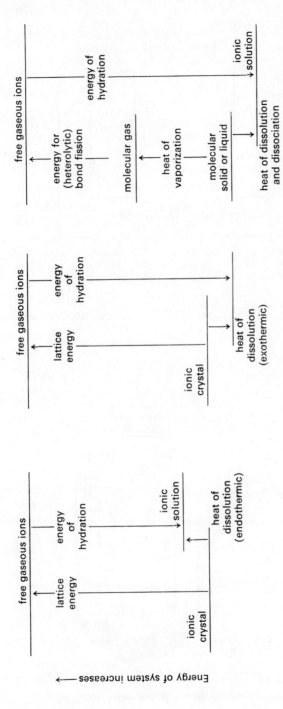

Fig. 1.1 Analysis of energy changes for hypothetical routes (thermochemical cycles) for the formation of electrolytic solutions

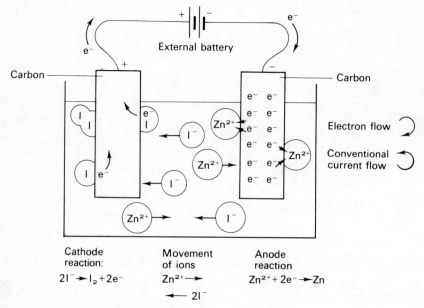

Fig. 1.2   Electrolysis. The processes comprising the electrolysis of aqueous zinc iodide solution

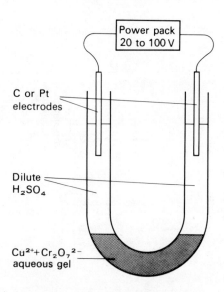

Fig. 1.3   Demonstration of the movement of ions during electrolysis

appears in the acid in which the negative electrode is placed, due to the migration of Cu^{2+}(aq) ions. Simultaneously, orange $Cr_2O_7^{2-}$(aq) ions migrate towards the positive electrode. Even with a potential difference of 20 V, about 15 minutes is required to give clearly visible colours in the limbs of the U-tube, which gives an impression of the slowness of the drift of ions. Practical details for setting up this demonstration, and also a version for individual work, are given in Appendix II (p. 194).

A similar but quicker demonstration is provided by the migration of MnO_4^- when electrodes with a potential difference (p.d.) of about 100 V d.c. are placed each side of a single crystal of potassium manganate(VII) on a filter paper moistened with dilute sulphuric acid. An elongated purple stain grows out from the crystal, on one side only.

The use of electrophoresis to separate ions for the purpose of qualitative analysis is the subject of a Project in Chapter 9.

1.3 Chemical changes in electrolysis

Unlike electronic conduction, electrolytic conduction is always accompanied by chemical changes at the electrodes. In some cases the electrodes are attacked, but in other cases they are inert, and then the chemical changes involve only the electrolyte. Despite the variety of possibilities, certain rules are obeyed in all electrolyses:

(1) At the negative electrode, electrons are forced to leave the metallic (or carbon) electrode and take part in an electron-absorbing reaction, most commonly the discharge of a metal ion or hydrogen ion. This results in the formation of a metal plating on the electrode, or the production of hydrogen gas.

(2) At the positive electrode, the externally imposed potential difference causes a deficiency of electrons, thereby encouraging any electron-releasing reaction such as the dissolution of the metal electrode in the form of positive ions, or the discharge of negative ions to produce oxygen, chlorine or another non-metal.

(3) The sum total of these 'half-reactions' at the two electrodes is a complete chemical reaction, but one which would not have occurred without the supply of electrical energy. It is often the exact reverse of a spontaneously occurring reaction.

The examples which follow will illustrate these general rules.

Examples of electrolysis

1. Molten lead bromide with inert electrodes
This experiment illustrates an electrolysis of no industrial importance, but one which provides a good introduction to the theory of electrolysis because the

results can be interpreted unambiguously. It is best shown as a lecture demonstration, preferably in a fume cupboard, because of the poisonous nature of the lead bromide fumes and bromine vapour (see Appendix II). Routine eye protection is recommended.

About 5 g dry powdered lead(II) bromide is placed in a porcelain 'boat' or crucible, supported on a drilled asbestos board. Two carbon electrodes, fixed in holes in a wooden bar, are clamped in place, touching the compound at points 1 to 3 cm apart (Fig. 1.4). The d.c. supply (about 12 to 20 V) with a rheostat and lamp in series, is switched on. No current passes.

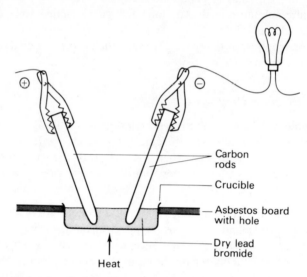

Fig. 1.4   Electrolysis of molten lead bromide

The crucible is heated with a bunsen flame; suddenly the lead bromide melts, and the lamp lights up. After this the heating effect of the current is often sufficient to keep the electrolyte molten. To confirm the point that solid lead bromide does not conduct even when in one piece, with good contact with the electrodes, the current is switched off until the melt solidifies, and then switched on again, no current passes until the solid is remelted.

The current is left on for 5 to 10 minutes. Brown fumes of bromine gas are seen at the positive electrode, and may be tested with starch–iodide paper. Silvery globules of molten lead may sometimes be seen during the electrolysis, but in any case the lead is easily found, after cooling, by dissolving away the residual lead bromide in boiling water.

Assuming that, since they appear to be unchanged, the carbon electrodes do not react, there is only one possible pair of electrode reactions:

At positive anode: Br^- ions arrive and are discharged: $2Br^- \rightarrow Br_2 + 2e^-$

At negative cathode: Pb^{2+} ions arrive and are discharged: $Pb^{2+} + 2e^- \rightarrow Pb$

2. Molten sodium chloride with inert electrodes

Sodium chloride melts at 801°C, which is inconveniently high. The addition of calcium chloride lowers this melting-point, and in the industrial process (the Downs Cell) a mixture of 42% by weight NaCl and 58% $CaCl_2$ is used, at 590°C. Despite the high proportion of Ca^{2+} ion (44 mole %) very little calcium is produced at the steel cathode; the molten sodium floats to the surface and is drawn off in an inert atmosphere. A steel grid separates the cathode region from the graphite anode, and prevents the chlorine from reaching the sodium.

The conductivity of the NaCl + $CaCl_2$ melt can be shown with the apparatus in Fig. 1.4, but no sodium metal will be obtained, since at the high temperature it oxidizes in the air instantly, unless the cathode is protected from air (e.g. by a glass sleeve). As a small-scale demonstration of the production of sodium or potassium by electrolysis, Humphry Davy's original experiment with solid NaOH or KOH may be imitated.[3]

3. Sodium fluoride solution (and other inert electrolytes) with inert electrodes

In this case the solvent is decomposed, while the ions only carry the current through the solution. About 0.5 M NaF or KF solution is electrolysed with carbon or platinum electrodes (caution: soluble fluorides are poisonous). The products are hydrogen at the (negative) cathode and oxygen at the anode; these gases may be collected and identified by simple tests. Since neither element is present in NaF, the overall electrode reactions must be the decomposition of water:

$$2H_2O(l) + 2e^- \text{ (from cathode)} \rightarrow 2OH^-(aq) + H_2(g)$$
$$H_2O(l) \rightarrow 2H^+(aq) + \tfrac{1}{2}O_2(g) + 2e^- \text{ (to anode)}$$

Since fluorides are slightly hydrolysed the solution is already alkaline, and it is not so easy to show the immediate production of H^+ and OH^- ions, whereas with a neutral solution, such as sodium sulphate(VI), this can be demonstrated readily by indicators (see §2.4).

Many electrolytes behave as inert current-carriers, with the decomposition of water as the electrolytic reaction: these include the sulphate(VI)s, nitrate(V)s, phosphate(V)s, carbonates and chlorate(VII)s of sodium, potassium, ammonium, calcium, magnesium etc.

The free acids give the same results, though the cathode reaction would be written a little differently:

$$2H^+(aq) + 2e^- \text{ (from cathode)} \rightarrow H_2(g)$$

The soluble hydroxides also give hydrogen and oxygen, and the anode reaction is probably the direct discharge of ionic OH^- initially to H_2O_2, which then decomposes catalytically at the electrode surface.[4] The overall half-equation is:

$$2OH^-(aq) \rightarrow H_2O(l) + \tfrac{1}{2}O_2(g) + 2e^- \text{ (to anode)}$$

[3] This demonstration is well shown in the TV broadcast 'Davy, Founder of Electrochemistry', in the Open University Course A202.

[4] For the effect of separating the anode from the electrolyte see Project 9.23.

Practical work

It is highly desirable that the electrolyses of various aqueous solutions should be repeated individually by all students. The apparatus is cheap and the experiments are easily set up. Details are given in §2.3 and Appendix II. As a lecture demonstration, however, or for the more accurate measurement of the volumes of gases, the electrolyses may be carried out in the Hofman Voltameter (Fig. 1.5).

4. Sodium chloride solution with inert electrodes

The products of electrolysis of aqueous sodium chloride appear to depend upon the concentration. Concentrated solutions with well separated carbon electrodes give hydrogen and chlorine, and the solution becomes alkaline around the cathode:

$$2H_2O(l) + 2e^- \text{ (from cathode)} \rightarrow 2OH^-(aq) + H_2(g)$$
$$2Cl^-(aq) \rightarrow Cl_2(g) + 2e^- \text{ (to anode)}$$

It is frequently stated that dilute solutions give $H_2 + O_2$, the dilute $Cl^-(aq)$ not being discharged; and that at intermediate concentrations a mixture of Cl_2 and O_2 is given at the anode (see Appendix II and Project 9.20).

The electrolysis of concentrated brine (NaCl) is performed industrially for the manufacture of H_2, Cl_2 and NaOH. The diaphragm cell (Fig. 6.12) is designed so that the electrolyte meets the steel cathode immediately after seeping through the

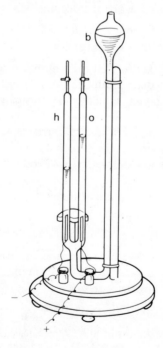

Fig. 1.5   A Hofmann Voltameter of 1870–1880

asbestos diaphragm; here the thin layer of solution is almost completely depleted of Cl⁻ ions, which are attracted back through the diaphragm towards the positive electrode, and concentrated NaOH solution drips off into the collecting troughs. The diaphragm also prevents the chlorine from diffusing through the solution and meeting the alkali, with which it would react (§6.6).

5. Copper(II) sulphate solution with inert electrodes

Oxygen is produced at the anode; the cathode (of any conducting material) is plated with copper, by discharge of Cu^{2+} ion:

$$Cu^{2+}(aq) + 2e^- \text{ (from cathode)} \rightarrow Cu(s)$$

The solution becomes more acid and, as the $Cu^{2+}(aq)$ concentration decreases, less blue in colour. The eventual increase in weight of the cathode may be used to measure the original concentration of copper ion (electrogravimetric analysis, §7.1). Solutions of Ag^+, Pb^{2+}, Sn^{2+}, Cd^{2+}, Hg_2^{2+} or Hg^{2+} and, with care, Ni^{2+}, Co^{2+} and Fe^{2+}, also give quantitative deposition of the metal at the cathode (mercury forms an amalgam). Even quite 'reactive' metals such as zinc may be deposited from solution, though some hydrogen is produced at the same time.

6. Copper(II) sulphate solution with copper electrodes

The result of this electrolysis is that the *average* concentration of copper(II) sulphate remains unchanged, while the cathode gains mass (as in example 5) and the anode is eaten away, losing a mass equal to that gained by the cathode:

$$Cu^{2+}(aq) + 2e^- \text{ (from cathode)} \rightarrow Cu(s)$$
$$Cu(s) \rightarrow Cu^{2+}(aq) + 2e^- \text{ (to anode)}$$

This experiment is often used to determine the relationship between the change of mass of the electrodes and the amount of electricity passed (§2.2). It is also the basis of copper plating (see §8.2 for practical details) and refining (§8.1).

The anode reaction is not dependent on the presence of Cu^{2+} ions already in solution, and a copper anode is almost invariably attacked during electrolysis. Anodes of lead, silver, zinc, soft iron, and in fact any soft metal except the very noble metals like gold or platinum, are usually corroded and produce the corresponding cations. Some hard metals such as steel, chromium, and nickel can act as inert anodes,[5] and then oxygen may be produced without any visible oxidation of these anodes. Cathodes, of course, may be made of any metal not attacked by water.

1.4 Summary

Electrolytic conduction is a property of molten (fused) salts and bases, and aqueous solutions of salts, acids and bases. Ions must be present, and free to move: positive

---

[5] Presumably due to the formation of thin protective but conducting oxide layers.

ions (cations) towards the cathode, which is negative in the case of electrolysis; and negative ions (anions) towards the anode. This movement of ions constitutes the electric current.

Chemical reaction must occur at both electrodes during electrolysis: at the (negative) cathode the reaction is always a reduction, that is, a half-reaction which absorbs electrons; and conversely, an oxidation always occurs at the anode.

The cathode reactions are usually either the discharge of the cation to give the metal, or the reduction of water to hydrogen, the latter being preferred to the discharge of metals more active than, say, zinc from aqueous solution. The reactive metals may, however, be produced from their molten salts.

Anode reactions may be: (1) discharge of simple anions of the less reactive non-metals; (2) oxidation of water or OH^- to oxygen; (3) attack of the anode metal.

Later in the book examples will be given of electrode reactions which involve changes of oxidation state without production or consumption of free elements (e.g. Chapter 5).

1.5 Exercises

1. The potential difference across the ends of a certain wire is 3.20 V when the current passing is 0.85 A. The wire is 300 cm long and 1.0 mm in diameter. What is (a) the resistance, (b) the resistance per cm, (c) the resistivity, and (d) the conductivity?

2. Solid sodium hydroxide does not conduct electricity, but it becomes conducting either when melted (m.p. 318°C) or when dissolved in water. Solid malonic acid $CH_2(COOH)_2$ does not conduct, *nor* does molten malonic acid (m.p. 135°C); but the aqueous solution is a conductor. Explain the difference.

3. A saturated solution of calcium hydroxide (0.16 g per 100 g water) has a conductivity of less than 1/200 that of saturated calcium chloride solution (74 g per 100 g water). Is this evidence that calcium hydroxide is a weak electrolyte?

4. Predict the products of the following electrolyses, and write the half-equations for the electrode reactions:

   (i) Lead(II) nitrate solution with carbon electrodes;
   (ii) Lead(II) nitrate solution with a carbon anode and a lead cathode;
   (iii) Lead(II) nitrate solution with a lead anode and a carbon cathode.

5. If sea-water contains the following ions: Na^+, K^+, Mg^{2+}, Cl^-, Br^-, and HCO_3^-, what products would you expect from the extended electrolysis of this mixture, with carbon electrodes?

6. Explain the following observations: A p.d. of about 2 V was applied across two copper wires dipping near together in dilute sulphuric acid. At first a gas was given off at *one* of the wires, but after a time this ceased, although the current did not diminish.

2

Electrode Reactions

2.1 Redox half-equations

When a current is passed through an electrolyte, causing electrolysis, the overall chemical reaction is a reduction–oxidation. The reaction is one which would not have occurred without the current, and since the products appear at separate electrodes there is little doubt that they are the result of electron gain or loss. For example, the result of the electrolysis of molten lead(II) bromide (§1.3) was:

$$PbBr_2 \rightarrow Pb + Br_2$$

In fact the same products would have resulted from the electrolysis of an aqueous solution of the salt. The separate electrode reactions are written thus:

$$Pb^{2+} + 2e^- \rightarrow Pb \quad \text{(reduction, at cathode)}$$
$$2Br^- \rightarrow Br_2 + 2e^- \quad \text{(oxidation, at anode)}$$

The converse of electrolysis is galvanic cell action, and this comes about when an oxidant is present at one electrode of a cell, and a reductant at the other. Lead and bromine would be an example, and the reactions would be the reverse of those given above. One difference is that in this case the reaction could be brought about quite independently of the cell, merely by bringing the reactants into contact, and it might not then be suspected that the reaction involved electron transfer.

Most redox reactions encountered in volumetric analysis, for example, can be shown to take place by the giving and receiving of electrons, simply by having the two reagents separately in the limbs of a U-tube, with a platinum (or carbon) electrode in each. A milliammeter will show a current flowing, with the electrons coming from the electrode in the reductant (Fig. 2.1). After some time there will be signs that the reaction is occurring 'at a distance'. For example, if the two solutions are potassium iodide and iron(III) chloride, iodine will be seen around one electrode, and in the region of the other electrode ionic iron(II) may be detected by its reaction with hexacyanoferrate(III).

The reactions at the two electrodes, though separate in space, are not independent of each other, the amounts of reaction being directly related by the necessity for the number of electrons leaving the electrolyte in given time to equal the number entering. No electricity accumulates in any electrolytic or galvanic cell (not even in an 'accumulator'!); in other words, the capacitance is negligible.

13

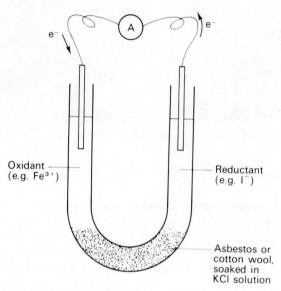

Fig. 2.1 Demonstration of electron transfer

The consequence of this is that the stoichiometric equation for the total chemical change can be separated into a pair of half-equations, which are equations containing electrons, and so representing either a reduction (electrons on left) or an oxidation (electrons on right). The half-equations must each contain the same number of electrons, but on opposite sides. This useful device can be applied to any redox reaction, whether taking place electrochemically or not.

For example, the reaction between potassium iodide and iron(III) chloride may be considered to be the sum of the following half-reactions:

$$2I^- \rightarrow I_2 + 2e^- \quad \text{(oxidation)}$$
$$Fe^{3+} + e^- \rightarrow Fe^{2+} \quad \text{(reduction)}$$

Because the numbers of electrons gained and lost must be equal, the second half-equation must be doubled (or the first one halved) before addition, giving as the full ionic equation:

$$2Fe^{3+} + 2I^- \rightarrow 2Fe^{2+} + I_2$$

This procedure (or the similar one using oxidation numbers) provides a useful means of balancing redox equations, which can be very awkward to do by simple inspection.

Worked example

'Obtain the balanced equation for the reaction of potassium manganate(VII) (permanganate) with hydrogen peroxide, in acidic aqueous solution.'

The student may care to spend a few minutes trying to balance the following by 'trial and error'

$$MnO_4^- + H_2O_2(+H^+ ?) \rightarrow Mn^{2+} + H_2O + O_2$$

In the systematic method, the two half-equations are considered separately, and balanced for atoms and then for charges, thus:

$$MnO_4^- + H^+ + e^- \rightarrow Mn^{2+} + H_2O \quad \text{(unbalanced)}$$

The four oxygen atoms lost by the MnO_4^- will require $8H^+$ to form $4H_2O$:

$$MnO_4^- + 8H^+ + ze^- \rightarrow Mn^{2+} + 4H_2O$$

Now from charge balance (conservation of charge) it follows that $z = 5$.
Similarly we arrive at the half-equation for the oxidation:

$$H_2O_2 \rightarrow 2H^+ + O_2 + 2e^-$$

So the equation for the oxidation of H_2O_2 by MnO_4^- is derived by adding the half-equations, each multiplied through to make the numbers of electrons equal:

$$2MnO_4^-(aq) + 16H^+(aq) + 10e^- \rightarrow 2Mn^{2+}(aq) + 8H_2O(l)$$

$$\underline{5H_2O_2(aq) \rightarrow 10H^+(aq) + 5O_2(g) + 10e^-}$$

$$2MnO_4^-(aq) + 5H_2O_2(aq) + 6H^+(aq) \rightarrow 2Mn^{2+}(aq) + 8H_2O(l) + 5O_2(g)$$

Two qualifying points should be noted:

(1) The fact that any redox reaction can be written as a pair of half-equations should not be taken to imply that the unconstrained reaction *necessarily* takes place by a mechanism of transfer of free electrons (e.g. there could be, in some cases, oxygen atom transfer).

(2) The state of the electron in the half-equation is not defined. Hydrated electrons are known in the free state, but are highly reactive and short-lived, and it is not this state which is implied by the symbol e^- in redox half-equations. This uncertainty makes any energy calculations from a *single* half-equation meaningless. See also p.73 .

2.2 The stoichiometry of electrolysis (Faraday's Laws)

If the stoichiometry of redox reactions is understood (see §2.10 q.1) only one new principle is required in order to extend the calculations to include electrolysis— namely, the idea of the mole of electrons. An electron is a particle with a definite mass (though this is negligible in comparison with atoms), and a definite charge $e = 1.602 \times 10^{-19}$ coulombs. By historical misfortune, the type of electrostatic charge which is now known to result from an excess of electrons was arbitrarily designated 'negative', so when a current flows across any potential difference, the electrons move from negative to positive.

Since electrons are (or at least behave like) separate particles, it is meaningful to speak of one mole of them—that is, L electrons, where L is 'Avogadro's number', the number of ^{12}C atoms in 12.000 g of ^{12}C, found by experiment to be about 6.023×10^{23}. This gives a value for the Faraday constant, F, which refers to the charge on one mole of electrons:

$$F = Le = 6.023 \times 10^{23} \times 1.602 \times 10^{-19} \text{ C mol}^{-1} = 9.649 \times 10^4 \text{ C mol}^{-1}$$

The value of F is normally taken as 96 500 C mol^{-1}.

Stoichiometric equations, though written as if they represent changes among a few atoms, molecules or electrons, always have another meaning. If they are (mentally) multiplied through by L, they then represent changes in the molar amounts of substances. Thus $O_2(g) + 2H_2(g) \rightarrow 2H_2O(g)$ contains the information that '2 moles of steam are formed when 1 mole O_2 reacts with 2 moles H_2', and this could be related to masses or volumes of the participants.

In exactly the same way, the half-equation:

$$Cu^{2+}(aq) + 2e^- \rightarrow Cu(s)$$

tells us that 2 moles of electrons, or $2 \times 96\ 500$ C of electricity, can bring about the production of 1 mole, or 63.55 g, of copper metal.

Worked example

A current of 250 mA was passed for 22 minutes 20 seconds through a 'copper coulometer' containing copper electrodes in acidified $CuSO_4(aq)$, with the addition of 5% ethanol to inhibit reoxidation of the deposited copper. What changes of mass of the electrodes would be expected?

$$\text{Quantity of electricity passed} = 250 \text{ mA} \times \frac{10^{-3} \text{ A}}{\text{mA}} \times ((22 \times 60) + 20)\text{s}$$

$$= 335 \text{ A s} \equiv 335 \text{ C}$$

$$\therefore \text{ Amount of electrons} = \frac{335}{96\ 500} \text{ mol}$$

The half-equations are: (cathode) $Cu^{2+}(aq) + 2e^- \rightarrow Cu(s)$

(anode) $Cu(s) \rightarrow Cu^{2+}(aq) + 2e^-$

$\therefore$ Loss of Cu at anode = gain of Cu at cathode = $\frac{1}{2}$ mole Cu per mole of electrons.

$$\therefore \text{ Changes in mass} = 63.55 \frac{g}{\text{mol Cu}} \times \frac{\frac{1}{2} \text{ mol Cu}}{\text{mol electrons}} \times \left(\frac{335}{96\ 500}\right) \text{mol electrons}$$

$$= 0.11 \text{ g}.$$

There are two important variations of this calculation:

(a) To calculate the amount of electricity from the change of mass of the electrodes. This can be used to check or calibrate an ammeter. It was also the basis of the *definition* of the international ampere, which was the flow per second of the quantity of electricity which caused a loss of 0.001 118 g from a silver anode (this definition is now obsolete, having been replaced by the 'Absolute' ampere, based on the force between parallel current-carrying conductors).

(b) Measurements of the amount of electricity *and* mass changes of substances involved may be used to deduce the half-equation.for the electrode process. This applies particularly when the product may be in one of several possible oxidation states.

To illustrate this pass a current in series through (1) an ordinary copper coulometer containing copper electrodes in acidified copper(II) sulphate solution; and (2) copper electrodes in boiling alkaline sodium chloride solution (Appendix II). In the second cell a red solid appears at the anode but does not adhere, and the loss of copper per mole of electrons passed is found to be 63 g. Therefore in the alkaline solution the anode half-equation must contain one electron for every atom of Cu, and the product must be a Cu(I) compound, probably hydrated Cu_2O:

$$2Cu(s) + 2OH^-(aq) \rightarrow Cu_2O(s) + H_2O(l) + 2e^-$$

Faraday's laws

Faraday announced at least three important laws of electrolysis. The first (1832) was actually a by-product of researches aimed at proving the essential identity of 'galvanism' (electricity from a galvanic cell) and electricity from an electrostatic friction machine. Almost incidentally, Faraday noticed that 'The chemical power'[1] of a current of electricity is in direct proportion to the absolute quantity of electricity which passes'. This law is the basis of our treatment of electrode processes as gain or loss of electrons; but although it might have suggested the possibility of particles of electricity associated with atoms, Faraday had no faith in the atom of 1832 (hard, spherical, and incapable of transmitting any influence except during contact). General recognition of the logical inevitability of the electron had to wait until after Helmholtz's famous Faraday Lecture to the Chemical Society in 1881.

Faraday seems to have attached considerable importance to his next law, of April 1833: 'A New Law of Electric Conduction: the assumption of conducting power during liquefaction, and the loss of it during congelation'. He observes that compounds become conducting (if at all) only when they are melted (e.g. $PbBr_2$, §1.3). This was a useful generalization, though recently exceptions have been found (p. 30).

The law which is known as the second was published in December 1833 in an extended discussion, of which the following sentence may be taken as representative:

'The equivalent weights of bodies are simply those quantities of them which contain equal quantities of electricity, or have naturally equal electric powers; it being the electricity which *determines* the equivalent number, because it determines the combining force.'

[1] The word 'power' here means 'measure of the extent of change caused', and not the modern 'rate of transfer of energy'.

Subsequently the law, as stated in textbooks, was made more operational, or theory free, but now that chemical equivalents have fallen out of use the wording becomes problematical, and there is little point in perpetuating it. The *principle* of Faraday's great discovery is implicit in the modern interpretation of electrode reactions, given earlier in this section. Specifically, from the half-equation

$$2H^+(aq) + 2e^- \rightarrow H_2(g)$$

it is seen that 2 moles of electrons produce 1 mole, or 2 grammes, of hydrogen molecules; therefore one mole of electrons can produce 1 g H_2, i.e. 'one equivalent'. For any other element, the half-equation will be one of the following:

$$M^{z+}(aq) + ze^- \rightarrow M(s) \quad \text{(metals)}$$
$$\text{or } X^-(aq) \rightarrow \tfrac{1}{2}X_2 + ze^- \quad \text{(non-metals)}$$

In either case, 1 mole of electrons (sometimes called 'one Faraday') will produce $1/z$ mole of the element, with a mass equal to (atomic mass)$/z$.

It is interesting that this law, which is the foundation for almost all subsequent study of electrodeposition, was announced on the basis of only three successful experiments, one poor result, and five attempts which failed to work. The reason is that Faraday thought that only fused salt electrolyses could give unambiguous quantitative evidence. The contemporary theory of aqueous electrolysis was that the current was carried by chains of water particles (§3.9); any metal produced *from solution* could be argued to be a product of the reaction of hydrogen (the 'primary product' of electrolysis) with the salt. So the theory would merely prove, in every case, that *hydrogen* was liberated in equal amounts by equal amounts of electricity—a fact already known from the First Law. So Faraday proved his new law with three examples: fused $SnCl_2$, $AgCl$, and $PbCl_2$; he tried but failed to electrolyse fused Sb and Bi compounds; and his results for K were erratic.

2.3 Practical work on simple electrolysis

Required   Electrolysis cell as in Fig. 2.2, or a pair of J-shaped electrodes.
10 cm^3 measuring cylinder.
Neutral NaCl and Na_2SO_4 solutions.
Litmus papers.
6 V d.c. supply (e.g. battery charger).
Milliammeter (0–500 mA).
Rheostat, about 1 A, 100 Ω.

Expt. 2–1.1. Half-fill the cell with tap water, and with the rheostat half in the circuit, switch on the 6 V d.c. Note the meter reading, and observe the electrodes. (Gas evolution is a more sensitive current detector than many milliammeters!)

Place two test-tubes full of water in position over the electrodes, then add a few cm^3 of dilute sulphuric acid to the cell, and stir. Collect the gases evolved, note the relative volumes, and the polarity of the electrodes. Identify the gases. Write the electrode half-equations.

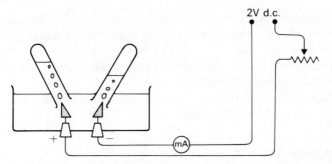

Fig. 2.2 Apparatus for simple electrolysis (see Appendix II for construction)

Expt. 2–1.2. Add a little potassium iodide solution to the very dilute sulphuric acid in the electrolysis cell. Note the different anode reactions at high and low currents, after adjustment of the rheostat. Suggest an explanation.

Expt. 2–1.3. Empty the cell and rinse the electrodes. Soak a piece of red litmus paper, and one of blue, in neutral sodium sulphate solution, and lay them in turn across both electrodes while the current is passed for a few seconds. Note any acidity or alkalinity resulting from the electrolysis. Explain this by appropriate half-equations. State a simple empirical rule for discovering the polarity of a d.c. supply using litmus paper soaked in tap-water ($CaSO_4$ solution).

Repeat the experiment, but use sodium chloride (not sulphate) solution. Note and explain any differences.

Expt. 2–1.4. Quantitative electrolysis. Starting with fresh water in the cell, fill and invert a 10 cm^3 measuring cylinder (or a test-tube graduated at 10 cm^3). Clamp the cylinder so that it will collect all the hydrogen evolved at the cathode, but before moving the cathode into position, switch on, add 50% sulphuric acid and stir, until the current is in the range 100 to 400 mA, and accurately measurable on the meter provided. Use the rheostat to adjust the current if necessary.

Move the cathode into position, note the time, and read the current. Keep the electrodes and receiver still, to ensure a steady current. Measure the time required for 10 cm^3 hydrogen to be produced. Record the temperature and barometric pressure.

Calculate the amount n (in moles) of H_2 collected, using the ideal gas equation $pV = nRT$, where $R = 8.31$ J K^{-1} mol^{-1}; T is the 'absolute' temperature calculated

Table 2.1 Saturated Vapour Pressure of Water

$\theta/°C$	10	15	20	25	30
$p/$mm Hg	9.2	12.7	17.5	23.8	31.8
$p/$N m^{-2}	1230	1700	2330	3170	4250

from the 'common' temperature θ thus: $T = (\theta/°C + 273)$ K, and p = partial pressure of H_2, that is, atmospheric pressure minus the saturated vapour pressure of water (see Table 2.1). Since $1 J = 1 N m$, p should be expressed in $N m^{-2}$ and V in m^3. For the conversion of barometer readings, take $1 mm Hg = 133.3 N m^{-2}$, or 1 standard atmosphere $= 101\ 325\ N\ m^{-2}$.

Also calculate the quantity of electricity passed, and hence the quantity (in coulombs) which would produce 1 mole H_2.

2.4 Concentration changes in aqueous electrolysis

For this qualitative discussion of concentration changes (a quantitative treatment, leading to transport numbers, will follow in Chapter 3), let us consider the cathode and the anode to be in separate compartments, divided by a porous partition which will allow the movement of ions under the influence of the electric forces, but which prevents random diffusion.

Several common examples of electrolysis will be analysed, to show that the visible production of solids or gases at the electrodes are not the only changes.

(a) $CuSO_4(aq)$, Cu electrodes.

Cathode	Partition	Anode
$Cu^{2+} + 2e^- \rightarrow Cu$	$Cu^{2+} \leftarrow \quad SO_4^{2-} \rightarrow$	$Cu \rightarrow Cu^{2+} + 2e^-$

During the passage of 2 moles of electrons, the cathode compartment loses 1 mole Cu^{2+} at the electrode. Meanwhile some Cu^{2+} ion arrives through the partition, but since the movement of charge by migration of ions must equal 2 moles e^-, and both Cu^{2+} and SO_4^{2-} ions carry two charges, the total movement of both ions *together* is 1 mole, so the arrival of Cu^{2+} is something less than 1 mole. Therefore the cathode compartment diminishes in $CuSO_4$ concentration. By similar reasoning, the anode compartment gains in concentration.

(b) $Na_2SO_4(aq)$, Pt electrodes.

Cathode	Partition	Anode
$2H_2O + 2e^- \rightarrow H_2 + 2OH^-$	$2Na^+ \leftarrow \quad SO_4^{2-} \rightarrow$	$H_2O \rightarrow \frac{1}{2}O_2 + 2H^+ + 2e^-$

At the cathode, Na^+ ion arrives but is not discharged (§6.4); instead, water is reduced to H_2 and OH^- ion. So the cathode region becomes alkaline (basic), as can be shown by indicators. In the anode compartment, SO_4^{2-} ion arrives, carrying the current, but again the water reacts more readily, being oxidized to $O_2 + H^+$, and so the acidity increases.

From the stoichiometry, the amount of OH^- produced at the cathode must equal the amount of H^+ produced at the anode, so if the partition were removed and the solution stirred, its pH would be the same as before electrolysis.

The stoichiometry also determines the 2:1 ratio of H_2 to O_2 by amount and hence (by Avogadro's Law) by volume.

A variation of the experiment, discovered by Humphry Davy, intrigued a generation of chemists. Three containers were set up as in Fig. 2.3. Each solution also contained an indicator such as litmus. It was known that Na_2SO_4 appeared to be separated into NaOH and H_2SO_4, as discussed above. But in this variation, when the anode compartment became acid, it had to be assumed that the H_2SO_4 had *passed through the NaOH* without combining with it. A mystery indeed!

(c) NaCl solution with C electrodes.

Cathode   Partition   Anode

$$2H_2O + 2e^- \rightarrow H_2 + 2OH^- \quad \underset{\longleftarrow}{2Na^+} \quad \underset{\longrightarrow}{2Cl^-} \quad \begin{cases} 2Cl^- \rightarrow Cl_2 + 2e^- \\ H_2O \rightarrow \tfrac{1}{2}O_2 + 2H^+ + 2e^- \end{cases}$$

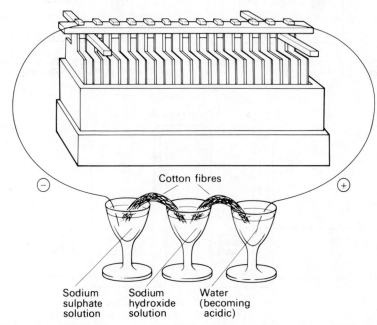

Cotton fibres

$\ominus$ $\oplus$

Sodium sulphate solution   Sodium hydroxide solution   Water (becoming acidic)

Fig. 2.3 Based on a Plate from *Conversations on Chemistry* by Mrs Jane Marcet, 1822: Voltaic battery of improved construction with instances of chemical decomposition by the same.

2.5 Galvanic cells

The basic difference between galvanism and electrolysis is this: the galvanic cell reaction must be capable of proceeding unaided (and not necessarily in the cell at all), and so the free energy of reaction ΔG (§4.7) must be negative. In contrast, the reaction brought about by electrolysis would not occur spontaneously, since it has a positive ΔG, and so there must be an external source of electrical energy in the circuit, to force electrons to flow through the electrolytic cell.

Otherwise there are many similarities. As we have seen (§2.1) the electrode processes are in each case a pair of oxidation–reduction reactions, and the stoichiometry is exactly the same.

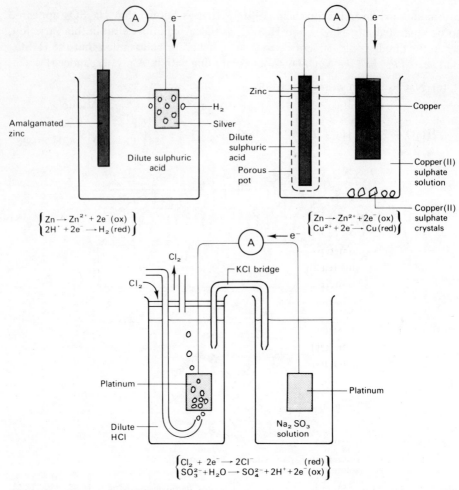

Fig. 2.4   Some galvanic cells (see text)

A galvanic cell can be based on any reaction which can occur spontaneously, at a reasonably rapid rate, to produce work. We will consider three examples:

(1) $\qquad Zn(s) + 2H^+(aq) \rightarrow Zn^{2+}(aq) + H_2(g)$

(2) $\qquad Zn(s) + Cu^{2+}(aq) \rightarrow Zn^{2+}(aq) + Cu(s)$

(3) $Cl_2(aq) + SO_3^{2-}(aq) + H_2O \rightarrow 2Cl^-(aq) + SO_4^{2-}(aq) + 2H^+(aq)$

In order to generate electricity from these reactions it is essential that the reactants should be kept apart, to prevent direct reaction; or that conditions be chosen which make direct ('local') action very slow.

If one of the reactants is a metal, it may act as an electrode. Otherwise some inert electronic conductor (platinum, gold, or carbon) must dip into the solution. For keeping solutions apart, a porous partition (e.g. unglazed earthenware) is used for practical cells, or a salt bridge in experimental cells. The concentration of any reactant can be maintained at saturation, if desired, by having excess solid present or, in the case of a gas, by bubbling it past or through the electrode.

These principles are followed in the design of cells making use of the three reactions mentioned above. The half-equations for the electrode reactions are given below each cell.

In the first two cells the zinc rods are amalgamated (by being rubbed with mercury(I) nitrate solution) to make direct action with the acid very slow. Hydrogen is more readily released at a silver surface, where the overpotential is lower than on zinc; and so the first cell needs no partition.

Zinc, even when amalgamated, reacts with ionic copper(II) by local action, so in the second cell the zinc is in dilute sulphuric acid, and separated from the copper sulphate solution by a partition. The reduction of Cu^{2+}(aq) to Cu takes place at a copper electrode (sometimes the whole container is of copper, acting as a large electrode); and as this reaction occurs more readily than the reduction of H^+(aq) ion, the second cell is more efficient than the first. It is in fact the Daniell Cell, once widely used for powering telegraphs.

The third cell is likely to be of theoretical interest only, probably for the purpose of measuring the cell potential. Little current will be taken from it, so the internal resistance need not be kept low; therefore a salt bridge of potassium chloride solution ensures that no dissolved chlorine meets the sulphate(IV).

In each case the *polarity* of the cell may be deduced from a knowledge of the cell reaction (§2.1). At the anode oxidation occurs, which produces electrons: these go into the metallic part of the circuit, and cause the anode of any galvanic cell to appear negative to a meter connected across the cell. Similarly, the reduction half-reaction at the cathode absorbs electrons, and tends to leave the cathode positively charged. Thus the relationship between polarity and the location of oxidation and reduction (and hence the names of the electrodes) differs for electrolytic and galvanic cells, as summarized in Table 2.2.

Table 2.2 Electrolytic and Galvanic Cells

Type of cell	Electrons enter cell at	Reduction half-reaction at	Polarity of cathode	Thermodynamic nature of cell reaction
Galvanic	Cathode	Cathode	Positive (self-generated)	Spontaneous
Electrolytic	Cathode	Cathode	Negative (imposed by external source)	Non-spontaneous

2.6 Electrode potentials

The measurable potential difference across any galvanic cell is found to decrease as the current drawn from the cell is increased. It is usual to regard the cell as having an electromotive force (e.m.f.) which is the potential difference (p.d.) which it would maintain if the transformation of chemical to electrical energy were taking place with maximum efficiency. This state of affairs is approached when the current flowing is infinitesimal—for instance when the p.d. is measured by an electronic voltmeter or a potentiometer (§4.2). An ordinary moving-coil voltmeter is actually an ammeter in series with a resistor, and draws some current from the cell: hence the p.d. measured by a cheaper meter (with a lower resistance) may be considerably less than the e.m.f. (see §4.8). Since potential differences of working cells depend upon the physical design (especially internal resistance) of the cell and the meter, it is convenient to define the *cell potential* as the p.d. which is measured at almost zero current—in other words, the e.m.f.

Cells of the Daniell cell type could be constructed (in theory) of any pair of metals, each in a solution of one of its salts. For example, zinc in zinc sulphate paired with silver in silver nitrate (both solutions 1 M), gives a cell potential of 1.56 V with the zinc negative. Similarly, zinc is 1.10 V negative to copper; and copper is 0.46 V negative to silver.

Though only potential *differences* between pairs of electrodes can be measured, the results are consistent with the proposal that each electrode has its own potential (on some arbitrary scale) which is constant, regardless of the other electrode with which it is paired.

So by pairing all metal/metal–ion half-cells against one chosen half-cell, an electrode potential series could be constructed. A metal high in the series will be negative compared to any lower metal, because its tendency to form ions, and release electrons, will be the greater. Note that an element which forms a negative electrode has a strong tendency to change to its positive (ionic) form, and is therefore said to be *electropositive*.

Besides the demonstration of the electrode potential series directly, two other experiments are commonly included at the elementary level. These are the displacement of metals and the reaction of metals with acids (see Appendix II). For example, pieces of zinc, iron and other metals react with dilute copper(II) sulphate(VI) solution to produce copper metal, but silver has no effect; but all these same metals *and* copper will displace silver from silver nitrate(V) solution. By considering the extent and speed of such displacement reactions, a series is drawn up such that any higher member can displace the lower ones from their salts.

2.7 The electrochemical series

The electrochemical (or electrode potential) series has come to be regarded as a unifying principle in elementary chemistry. Fig. 2.5 is taken from the widely used

	Combustion	Action on WATER	Action on ACIDS	Reduction of heated oxides by hydrogen	Action of heat on oxides	Action of water on oxides	Character of hydroxides	Character of carbonates	Action of heat on nitrates	Solubility of sulphides
K		Decompose cold water				Oxides react to form hydroxides	Soluble in water therefore bases and alkalis	Soluble and not decomposed by heat	Nitrates decompose to nitrite	Sulphides soluble in water
Na										
Ca	Burn in air to oxygen readily		Attacked by dilute acids	NOT RE-DUCED	Stable when heated					
Mg		Decompose steam at red heat								Sulphides insoluble in water but soluble in dilute hydrochloric acid
Al							Hydroxides insoluble bases only	Insoluble and decomposed by heat	Nitrates decompose to oxide	
Zn										
Fe						Oxides do not react with water				
Pb	oxidize when heated in air	Do not decompose water or steam at red heat	Attacked by oxidizing acids	RE-DUCED						
Cu										Sulphides insoluble in water and dilute hydrochloric acid
Hg					De-compose		Hydroxides not formed	Carbonates unstable	Nitrates decompose to metal	
Ag	Unaffected by oxygen		Not attacked							
Au										

Fig. 2.5 The electrochemical series used as an aid to systematization

'School Certificate Chemistry'[2] by Holderness and Lambert, who were the first authors to make extensive use of the E.C.S. in an intermediate text. It may be seen from this table that reactions as diverse as the attack of metals by acids and the decomposition of carbonates by heat have been brought together by means of the E.C.S.

In the Nuffield Chemistry Sample Scheme, Topics A7 and B10 (1975), the 'reactivity series' is established from the 'vigour' of reaction of the metals with oxygen, and then used for predictions of the power of carbon to reduce oxides, and the order of displacement of metals from their salts.

It is right to ask how closely 'reactivity' is truly related to electrode potential, and how much of the agreement is loose or even fortuitous. I would suggest that the term is ambiguous in that it glosses over the distinction between the rate of reaction and the position of equilibrium to which the reaction tends to proceed.

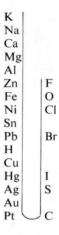

It is true that the Nuffield Scheme refers to the series as one of 'apparent reactivity', but this hardly makes for clarity since the added implication is not discussed. The terms 'reactive' and 'vigorous' are subjective judgments, being based on direct observation only, and are inevitably a composite of 'fast' and 'exothermic', neither of which qualities is *necessarily* predictable from electrode potentials (see §4.7). Yet it does appear that, for the comparison of reactions of a similar kind, under closely similar conditions, qualitative predictions from the E.C.S. are very often correct. And when they are not, this may be explained away in terms of factors such as hardness, surface oxide films, insolubility of the product, etc.

Even after the point about rate has been made, and it is recognized that predictions from electrode potentials should, strictly, be kept to tendency (feasibility), there remains the question of how widely the E.C.S. is valid. In the case of electron-transfer reactions in aqueous solution, the connection is definite enough: if metals

[2] Now entitled *A New Certificate Chemistry* (4th edn.). Fig. 2.5 reproduced by kind permission of the publishers, Heinemann Educational Books Ltd.

A and B are both placed in a mixture of soluble salts of A and B, the metal A which is higher in the E.C.S. (i.e. has the more negative reduction potential) will *tend* to dissolve, and ionic B will tend to be reduced to metallic B. The displacement series can be extended to cover the reaction of metals with non-oxidizing[3] acids, since the reduction of the hydrogen ion to hydrogen gas is closely similar to the reduction of metal ions. However there is a reluctance of hydrogen to react or to be produced (at ambient temperatures) which is measured by its high overpotential (§6.2) of about 0.5 V, so that the reaction of metals above H in the E.C.S., but by less than 0.5 V, is negligibly slow. That is, Co, Ni, Sn, Pb and Cd fail to produce H_2 from 1 M acids at 298 K. Conversely, hydrogen does not displace metals such as copper from their salts under normal circumstances, though reaction can be shown to occur under pressure (see Appendix II for a description of H. G. Andrew's 'hydrogen bomb') or at a catalyst.

When the E.C.S. is used for predictions concerning redox reactions in the solid state (e.g. reaction of hot metals with steam, the reduction of metal oxides by CO or C, etc.) the connection becomes far less straightforward. Firstly it is important to make the distinction between two rather similar terms, the oxidation potential (= the 'electrode potential' with opposite sign, see §4.6) and the ionization potential, since the half-reactions to which they refer differ only in the states of the participants, thus:

$$\text{oxidation potential: } M(s) \rightarrow M^{z+}(aq) + ze^-$$
$$\text{ionization potential: } M(g) \rightarrow M^{z+}(g) + ze^-$$

Now, while the reactions involving the oxidation of a metal or the reduction of an oxide clearly have energies which depend upon the ionization potential, they will not be related directly to the electrode potential because (1) energies other than that of ionization (e.g. lattice energy) must be incorporated in any comparison, and (2) the electrode potential relates to aqueous solution, and so incorporates the energy of hydration (see Fig. 1.1) of the ion, which is irrelevant to the solid metal/oxide system. It is not intended to give the full thermochemical analysis here, but simply to show that there are important complicating factors.

In the case of the non-redox decompositions of crystalline solids (nitrates(V), carbonates, etc.) or the solubilities of metal compounds, the accordance with predictions from the E.C.S. should be regarded as a piece of good luck. The relationship is not one of cause and effect, but rather that of two different 'effects' of a common, more fundamental 'cause'—namely atomic size and charge.

2.8 Practical cells

Cells which are used as sources of electrical power can be classified into three groups:
  (1) Primary or expendable cells.
  (2) Secondary or re-chargeable cells.
  (3) Fuel cells.

---

[3] Meaning that the anion is non-oxidizing; H^+(aq) is an oxidant in any acid.

This classification is for convenience only, and most primary cells can be reversed to some extent; but unless the cell is specially designed this regeneration is very inefficient, and not normally worthwhile.

The name Fuel Cell is usually given to a cell which operates by the reaction of oxygen with hydrogen, hydrocarbons or other organic substances; but the distinctive features are technological rather than chemical. For this reason they will be considered in §8.6, under 'applications'.

The design and manufacture of primary and storage batteries is an important industry,[4] but space permits a description of no more than the two most important cells, and a mention of some others.

Primary cells

Among the requirements for a well designed primary cell are (a) a high e.m.f., of at least 1 V; (b) little 'polarization' when the cell is under load; (c) long 'shelf-life'; (d) high ratio of electrical capacity to volume, mass and/or cost.

The first two of these features, at least, are consequences of the chemical system on which the cell is based, The initial e.m.f. follows from the electrode potentials (§2.6; and chapter 4), but when a current is drawn, the effective e.m.f. of some cells falls considerably. This effect is known as *polarization*, and is partly due to the accumulation of the products of the cell reaction, which cause the e.m.f. to decrease in accordance with the Nernst equation (§4.10). Substances which reduce this effect are often called depolarizers—an unfortunate name (since they *increase* the polarity of the cell) derived from an outmoded theory of their action.

All the principles of a good cell are illustrated in the Dry Leclanché Cell, by far the most commonly used primary cell. It is not really 'dry', since the electrolyte is a moist paste of ammonium chloride solution and starch, with additives. Zinc is the anode (negative), and at one time served as the container as well (Fig. 2.6a). As the cell operates, the metal is oxidized to ionic Zn^{2+} which is partly removed by complexing with ammonia:

$$Zn(s) \rightarrow Zn^{2+}(aq) + 2e^-\ ;\ E^{\ominus}_{ox} = +0.76\ V$$
$$Zn^{2+}(aq) + 2NH_4^+ + 2OH^-(aq) \rightleftharpoons Zn(NH_3)_2^{2+} + 2H_2O$$

Although 'local action' could result if this oxidation were paired with the reduction of H_2O or NH_4^+ to hydrogen, it is in fact almost negligible because of the high overpotential (§6.2) of hydrogen on zinc, especially smooth amalgamated zinc.

The cathode is a carbon rod surrounded by a mixture of manganese(IV) oxide (dioxide) and carbon granules, and the predominant electrode reaction seems to be the reduction of manganese (IV) to (III), though this is still not well characterized even after extensive investigation:

$$MnO_2(s) + H_2O + e^- \rightarrow MnO(OH)(s) + OH^-(aq)$$

It is the OH^- ion from this reaction which diffuses to the anode and assists the

---

[4] See Bibliography.

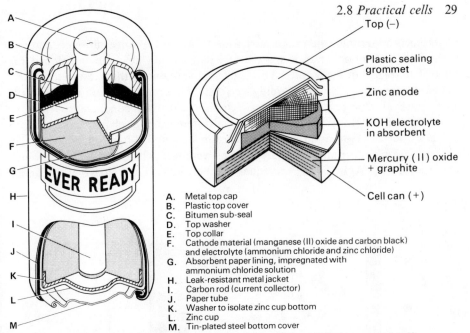

A. Metal top cap
B. Plastic top cover
C. Bitumen sub-seal
D. Top washer
E. Top collar
F. Cathode material (manganese (II) oxide and carbon black) and electrolyte (ammonium chloride and zinc chloride)
G. Absorbent paper lining, impregnated with ammonium chloride solution
H. Leak-resistant metal jacket
I. Carbon rod (current collector)
J. Paper tube
K. Washer to isolate zinc cup bottom
L. Zinc cup
M. Tin-plated steel bottom cover

Fig. 2.6   (a) The Leclanché dry cell (torch battery), (b) the Mallory mercury cell

formation of the complex ion; and when this exceeds a certain concentration, it forms solid $Zn(NH_3)_2Cl_2$, which increases internal resistance. A worn-out dry cell can often be restored to some extent by being kept for a few hours in a warm place (60–80°C) to enable this unwanted product to diffuse away.

The p.d. of the Leclanché dry cell is not very constant, especially during heavy use; it starts at 1.5 V, but falls steadily during continuous discharge to about 0.8 V. After 24 hours rest, however, the cell may regain a p.d. of 1.3 V or so. These cells are made in several sizes, and in series batteries for high p.d. But they are not as suitable for miniaturization as, for example, the 'mercury cell' (Zn/KOH(aq)/ HgO, C).

Other primary cells of continuing importance are those designed for use as standards for potentiometry, such as the Weston cadmium cell, and those which maintain an exceptionally steady p.d. during heavy use, such as the Mallory mercury cell (Fig. 2.6b).

Invention of new cells still continues. Among recent developments are cells based on the use of a metal/insoluble salt depolarizing electrode such as the copper/copper(I) chloride cathode in which the reduction half-reaction is:

$$CuCl(s) + e^- \rightarrow Cu(s) + Cl^-(aq).$$

Cells using this cathode and a magnesium anode are manufactured complete except for the electrolyte, and connected in circuit with a lamp. They begin to operate automatically if immersed in sea-water, for example after a shipwreck.

Most cells have aqueous electrolytes, and suffer from a disadvantage that might become serious when unusually wide temperature ranges are encountered, such as on the moon or in a space–craft: that is, they cease to function if the electrolyte freezes or evaporates. This is overcome in one of the latest innovations, the *really* dry 'dry cell', with a solid electrolyte. Silver bromide and iodide, in the solid state at elevated temperatures exhibit electrolytic conductance—that is, movement of ions under an applied potential difference. If a cell is constructed with one electrode of silver, and the other of carbon surrounded by bromine vapour, in contact with silver bromide (Fig. 2.7), some silver atoms change to Ag^+ ions, which migrate into the AgBr lattice; an equal number of Ag^+ ions arrive at the anode

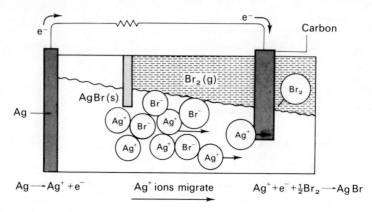

Fig. 2.7   The solid-state 'dry cell'.

where they accept electrons and react with Br_2 molecules to form more AgBr. The e.m.f. is about 1.1 V. Similar cells, with e.m.f.'s of around 0.6 V, can be made for use from $-75°C$ to $150°C$. These use as the solid electrolyte a mixed crystal of silver and rubidium (or potassium) iodides, Rb_4AgI_5. This has a lattice structure determined by the large Rb^+ and I^- ions, with the smaller Ag^+ ions occupying only a quarter of the remaining 'holes'—so the Ag^+ ions can move almost as freely as in a liquid.

Secondary (rechargeable) cells

Secondary cells (often called storage batteries) are electrochemically similar to primary cells, but the electrode reactions are chosen so that all reactants and products are insoluble in the electrolyte, and so the electrodes keep their shape during charging and discharging. Only a few systems have proved fully satisfactory, and the commercially available cells are listed in Table 2.3. Of these, the lead–acid cell is by far the most widely used, and a short description is called for.

The usual car battery consists of 3 or 6 cells connected in series, giving a nominal 6 or 12 V. Each cell is independent, and situated in a separate compartment of the hard-rubber casing. In order to provide large surface area for the electrodes, each

Table 2.3 Secondary Cells

Cell	Electrodes + (for discharge)	Electrodes − (for discharge)	Electrolyte solution	E.m.f./V	reduction (during discharge)	oxidation (during discharge)	Remarks
0. Grove	Pt, O_2	Pt, H_2	KOH	1.2	$\frac{1}{2}O_2 + H_2O + 2e^- \rightarrow 2OH^-$	$H_2 + 2OH^- \rightarrow 2H_2O + 2e^-$	First 'fuel cell'
1. Lead–acid	PbO_2	Pb	H_2SO_4	2.04	$PbO_2 + SO_4^{2-} + 4H^+ + 2e^- \rightarrow PbSO_4 + 2H_2O$	$Pb + SO_4^{2-} \rightarrow PbSO_4 + 2e^-$	See text
2. Nickel–cadmium	$Ni(OH)_3$	Cd	KOH	1.30	$Ni(OH)_3 + e^- \rightarrow Ni(OH)_2 + OH^-$	$Cd + 2OH^- \rightarrow Cd(OH)_2 + 2e^-$	Capacity/mass ratio twice that of cell 1, and less self-discharge. High currents possible
3. Nickel–iron (NIFE)	$Ni(OH)_3$	Fe	KOH	1.37	ditto	$Fe + 2OH^- \rightarrow Fe(OH)_2 + 2e^-$	Cheaper than cell 2. Same advantages but more self-discharge
4. Silver–zinc	AgO, Ag_2O	Zn	KOH	1.50	$2AgO + H_2O + 2e^- \rightarrow Ag_2O + 2OH^-$; $Ag_2O + H_2O + 2e^- \rightarrow 2Ag + 2OH^-$	$Zn + 2OH^- \rightarrow Zn(OH)_2 + 2e^-$	Very high current/mass ratio. Expensive
5. Sulphur–sodium	$Na_2S_5(l)$	Na	solid	2	$S_5^{2-} + 8e^- \rightarrow 5S^{2-}$	$Na \rightarrow Na^+ + e^-$	See text

one consists of a number (often 6) plates, connected together at the top. The two sets of plates slot together, and porous plastic separators are inserted to prevent short-circuits.

Each plate is manufactured as a grid of hard antimony–lead alloy, supporting a paste of lead sulphate. Then the plates which are to be the positives are made the anode in an electrolytic cell, and those which are to be the negatives are made the cathode, with sulphuric acid as electrolyte. Electrolysis under carefully controlled conditions converts the $PbSO_4$ to PbO_2 and Pb respectively:

$$\text{Anode (positive)} \quad PbSO_4 + 2H_2O \rightarrow PbO_2 + SO_4^{2-} + 4H^+ + 2e^-$$
$$\text{Cathode (negative)} \quad PbSO_4 + 2e^- \rightarrow Pb + SO_4^{2-}$$

These are the reactions which occur during the charging of a run-down cell. Note that H_2SO_4 is produced, and so the density of the acid increases during charging (and decreases during discharge). If acid of known density (1.20 g cm^{-3}, that is 2.3 mol dm^{-3}) is put into the battery when the plates are in a fully charged condition, the fall in density is a good guide to the state of discharge. When 1.10 g cm^{-3} is reached the cell potential will have fallen to 1.7 V, and further discharge may damage the cell by the formation of a hard unreactive layer of $PbSO_4$.

On standing, the cell slowly discharges itself by 'local action', that is, reaction of the electrodes with impurities (such as iron) without transfer of electrons to or from the external circuit. This self-discharge may be 1 to 2% per day, and is made worse if impure water is used to 'top up' the electrolyte. A battery which is to be stored for a long time should be fully charged, and then drained of its electrolyte.

The search has gone on for secondary cells which have, mass for mass, higher energy capacity than the lead–acid cell, and also higher energy conversion efficiency. Recently a cell which seems to have commercial possibilities (for electric vehicles) has been developed by exploiting molten electrolytes and ion-permeable lattices. The *sulphur–sodium cell* operates at about 300°C, and consists of two compartments separated by a solid state electrolyte (Al_2O_3 + a little Na_2O) through which sodium ions can migrate. In one compartment is molten sodium, and in the other, molten sodium sulphide—each with a graphite current collector. The whole unit is sealed in a stainless steel case. Charging the cell produces more sodium, and sulphur which remains in solution as Na_2S_x ($x = 2$–5). These reactions are reversed when a current is drawn, and it is claimed that the stored energy is then recovered at almost 100% efficiency.

2.9 Summary

The net chemical reaction in either a galvanic or an electrolytic cell is invariable an oxidation–reduction, so it can always be shown as the sum of two *half-equations* involving the gain or loss of electrons. The stoichiometry of these half-reactions requires a definite connection between the amount of substance produced or consumed at an electrode, and the amount of current passed—a connection first observed by Faraday.

Many electrochemical reactions cause changes in the electrolyte as well as at the electrodes, and concentration changes may occur.

The *potential difference* created by a galvanic cell is determined by the net cell reaction. Metals can be arranged in an order of effectiveness as anodes (negative poles), and non-metals in a similar order as cathodes. This is the electrochemical series, and it is closely connected with the reactivity of the elements in a variety of chemical reactions.

Practical cells are designed to give a steady current for long periods. Primary cells are expendable, secondary cells are rechargeable, and fuel cells have a renewable supply of reactants.

The zinc/ammonium chloride/manganese dioxide/carbon cell is the most widely used primary cell (the 'dry battery'), while the lead/sulphuric acid/lead dioxide secondary cell is probably the most important technological application of electrochemistry up to the present time.

2.10 Exercises

1. *Half-equations.* Divide each of the following redox equations into a pair of half-equations, one for the reduction and one for the oxidation. The number of electrons in each should be equal. All the aqueous electrolytes are fully ionized, and non-participating ions should be omitted.

(a) $2KI(aq) + Cl_2(g) \rightarrow 2KCl(aq) + I_2(aq)$

(b) $3KI(aq) + Cl_2(g) \rightarrow 2KCl(aq) + KI_3(aq)$

(c) $K_2Cr_2O_7(aq) + 7H_2SO_4(aq) + 3Zn(s) \rightarrow K_2SO_4(aq) + Cr_2(SO_4)_3(aq)$
$\qquad\qquad\qquad\qquad\qquad + 3ZnSO_4(aq) + 7H_2O(l)$

(d) $CuSO_4(aq) + 2KI(aq) \rightarrow CuI(s) + K_2SO_4(aq) + \frac{1}{2}I_2(aq)$

2. Each of the reactions in q. 1 could, in theory, be used to generate electricity in a galvanic cell. How much electricity (in coulombs) could be obtained from 1 gram-equation, or 1 mole of reaction, in each case?

3. *Stoichiometry.* For how long must a current of 2.50 A pass in order to produce 1.00 g of each of the products underlined in the following equations for electrolyses?

(a) $Cu^{2+}(aq) + H_2O(l) \rightarrow \frac{1}{2}O_2(g) + 2H^+ + \underline{Cu(s)}$

(b) $(CH_3)_2CO(aq) + 3I^-(aq) + 3H_2O \rightarrow \underline{CHI_3(s)} + CH_3COO^-(aq) + 2OH^-$
$\qquad\qquad\qquad\qquad\qquad$ (at anode)
$\qquad\qquad\qquad\qquad\qquad\qquad\qquad\qquad + 3H_2(g)$
$\qquad\qquad\qquad\qquad\qquad\qquad\qquad\qquad$ (at cathode)

(Hint: the anode reaction in (b) is best considered as an oxidation of I^- to I_2, followed by the non-electrochemical attack of $(CH_3)_2CO$ by I_2 or IO^-).

4. Three electrolytic cells were connected in series, and a certain amount of electricity was passed through. In one, a $Cu/CuSO_4/Cu$ cell, the cathode gained 0.635 g while the anode lost the same mass. In the second, a $Pt/H_2SO_4/Pt$ cell, gases were produced at each electrode: What volumes would these have occupied, at 27°C and 760 mmHg (101.3 kN m^{-2})? In the third cell, a $Pt/CdSO_4/Pt$ cell, the cathode was plated with a metal, while the solution became more acidic as a result of the anode reaction. What volume of 0.50 M NaOH would have to be added in order to bring this solution back to its former pH?

5. A sample of one of the oxides of rhenium was dissolved in hydrochloric acid (without producing any chlorine) and electrolysed at controlled potential until all the rhenium had been deposited on the platinum cathode, but no hydrogen had been produced. This took 27 minutes at an average current of 0.1 A, and the cathode gained about 80 mg. What was the empirical formula of the oxide? (At. wt. Rh = 186).

6. *Galvanic cells.* The following reactions are spontaneous ($\Delta G^{\ominus}$ negative) and rapid. Which of them could be used to produce electricity? Design cells to make use of each useable reaction, state whether any partition is required, and deduce the polarity from the half-equations.

   (a) $MnO_4^- + 5I^- + 8H^+ \rightarrow Mn^{2+} + \frac{5}{2}I_2 + 4H_2O$

   (b) $Na_2CO_3 + 2HCl \rightarrow 2NaCl + CO_2 + H_2O$

   (c) $Fe + Pb(NO_3)_2 \rightarrow Fe(NO_3)_2 + Pb,$

   (d) $Na + H_2O \rightarrow NaOH + \frac{1}{2}H_2$

7. *Electrode potential series.* Metal P reacts with a solution of QSO_4 to produce metallic Q, and with RSO_4 to produce metallic R. One of the metal oxides is reduced by hydrogen at 150°C, but all three oxides are reduced by carbon at high temperature. R and one of the other metals react with dilute hydrochloric acid.

   (a) How, if at all, would Q react with (i) RSO_4 soln., (ii) dilute hydrochloric acid, (iii) warm 10 M HNO_3?

   (b) How, if at all, would R react with (i) PSO_4 soln., (ii) QSO_4 soln., (iii) a mixture of PSO_4, QSO_4 and H_2SO_4 solutions?

   (c) Which combination of P, Q, R or H_2/Pt, in contact with 1 M solutions of P^{2+}, Q^{2+}, R^{2+} or H^+ ions respectively, would give the largest e.m.f., and which would be the positive electrode?

3

Electrolytic Conduction

3.1 Introduction

Electrical conduction in general was discussed in the opening section of this book. The terms conductance (G) and conductivity (κ) were defined, the former being simply the ratio of current to potential difference, as observed in an experiment. To the chemist the conductivity is the more interesting quantity, since it is dependent only on the nature (and temperature) of the conducting substance, and not on the shape or size of the sample:

$$G = \frac{I}{E} = \kappa \frac{a}{l}$$

The cell constant

Only in certain specially designed conductivity cells can the area and path length be obtained by direct measurement. Usually the effective area is not equal to the geometrical area because some current is carried by ions which are outside the volume of solution directly between the electrodes. So the cell behaves as if the ratio l/a has some value, known as the 'cell constant', which is not exactly equal to that obtained by geometry.[1] It is not at present possible to calculate theoretically the effective current path between electrodes except in very restricted cases. Therefore the cell constant is obtained by measuring the conductance of a solution for which the conductivity has been published in the literature. The most commonly used solutions are of potassium chloride, and the conductivities are given in Table 3.1.

Naturally, if the same apparatus is used to measure conductances of a number of liquids in turn, the *relative* conductances will equal the relative conductivities, since the area (a) and the path length (l) remain the same. In practice, commercially made conductivity cells (see Fig. 3.5) have specified cell constants, and conductivities are simply calculated thus:

conductivity = measured conductance × cell constant

[1] See Project 9.17.

35

Table 3.1   Conductivities of Certain KCl Solutions

Concentration/mol dm^{-3}	$\dfrac{\text{Mass of KCl}}{\text{Mass of H}_2\text{O}} \times 10^3$	Conductivity/Ω^{-1} m^{-1} 18°C	25°C
0.010	0.746	0.1221	0.1409
0.10	7.48	1.117	1.286
1.00	76.6	9.784	11.13

The circuit mentioned on p. 1 may be used to demonstrate certain simple facts:

(1) The conductivity of distilled water is increased ten thousandfold by the addition of a few drops of a concentrated solution of any strong electrolyte.

(2) Tap-water has a conductivity 10^2 or 10^3 times that of ordinary distilled water.

(3) Equimolar (say 0.1 M) solutions of various 1:1 electrolytes have conductivities which are of the same order. KCl conducts about 20% better than NaCl. But 0.1 M HCl conducts nearly four times better.

(4) Conductivities of solutions of strong electrolytes are roughly proportional to concentration. κ for 0.2 M KCl is almost double κ for 0.1 M KCl.

(5) Conductivities of solutions of weak electrolytes such as aqueous ammonia are not, even roughly, proportional to concentration. 0.2 M ammonia solution conducts only slightly better than 0.1 M.

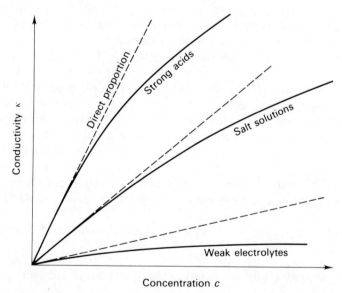

Fig. 3.1   Variation of conductivity with concentration

(6) In the case of liquids (such as pure ethanoic acid) which react with water to form ions, the conductivity can actually increase with dilution, up to a point.

3.2 Measuring conductances by d.c. with non-polarizable electrodes

During the measurement of conductance by direct current, electrolysis occurs and in most cases the products have a serious effect on the proportionality between current and applied p.d. This makes it difficult to get accurate or even reproducible conductances from the experiment described above, which was intended only as an introduction. The accepted answer to the difficulty is to use alternating current (a.c.), and this method will be described below (§3.3). But a.c. bridges are expensive compared to d.c. meters, and many laboratories will not possess enough for a large class. For this reason we will look a little closer at the d.c. method, to see how the accuracy can be improved. After all, much of the pioneer work by Kohlrausch and others was done with d.c. This point is taken up again in Project 9.9.

The most successful d.c. conductance measurements result from the elimination of polarization by careful choice of electrodes. If the electrolysis produces no substances which were not present already, polarization may be negligible. Of course this requirement limits the number of solutions which can be used, but the method of mixed electrolytes (§9.9) partially overcomes this.

One type of electrolysis which produces no new substance is that involving two identical metal electrodes in a solution of a salt of that metal—for example, $Cu/Cu^{2+}(aq)/Cu$. Another case is that using a pair of metal–insoluble salt electrodes such as $Ag–AgCl/Cl^-(aq)/AgCl–Ag$.

Practical work

Expt. 3–1

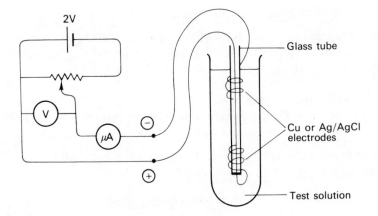

Fig. 3.2 Circuit for d.c. conductance measurements

Required   2 V d.c. source: battery charger, or accumulator.
Rheostat, about 200 Ω to act as potential divider.
Voltmeter, 0–1.5 V.
Microammeter, 0–500 μA or similar.
Copper and/or silver–silver chloride electrodes as shown in Fig. 3.2 (see Appendix II).

With copper electrodes

(i) Immerse the electrodes to the same level each time, and rinse before and after with distilled water. Using 0.1 M $CuSO_4$ and copper electrodes, take current readings for a range of applied potential differences: aim to cover the full range of the microammeter. Plot a graph of current versus p.d., and discover how closely Ohm's Law is obeyed. If a straight line is obtained, measure the slope and calculate the conductance:

$$\frac{\text{conductance}}{\Omega^{-1}} = \frac{\text{current}}{A} \div \frac{\text{p.d.}}{V}$$

(ii) The conductivity of 0.1 M $CuSO_4$ ($= 0.2$ M $\frac{1}{2}CuSO_4$) is 0.87 Ω^{-1} m^{-1} at 298 K. From this, and your result for conductance, calculate the cell constant l/a:

$$\kappa = \frac{I}{E} \times \text{cell constant}$$

(iii) Repeat the experiment (2 or 3 readings of I/E) with different concentrations, for example, 0.05 M, 0.02 M and 0.01 M ($\frac{1}{2}CuSO_4$), and show graphically the variation of conductivity with concentration.

(iv) Measure the conductivity of one solution at several temperatures in the range 305 to 345 K.

(v) Then measure κ for 0.05 M $\frac{1}{2}Cu(NO_3)_2$ and $\frac{1}{2}CuCl_2$, to demonstrate the different conducting power of different anions.

If the copper ion carries two-fifths of the current in $CuSO_4$ solution, and carries the same amount of current per volt (i.e. has the same mobility) in the other solutions, what are the relative speeds of $\frac{1}{2}SO_4^{2-}$, NO_3^- and Cl^-?

With silver–silver chloride electrodes

Alternatively, very similar experiments can be carried out using Ag–AgCl electrodes in KCl solution. Investigate:

(i) The relationship between current and applied p.d.

(ii) The cell constant (see Table 3.1).

(iii) The variation of conductivity with concentration.

(iv) The variation of conductivity with temperature.

(v) The different conducting powers (mobilities) of different cations, from results with 0.05 M KCl, NaCl, $\frac{1}{2}MgCl_2$, HCl, $\frac{1}{2}CuCl_2$.

The Cl^- ion carries 51 % of the current in 0.05 M KCl; if the amount of current (not the *proportion*) carried by Cl^- is the same in all the solutions, what are the relative conductivities of the cations? (This question is taken further in §3.6, 3.7.)

3.3 Simple a.c. conductance measurements

The interferences due to minimum decomposition potential (§6.1), which make it difficult or impossible to measure the conductances of some solutions by d.c., disappear if alternating current of sufficiently high frequency is used. Any electrolysis occurring during one half-cycle will be reversed in the next half-cycle, and no net change results.

Since power-packs supplying low potential a.c. are available quite cheaply, and also a.c. ammeters (either rectifier attachments for d.c. ammeters, or in multi-range meters) it is a logical step to experiment with simple a.c. conductivity circuits. However it is found (Expt. 3–3.1) that ordinary 50 Hz a.c. is too slow to prevent electrolysis altogether, and overpotentials are not eliminated. Yet the technique offers a considerable improvement over simple d.c., since there is no net change in concentration at the electrodes, so concentration polarization is eliminated, and the circuit is suitable when no great accuracy is required (e.g. conductimetric titrations, Expt. 3–6).

For accurate conductivity measurements the a.c. bridge (§3.4) is used.

Practical work

Expt. 3–2. Use the apparatus in Fig. 3.13 (p. 56), with a known volume of water in the cell, and a concentrated solution of an electrolyte in the burette, so that solutions of increasing concentration can be produced in the cell. Platinum electrodes of the 'dip' type are preferable.

(1) Have 1 M H_2SO_4 (i.e. 2 M $\frac{1}{2}H_2SO_4$) in the burette. Note the conductance of 200 cm^3 distilled water in the cell (approx. zero), then run in sufficient acid to produce 0.001, 0.005, 0.01, 0.02, 0.04, 0.06, 0.08 and 0.10 M $\frac{1}{2}H_2SO_4$, noting the conductance each time. Also observe the electrodes, and notice any gases evolved. (What are they?) Plot a graph of conductance κ versus concentration c.

(2) Repeat, using ethanoic acid and then, if time permits, potassium chloride. Compare the three results.

3.4 The Wheatstone bridge

It was seen in Expt. 3–2 that electrolysis is not prevented by the use of a.c. at 50 Hz, and overpotential effects will interfere with accurate conductivity measurements.

However this interference may be reduced virtually to zero by the following refinements:

(1) Platinized platinum or special graphite electrodes are used to reduce over-potential;

(2) higher frequency a.c., about 1000 Hz, is used to avoid the build-up of electrolysis products;

(3) a null-point method is used so that the final reading of conductance is taken at zero current and hence zero overpotential.

An example of a null instrument is the Wheatstone Bridge, which was originally devised for measuring (or comparing) resistances of ordinary electronic conductors, for which d.c. is suitable. Therefore the d.c. circuit, which is somewhat simpler, will be described first (Fig. 3.3).

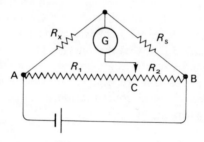

Fig. 3.3   D.c. Wheatstone bridge

AB is a uniform resistance wire on a metre scale (i.e. a potentiometer wire), and can be 'tapped off' at any point C. R_s is a standard known resistance, preferably of about the same value as the unknown resistance R_x. G is a galvanometer with several ranges of sensitivity. A source such as a lead–acid cell maintains a constant p.d. across AB.

If the probe C is tapped on to the wire, a current will flow through the galvano-meter (from D, if C is too near to A; towards D if AC is too large); the *balance-point* is sought, at which no current passes through G. The situation must then be that C and D are at the same potential, and since the same potential drop exists from A through D to B as from A through C to B, the resistance R_x must be the same fraction of $(R_x + R_s)$ as R_1 is of $(R_1 + R_2)$.

Since R_1 and R_2 are proportional to the distances AC and CB, at the balance-point

$$\frac{R_x}{R_x + R_s} = \frac{R_1}{R_1 + R_2}$$

it follows that

$$\frac{R_x}{R_s} = \frac{R_1}{R_2} = \frac{\text{AC}}{\text{CB}}$$

that is, the unknown

$$R_x = \frac{AC}{CB} \cdot R_s$$

A similar circuit (Fig. 3.4) can be used with a.c. if the e.m.f. source is replaced by an oscillator, and the galvanometer by a telephone (which gives an audible buzz which is a minimum at the balance-point) or a rectifier + milliammeter. In commercially built instruments the bridge wire is replaced by variable resistances, with

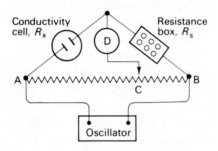

Fig. 3.4   A.c. Wheatstone bridge

the range selected by switching in other fixed resistances; the null-current detector may be a 'magic eye' valve. Conductance bridges of 'student' quality are available for as little as £40 (1975) without the cell. The 'dip-type' cell (Fig. 3.5) is probably the most versatile, and the cell constant is often about 1 cm^{-1}. For accurate results, thermostatting is important.

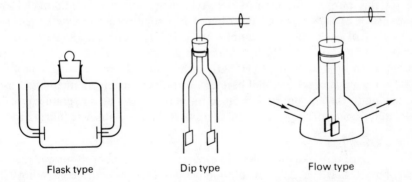

Fig. 3.5   Conductivity cells

3.5 Molar conductivity

It is found from simple conductivity measurements, such as those described in §3.2, that the conductivity of a solution of any strong electrolyte is roughly proportional to its concentration. This is to be expected, since the conductivity depends upon the number of ions available to carry the current. More accurate measurements reveal that there are marked and systematic deviations from the conductivity–concentration proportionality, and these are most clearly brought out by considering the variations in the conductivity/concentration ratio.

This ratio is named *molar conductivity*, and given the symbol Λ (Lambda):

$$\Lambda = \kappa/c$$

There is the possibility of some confusion over the *units* of Λ. Of course no difficulty arises with basic SI units, for then:

$$\frac{\Lambda}{\text{unit of } \Lambda} = \frac{\kappa}{\Omega^{-1}\,\text{m}^{-1}} \div \frac{c}{\text{mol m}^{-3}}$$

$$\text{unit of } \Lambda = \frac{\Omega^{-1}\,\text{m}^{-1}}{\text{mol m}^{-3}} = \Omega^{-1}\,\text{m}^2\,\text{mol}^{-1}$$

But the commonly used unit of concentration is mol dm^{-3} ('molarity'), which, if unconverted, leads to the unacceptable mixture, $\Omega^{-1}\,\text{m}^{-1}\,\text{mol}^{-1}\,\text{dm}^3$ as the unit of Λ; this must not be used.

Another procedure, widely used in the past, was to express concentrations in mol cm^{-3} and conductivities in Ω^{-1} cm^{-1}; then the unit of Λ appeared as Ω^{-1} cm^2 mol^{-1}, which is acceptable, as long as it is stated explicitly (it was frequently omitted in older literature).

In the comparison of molar conductivities of different electrolytes, perhaps having ions with different charges, it is most meaningful if the amounts of substances constituting 'one mole' are those which carry the same number of charges. Therefore for this purpose the mole is *not* Avogadro's number of empirical formula groups (such as H_2SO_4 or $CuSO_4$) but that amount of electrolyte which carries one faraday of each charge. Examples are $\frac{1}{2}H_2SO_4$, $\frac{1}{2}CuSO_4$, $\frac{1}{4}K_4Fe(CN)_6$, KCl. One speaks of a solution which contains 98 g sulphuric acid per litre as having a concentration of 2 mol dm^{-3} $\frac{1}{2}H_2SO_4$, rather than the more usual 1 mol dm^{-3} H_2SO_4. The mole of a fractional part of a formula is merely an unambiguous way of referring to the amount of substance formerly known as the 'gram-equivalent', while molar concentrations using these units replace the obsolete 'normality'.

Worked examples

A solution of 0.10 mol dm^{-3} KCl in a certain conductance cell showed a conductance of 0.006 45 Ω^{-1} at 25°C. A solution of lanthanum chloride, containing 0.818 g anhydrous $LaCl_3$ per dm^3, showed a conductance of $6.1 \times 10^{-4}\,\Omega^{-1}$ in the same cell, also at 25°C.

Calculate (a) the cell constant (using data from Table 3.1); (b) the conductivity of the $LaCl_3$ solution; (c) its molar conductivity.

(a) $$\kappa = G \times \frac{l}{a} = G \times \text{cell constant}$$

From Table 3.1, κ for 0.10 mol dm^{-3} KCl = 1.286 Ω^{-1} m^{-1} at 25°C.

$$\therefore \text{ cell constant} = \frac{\kappa}{G} = \frac{1.286 \, \Omega^{-1} \, m^{-1}}{0.006 \, 45 \, \Omega^{-1}} = 200 \, m^{-1} = 2 \, cm^{-1}$$

(b) For the $LaCl_3$ solution, $\kappa = 6.1 \times 10^{-4} \Omega^{-1} \times 2 \, cm^{-1}$
$$= 1.22 \times 10^{-3} \, \Omega^{-1} \, cm^{-1}$$
$$(= 0.122 \, \Omega^{-1} \, m^{-1})$$

(c) The concentration of lanthanum chloride must be in units of mol ($\frac{1}{3}LaCl_3$) dm^{-3}.

$$M_r(\tfrac{1}{3}LaCl_3) = \frac{245.4}{3} = 81.8 \text{ g mol}^{-1}$$

$$\frac{0.818 \text{ g dm}^{-3}}{81.8 \text{ g mol}^{-1}} = 0.010 \text{ mol } (\tfrac{1}{3}LaCl_3) \text{ dm}^{-3}.$$

$$\Lambda = \frac{\kappa}{c} = \frac{1.22 \times 10^{-3} \, \Omega^{-1} \, cm^{-1}}{0.010 \text{ mol dm}^{-3}}$$

$$= \frac{1.22 \times 10^{-3} \, \Omega^{-1} \, dm^3}{1.00 \times 10^{-2} \text{ mol cm}} \times \frac{10^3 \text{ cm}^3}{dm^3}$$

$$= 1.22 \times 10^2 \, \Omega^{-1} \, cm^2 \, mol^{-1}$$

$$= 1.22 \times 10^{-2} \, \Omega^{-1} \, m^2 \, mol^{-1}$$

Note: It is worth remembering that the molar conductivities of all *strong* electrolytes have values not far from the above; and therefore any literature value of 100 to 400 for Λ will be in units of Ω^{-1} cm^2 mol^{-1}, even if these are not stated.

3.6 Variation of molar conductivity with concentration

Preliminary exercise

Consider an apparatus for demonstrating the effect, if any, of dilution on the molar conductivity Λ. The actual measurement made will be the current ($I = G \cdot E$), and so ideally, for demonstration purposes, the current should be a direct measure of Λ, and should not change with dilution of the electrolyte unless Λ changes. What feature of the conductance cell is necessary if this is to be so?

We have seen that molar conductivities can be determined by (i) measuring the current through, and p.d. across, a conductivity cell of fixed electrode area and separation; (ii) knowing the effective distance/area ratio (the cell constant); and (iii) knowing the concentration of the electrolyte. Even if the molar conductivity did not change with dilution, the conductance would vary, in the usual cell, because the amount of ions between the electrodes would decrease. In other words, the conductivity cells in Fig. 3.5 are for measuring conductivity—and it is fairly obvious that this will vary with concentration; but they do not *directly* measure molar conductivity, which is the conducting power of the ions, and it is the variation in this that we are now interested in. So it is best to abandon the fixed area cell and think again about what is really required.

In answer to the question at the start of this section: molar conductivity is the conducting power of a certain number (Avogadro's number) of ions. So it is necessary that the same amount of electrolyte should remain between the electrodes at all the concentrations used. This is the case when the electrolyte solution partly fills a tall vessel with vertical sides, and with tall, parallel-sided, vertical electrodes which extend right to the bottom. Then, however much water is added, all the electrolyte (or a fixed proportion of it) remains between the electrodes.

In the case of a rectangular vessel such as that in Fig. 3.6, with two *entire* facing sides acting as electrodes, the addition of water decreases the concentration but increases the area (a) of electrodes submerged proportionately. If l is the separation of the electrodes, then the volume $= l \cdot a$, and the concentration c is connected with n, the amount of electrolyte by: $c = n/(l \cdot a)$.

$$\therefore G = \kappa \frac{a}{l} = \Lambda c \frac{a}{l} = \Lambda \frac{n}{al} \left(\frac{a}{l}\right) = \Lambda \cdot \frac{n}{l^2}$$

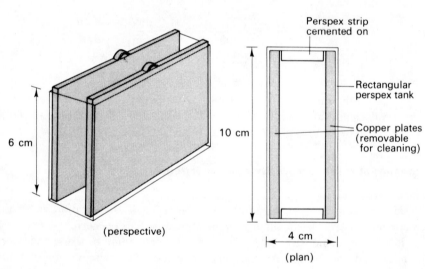

(perspective)

Perspex strip cemented on

Rectangular perspex tank

Copper plates (removable for cleaning)

6 cm

10 cm

4 cm

(plan)

Fig. 3.6 Cell for molar conductivity measurements (after E. R. Ridley. See Appendix II for class experiment model)

Practical work

Expt. 3–3

Required Cell as described (see Fig. 3.6)

Low tension a.c. supply (power-pack or transformer) 4–8 V.
a.c. voltmeter (may be on the power-pack).
a.c. ammeter (e.g. Avometer).

Rheostat.

Concentrated solutions of KCl, NaOH, NH_4NO_3, $CuSO_4$, $CuCl_2$, $Cu(NO_3)_2$.

Moderately concentrated (8 M) H_2SO_4, CH_3COOH.

Place sufficient concentrated KCl solution to reach up 1/10 of the height of the cell, or 2 cm, whichever is the greater. Measure this height, allowing for the thickness of the base. Complete the circuit and record current and p.d.

Switch off the current, and add an equal volume of distilled water, as measured by the height. Stir well, and measure the conductance again.

Repeat the procedure until the cell is full. If the p.d. has remained approximately constant, you may take molar conductivity to be proportional to the current I; but otherwise, proportional to the conductance G (current $\div$ p.d.). Plot a graph of I (or G) versus height of solution level, h; this is in effect a graph of Λ versus dilution V, the volume which contains one mole. Comment on the constancy (or otherwise) of Λ. For comparison, roughly sketch in on the same graph a possible line for the change of conductivity κ with V. (Hint: at what concentration does $\Lambda = \kappa$? And what is the value of κ at high dilution?)

Repeat the experiment with the other electrolytes,[2] and treat the results in the same way. What are the limiting values of Λ as the dilutions become very large?

Your graphs have been of the form Λ versus dilution, or volume. Since dilution is inversely proportional to concentration, the concentration is measured by the reciprocal of the height, i.e. $1/h$. Now re-plot one of the graphs in the form Λ versus concentration.

The behaviour of weak and strong electrolytes is conveniently summarized in the graphs in Fig. 3.7. Conductivity is *roughly* proportional to concentration for strong electrolytes, as shown by the 'strong' line in Fig. 3.7(a) which is a mild distortion of a straight line through the origin. It follows that molar conductivity plotted against concentration will not be far off a horizontal straight line, and in Fig. 3.7(b) it is seen that Λ for a strong electrolyte decreases somewhat with concentration (about 14% for the change from 10^{-3} to 10^{-1} mol dm^{-3}). Since the points for dilute solutions are crowded in at the left of (b), a better display of the information is given by Fig. 3.7(a), in which Λ is plotted against 'dilution', defined as the reciprocal of concentration. Λ increases with dilution, but levels off to a limiting value. This value may be referred to as the molar conductivity at infinitesimal concentration,[3] symbolized Λ^0.

Weak electrolytes (such as ethanoic acid) behave completely differently. κ does not increase even roughly in proportion to c, showing that increase in concentration does not provide a proportional increase in current carrying ions. Λ is not at all

---

[2] The NH_4NO_3 and copper salts may be omitted if time is limited, but they give interesting and unexpected results.

[3] In the past it has been known alternatively as the molar conductivity at infinite dilution, and symbolized Λ^∞.

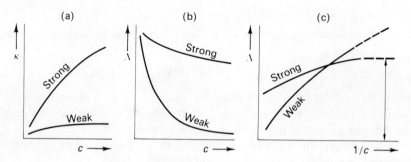

Fig. 3.7

constant, and decreases sharply (by a factor of about 10 for an increase from 10^{-3} to 10^{-1} mol dm^{-3}). In Fig. 3.7(c) Λ increases greatly with dilution, and is still increasing when the experimental limit is reached (say, $1/c = 10^4$ dm^3 mol^{-1}) and so Λ^0 for a weak electrolyte cannot be obtained by extrapolation.

For a strong or intermediate electrolyte, however, Λ^0 can be obtained from Λ measurements at a series of dilutions, since a plot of Λ versus $\sqrt{c}$ becomes linear at low concentrations (Fig. 3.8). The relationship, discovered empirically by Kohlrausch, is

$$\Lambda = \Lambda^0 - b\sqrt{c}$$

The Arrhenius theory of ionic dissociation (§1.2) gives a satisfactory account of the behaviour of weak electrolytes. In solution, unionized molecules are in

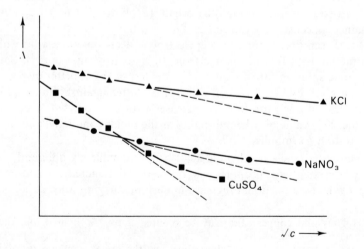

Fig. 3.8   Molar conductivity versus $\sqrt{}$concentration

equilibrium with ions, and in accordance with the equilibrium law, the proportion of ions to molecules increases with dilution. For a weak acid HA,

$$HA(aq) \rightleftharpoons H^+(aq) + A^-(aq)$$

$$\frac{[H^+][A^-]}{[HA]} = K$$

Consider a solution of this acid, with equilibrium concentrations $[H^+]_1$, $[A^-]_1$, and $[HA]_1$. If water is added, to increase the volume from V to xV ($x > 1$), the concentrations become, momentarily, $(1/x)[H^+]_1$, etc., and so:

$$\frac{[H^+][A^-]}{[HA]} = \frac{\frac{1}{x}[H^+]_1 \cdot \frac{1}{x}[A^-]_1}{\frac{1}{x}[HA]_1} = \frac{1}{x}K.$$

But $(1/x)K$ is less than the equilibrium constant K, and in order to restore equilibrium, reaction must occur in such a way as to increase $[H^+]$ and $[A^-]$ and decrease $[HA]$. That is, dilution causes an increase in the degree of ionization, α, defined as the fraction of the electrolyte which has ionized.

At the limit of infinitesimal concentration, the degree of ionization would become unity, and the molar conductivity reach its maximum, Λ^0. If conductivity depended only on the *number* of ions present (that is, if their speed for a given p.d. were constant against concentration) then at finite concentrations Λ would be proportional to α, and $\Lambda/\Lambda^0 = \alpha/\alpha^0 = \alpha$ (since $\alpha^0 = 1$). The ratio Λ/Λ^0 is thus a very useful measure of the degree of dissociation of a weak acid or base, and values of α found in this way agree with those from pH, catalytic activity, osmotic pressure, freezing point, etc.

However, a certain difficulty must be overcome. It was shown above (Fig. 3.7(c)) that Λ^0 for a weak electrolyte cannot be obtained by measuring Λ for various dilutions, and extrapolating the curve, since Λ is still increasing rapidly when the solutions become too dilute for reliable measurements.

The answer was found by Kohlrausch. He had noticed that in the comparison of pairs of Λ^0 values for the potassium and sodium salts of various anions, the difference was a constant. These and other observations led him to propose his *Law of independent migration of ions*: 'Each ion contributes a definite amount to the total molar conductivity of the electrolyte at infinitesimal concentration, irrespective of the nature of the other ion present.'

Thus for any electrolyte, $\Lambda^0_{total} = \Lambda^0_+ + \Lambda^0_-$. With a knowledge of transport numbers (§3.7) it is possible to calculate values for Λ^0_+ and Λ^0_- separately, but even without that, Kohlrausch's Law gives an arithmetical method of calculating Λ^0 for a weak electrolyte.

Strong electrolytes

Since Λ for finite concentrations is less than Λ^0, the ratio Λ/Λ^0 was at one time identified with the 'degree of dissociation' for strong, as well as weak, electrolytes. This can be shown to be a misinterpretation, and there is no association to molecules in dilute solutions of electrolytes such as HCl, KCl, or $Ba(NO_3)_2$. The decrease in Λ with concentration is accounted for by a different theory entirely (§3.8). However, some electrolytes, notably those containing transition metal ions and small or multivalent anions, show an intermediate behaviour, with some combination of ions, for example:

$$Fe^{3+} + 3Cl^- \rightleftharpoons FeCl^{2+} + 2Cl^-$$

3.7 Transport numbers

Generally, all ions in a solution contribute to carrying the current, and the fraction of the current carried by any particular species is known as its *transport number* (or transference number). For a single electrolyte, the transport numbers of a cation and an ion respectively are represented by t_+ and t_-.

$$t_+ = \frac{\text{current carried by cations}}{\text{total current}}$$

$$t_- = \frac{\text{current carried by anions}}{\text{total current}}$$

$$t_+ + t_- = 1$$

Transport numbers are meaningful only if the nature of the total electrolyte is specified; e.g. t_{Na+} will be different in different sodium salts. Transport numbers also vary somewhat with temperature and concentration, but extreme variation is an indication of some chemical reaction such as complex formation.

Transport numbers may be measured by three methods: (1) observations of concentration changes in the electrode regions; (2) direct observation of a moving boundary; (3) e.m.f.'s of some concentration cells (see §5.4). Practical details for the first two methods appear in §3.10.

The velocity of an ion v and the *ionic mobility* u have the relationship:

$$v_+ = u_+ \, dE/dl \quad \text{and} \quad v_- = u_- \, dE/dl$$

where dE/dl is the potential gradient, usually measured in V cm^{-1} or V m^{-1}.

v^0 and u^0 are specific properties of an ion (in a given solvent at stated temperature) and are, unlike t^0, independent of the other ions present. The relationships with molar conductivity Λ are as follows:

$$\Lambda^0 = F(u_+^0 + u_-^0)$$

$$\Lambda_+ = \alpha u_+ F \quad \text{and} \quad \Lambda_- = \alpha u_- F$$

$$\Lambda_+^0 = t_+^0 \Lambda^0 \quad \text{and} \quad \Lambda_-^0 = t_-^0 \Lambda^0$$

Table 3.2 gives selected molar ionic conductances. From these data, transport numbers and ionic mobilities can readily be calculated, as can (by simple addition) the limiting molar conductivity of any electrolyte.

Table 3.2   Limiting Molar Ionic Conductivities at 298 K

Cations	$\Lambda^0_+/\Omega^{-1}\,cm^2\,mol^{-1}$	Anions	$\Lambda^0_-/\Omega^{-1}\,cm^2\,mol^{-1}$
H^+	349.8	OH^-	198.3
Li^+	38.7	F^-	55.4
NH_4^+	73.4	Cl^-	76.4
Na^+	50.1	Br^-	78.1
$\frac{1}{2}Mg^{2+}$	53.1	I^-	76.8
$\frac{1}{3}Al^{3+}$	63.0	$\frac{1}{2}CO_3^{2-}$	59.3
K^+	74.5	HCO_3^-	44.5
$\frac{1}{2}Ca^{2+}$	59.5	CN^-	82
$\frac{1}{2}Fe^{2+}$	54	NO_3^-	71.4
$\frac{1}{3}Fe^{3+}$	68.4	$\frac{1}{3}PO_4^{3-}$	80
$\frac{1}{2}Ni^{2+}$	53	$\frac{1}{2}SO_4^{2-}$	79.8
$\frac{1}{2}Cu^{2+}$	53.6	HSO_4^-	52
$\frac{1}{2}Zn^{2+}$	52.8	ClO_3^-	64.6
Ag^+	61.9	ClO_4^-	67.4
$\frac{1}{2}Ba^{2+}$	63.6	MnO_4^-	61
$\frac{1}{3}La^{3+}$	69.6	$HCOO^-$	54.6
$\frac{1}{2}Hg^{2+}$	63.6	$CH_3CO_2^-$	40.9
Tl^+	74.7	$C_2H_5CO_2^-$	35.8
$\frac{1}{2}Pb^{2+}$	59.4	$\frac{1}{3}Fe(CN)_6^{3-}$	101.0
		$\frac{1}{4}Fe(CN)_6^{4-}$	110.5

3.8 Interionic attraction theory

The decrease in molar conductivity with concentration is explained for weak electrolytes by the Arrhenius theory of partial ionization; but although Λ for a strong electrolyte also decreases with concentration, a closer inspection shows that this cannot be due to an equilibrium with an un-ionized form.

If an equilibrium exists between ions and molecules, and α is the degree of ionization, then the concentrations at equilibrium are:

$$AB \rightleftharpoons A^- + B^+$$
$$(1-\alpha)c \quad \alpha c \quad \alpha c$$

So, from the equilibrium law:

$$\frac{[A^-][B^+]}{[AB]} = \frac{\alpha c \cdot \alpha c}{(1-\alpha)c} = \frac{\alpha^2 c}{1-\alpha} = K$$

This expression, for the decrease in α with increasing c, is known as Ostwald's Dilution Law. When α is calculated from Λ/Λ^0 for a series of concentrations, and the expression $\alpha^2 c/(1 - \alpha)$ (or a similar one for electrolytes which dissociate into more than two ions) worked out for each concentration, it is found to be a constant for weak electrolytes, but not at all a constant for strong electrolytes. Hence some different explanation is required, and the most successful theory to date (though it applies exactly only to very dilute solutions) is that of Debye, Hückel and Onsager. Only a mention of the main points of this theory is appropriate here, but a fuller account is to be found in any advanced text.

Debye and Hückel showed that although strong electrolytes are completely ionized, the distribution of ions is such that each positive ion will have more negative ions than positive amongst its nearest neighbours. Each ion is surrounded by an ionic atmosphere whose net charge is, on the average, opposite to that of the central ion.

The influence of this ionic atmosphere will increase with concentration, and with the square of the charge, of each ion; and this is measured by a quantity known as the *ionic strength* μ of the solution:

$$\mu = \tfrac{1}{2}\Sigma c_i z_i^2$$

Fig. 3.9 shows the situation, with (a) ions in random thermal motion, but with more $-$ than $+$ ions around the $\oplus$ ion on which our attention is fixed, and (b) this arrangement idealized for simplicity. When a potential gradient is applied (c) the ions begin to move, $\oplus$ to the left and the negative 'atmosphere' to the right.

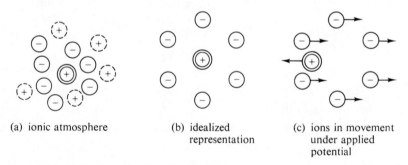

(a) ionic atmosphere

(b) idealized representation

(c) ions in movement under applied potential

Fig. 3.9   Debye–Hückel model of an ionic solution

As the $\oplus$ leaves its most stable position at the centre of the atmosphere, it feels a net backward pull, which contributes to the electrical resistance. This effect is called the *asymmetry effect* or the *relaxation effect* since it refers to the period of relaxation, or decay, of the ionic atmosphere.

A second retarding force is the friction arising as the ions, with their large hydration spheres, pass in opposite directions. Since this effect is due to ionic movement, it is known as the *electrophoretic effect*.

A quantitative treatment of these effects led to an equation relating Λ to Λ^0 and c:

$$\Lambda = \Lambda^0 - (a + b\Lambda^0)\sqrt{c}$$

where a and b are constants which can be derived from the theory in terms of temperature, dielectric constant and viscosity of the solvent, and the charges on the ions. For the special case of $1:1$ electrolytes in water at 298 K, the numerical values of the constants are $a = 59.8\ \Omega^{-1}\ cm^2\ mol^{-1}\ (mol\ dm^{-3})^{-1/2}$ or 1.89×10^{-4} $\Omega^{-1}\ m^{7/2}\ mol^{-3/2}$, and $b = 0.227\ (mol\ dm^{-3})^{-1/2}$ or $7.18 \times 10^{-3}\ m^{3/2}\ mol^{-1/2}$. The Debye–Hückel–Onsager equation agrees with experiment fairly well up to about $10^{-2}\ mol\ dm^{-3}$, and correctly predicts the slopes of the straight-line portions of the curves for strong electrolytes on the Kohlrausch plots of Λ versus $\sqrt{c}$ (Fig. 3.8). A satisfactory model for more concentrated electrolyte solutions is, however, still awaited.

3.9 The ionic conductivity of aqueous H^+ and OH^-

Table 3.2 shows that the limiting molar conductivity of the aqueous hydrogen ion is nearly five times greater than that of any other cation, and the hydroxyl ion conducts nearly three times as well as the other anions. It is tempting to attribute the high mobility of H^+ to its small size, but it must not be forgotten that small ionic radius may lead to a high degree of hydration, and this may put the *effective* sizes of the hydrated ions into a reverse order from that of the ionic radii. A comparison of the limiting molar conductivities of K^+, Na^+ and Li^+ will bear this out, since they decrease from K^+ to Li^+, suggesting an *increase* in effective size. At infinite dilution the electrical resistance of an electrolyte solution is due to (i) random thermal motion, which hinders the ionic drift, and (ii) friction between the hydrated ions and free water molecules. The second effect will be increased by the greater number of water molecules attached to Li^+ as compared to K^+. It is likely then that even if H^+ is no more hydrated than Li^+, it will not be small enough to account for the high mobility. Nor can the high mobility of OH^- be explained by size.

The currently held explanation is an interesting case of a theory which was first proposed on a scanty factual basis, then rejected in the light of further evidence, only to be revived many years later. It has become known as Grotthus' Chain Theory, although it is only on the strength of an important modification by Faraday that the theory is of interest to us today. In 1806, only six years after the discovery of electrolysis, Grotthus suggested[4] that the reason why both hydrogen and oxygen did not bubble up at all points along the current path (where, it was presumed, molecules of water were being disrupted) was that while, for instance, the hydrogen produced near the negative electrode was attracted to it and liberated, the oxygen was attracted towards the distant positive electrode, but never got there because on the way it met, and combined with, an atom of hydrogen coming the other way.

[4] *Ann. Chim. Phys.* **58**, 54.

Faraday's improvement on this theory (1833) was to propose that the molecules of water were not only polarized and oriented by the electric field (the positive pole attracting the oxygen end of the water molecule, then believed to be HO, and repelling the hydrogen), but that the bonding was distorted. The hydrogen atom, repelled by the positive pole, experienced an increased attraction to the oxygen of the next molecule, and combined with it. This released a hydrogen which in turn removed an oxygen from the adjacent water molecule in the direction of the negative pole, and so on until, at the end of the chain, a hydrogen atom was set free. Fig. 3.10(a)–(d) shows the successive stages in this proposed sequence, including the molecular rotations presumably necessary before it could be repeated.

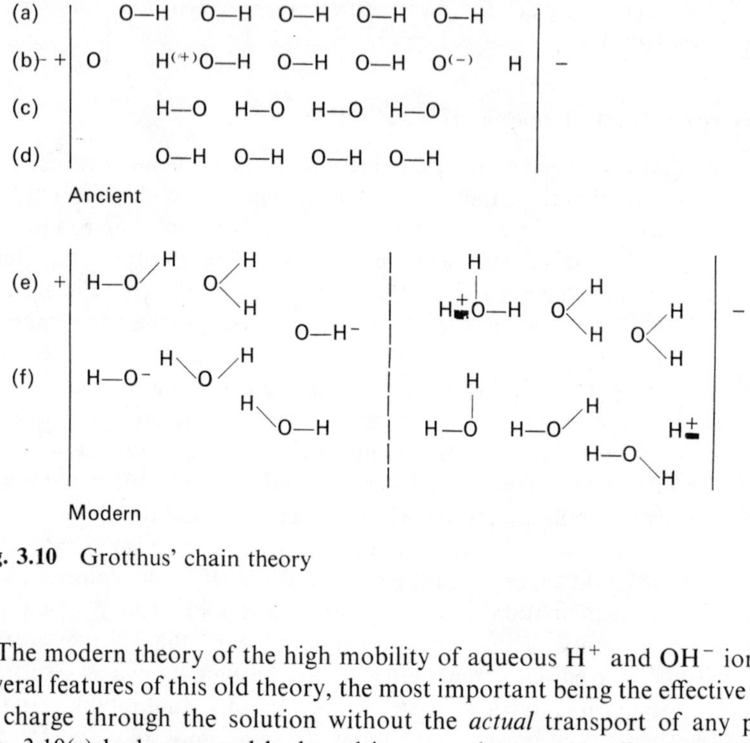

Fig. 3.10   Grotthus' chain theory

The modern theory of the high mobility of aqueous H^+ and OH^- ions borrows several features of this old theory, the most important being the effective movement of charge through the solution without the *actual* transport of any particle. In Fig. 3.10(e) hydrogen and hydroxyl ions are shown some distance from the electrodes, with water molecules in between; in (f) the ions have apparently moved to the surface of the electrodes, but this has been done by rearrangement of the bonds, and without the physical movement of any atom. If we assume that electrons can move more rapidly than atoms, we have a mechanism to account for the high mobility of H^+ and OH^- *in water*. But H^+ ions do not show this high conductivity in aprotic solvents, such as dioxan, which are incapable of ionizing to H^+.

An important practical application of the abnormally high conductivity of H^+ and OH^- ions is the *conductimetric titration*, for which practical details appear below. A neutralization reaction will bring about the destruction of H^+ or OH^- ions, and their replacement by other, less mobile, ions; therefore the conductance of the solution will reach a minimum at the end-point, and this is detected by use of an a.c. milliammeter. With care, the same method can be used to indicate the equivalence point of a precipitation reaction, since the concentration of ions, and hence the conductance, is then a minimum.

A similar application is the use of conductance to follow the *rate of reaction*. This is possible whenever a slow reaction consumes or produces ions, or replaces H^+ or OH^- ions by slower ones. A well known example is the saponification of an ester; another might be the dehydration of an alcohol by concentrated sulphuric(IV) acid.

3.10 Practical work

Expt. 3–4. Determination of transport numbers by Hittorf's method. Apparatus as in Fig. 3.11.

Required   Hittorf transport cell: alternatively two copper electrodes in 50 cm³ beakers containing 0.2 mol dm⁻³ CuSO₄, linked by a salt bridge tube of the same solution.

Battery (B) or d.c. source of about 12 V.

Variable resistor (R).

Ammeter (A) 0–250 mA.

Coulometer (C), see §2.2 (for accurate work).

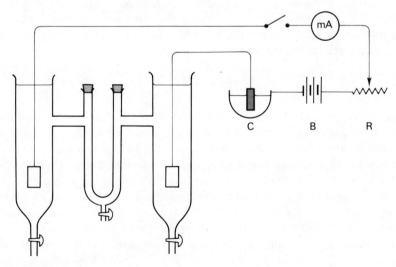

Fig. 3.11   Hittorf's apparatus

Refer to §2.4 for the discussion of concentration changes which accompany electrolysis. Hittorf showed that a measurement of such changes can be used to determine transport numbers.

Set up the apparatus as in Fig. 3.11, with copper electrodes and 0.2 M CuSO$_4$ solution; adjust the rheostat to give about 200 mA, and note the time. For accurate work a coulometer (copper, silver, or iodine) should be used to measure the total amount of electricity which passes. Otherwise the current can be kept steady by continuous adjustment of the rheostat, and the amount calculated as current × time.

After 10 to 15 minutes, break the circuit, and remove the solution from the central compartment, or in some other way isolate the anolyte (the contents of the anode compartment) from the catholyte. Remove the whole of the anolyte, stir it, measure its volume, and analyse it (titrimetrically) for Cu^{2+} concentration. Measure and analyse the catholyte similarly.

Treatment of results. Calculate the amount of Cu^{2+} gained by the anolyte and lost by the catholyte, and also the quantity of electricity which passed. By considering the half-equation for the cathode reaction, calculate the amount of Cu^{2+} lost from the catholyte by electrodeposition; and by considering the charge on the Cu^{2+} ion, and using t_+ to represent the fraction of the current carried by these cations, calculate the gain of Cu^{2+} by migration into the catholyte. The net loss of Cu^{2+} is known, so t_+ can be found.

Note that the net loss of Cu^{2+} must equal the gain of SO$_4^{2-}$ by migration; this follows since $t_- = 1 - t_+$.

See §3.12, q. 7 for an example of this calculation, also §9.31 for an extension of the enquiry into ionic transference.

Expt. 3–5. Determination of transport numbers by Lodge's moving boundary method. The apparatus (Fig. 3.12) permits the movement of ionic species to be observed and measured directly. This enables the transport numbers to be calculated, since these are related to the ionic velocities:

$$t_+ = \frac{v_+}{v_+ + v_-}$$

The electrolysis cell consists of a narrow vertical tube, surrounded by a thermostatted water jacket (since considerable heat is generated by the current). For this particular demonstration[5] the tube is filled with 0.2 M NaCl solution coloured with bromothymol blue indicator, and made *slightly* alkaline (green). The anode, at the bottom, is a rod of cadmium or copper; the cathode is of platinum or, better, Ag/AgCl.[5] As the resistance of the solution is high, a p.d. of 150–200 V is necessary, to give a current of about 25 mA. As the current flows, the cadmium anode is attacked, and a solution of cadmium chloride is formed, which is slightly acidic due to hydrolysis. The boundary between this solution and the sodium chloride

---

[5] See Appendix II.

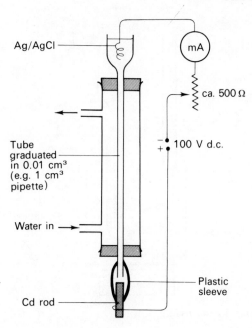

Ag/AgCl

mA

ca. 500 Ω

Tube
graduated
in 0.01 cm³
(e.g. 1 cm³
pipette)

100 V d.c.

Water in →

Plastic
sleeve

Cd rod

Fig. 3.12 Moving boundary experiment

remains sharp throughout the experiment, because the speed of the Cd^{2+} ion is less than double that of the Na^+, and so if any Na^+ ion diffuses into the lower solution, it will migrate upwards faster than the surrounding Cd^{2+}, and the boundary will reform.

Procedure. Switch on the current and wait for the boundary to rise to the capillary tube (this takes several hours). Then measure the time required for the boundary to cover the distance between two graduations enclosing a known volume V. As the $CdCl_2$ solution has a lower conductivity than the NaCl, the current may decrease with time, and should be noted at regular intervals. (N.B.—Cadmium compounds are very poisonous.)

Treatment of results. From the current readings, and the time intervals, the quantity of electricity Q is obtained. If the concentration of the acid is c, then cV moles of Na^+ ion have passed the upper mark, and have carried t_+Q of electricity (measured in coulombs). Since 1 mole would carry F coulombs, $cVF/Q = t_+$.

Expt. 3–6. Conductimetric titrations. Many variations in the apparatus are possible, and one of the simplest is shown here. Greater precision is possible with an a.c. conductivity bridge, but d.c. measurements are usually adequate.

Required Pair of electrodes, as in Fig. 3.13 (see Appendix II).

250 cm³ tall-form beaker.

Stirring device (magnetic, or air bubbles).

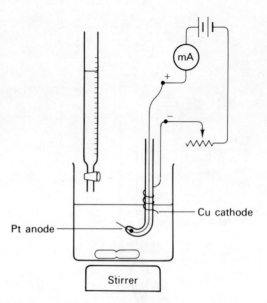

Fig. 3.13   Conductimetric titration apparatus

50 cm³ burette.
12 V d.c. supply (e.g. car battery).
Milliammeter.
Rheostat (ca. 100 Ω).

For each titration fill the burette with 0.10 M NaOH.

(i) Place 80 cm³ HCl(aq) (approx. 0.01 M) in the beaker, and adjust the circuit to give an almost full-scale deflection on the meter. Run in 20 cm³ of the 0.10 M NaOH, reading the current after every 2 cm³. Plot a graph of current vs. volume of titrant, and draw two intersecting straight lines through the points.

Repeat the experiment, reading the current after every 0.5 cm³ addition, but only in the region 5 cm³ before and after the expected equivalence point. (It might be interesting to have an indicator such as phenophthalein in the solution, and to compare the equivalence points given by the two methods.)

(ii) Find the concentration of ethanoic acid in a sample of vinegar. A suitable degree of dilution must be found by experiment; 1 to 50 would be reasonable for the first trial. (Note:—accurate a.c. measurements are essential in this case.)

Comment on the slopes of the lines.

(iii) Titrate the zinc(II) sulphate(VI) and lead(II) nitrate(V) solutions provided. Explain the changes in conductance and calculate the concentrations of the solutions.

A special case of a precipitation reaction which removes *all* the ions is the conductimetric titration of dilute sulphuric(VI) acid by standardized barium hydroxide solution, which makes a foolproof demonstration of the principle.

Expt. 3–7. The solubility of calcium sulphate(VI) conductimetry. Calcium sulphate(VI) is sparingly soluble in water (around one part per thousand by mass), which makes direct methods for the determination of its solubility—such as the evaporation of a saturated solution, or the complete dissolution of a pre-weighed quantity—rather difficult. Conductivity measurements provide a quick and simple solution to the problem. Put a few grams of powdered hydrated calcium sulphate(VI) and about 200 cm³ purified water in a bottle and shake frequently for about 15 minutes. Allow most of the solid to settle, then decant the slightly turbid liquid into a conductivity cell, and measure the conductance. It is not necessary to know the cell constant, nor to calculate the conductivity. If the applied potential is steady, the current reading is sufficient.

The intention is to find the concentration by comparison of the conductance with the conductances of other solutions of known concentration. Standard solutions of calcium sulphate are difficult to prepare (because of the low and also the slow solubility), and so magnesium sulphate is used instead. It may be assumed that these salts, with the sulphate(VI) ion in common and the cations of the same charge and similar size, will have roughly the same molar conductivity (the error is in fact less than 4%).

Prepare 100 cm³ 0.10 M $MgSO_4$ solution by weighing, and put some of it in a burette. Place a measured volume (say 50 cm³) pure water in the conductivity cell (enough to cover the electrodes), and run in the magnesium sulphate, a little at a time, with agitation, until the conductance equals that of the saturated calcium sulphate solution. The (molar) concentration of the magnesium sulphate solution thus formed is easily calculated, and is taken to be equal to that of saturated calcium sulphate.

It is instructive to measure the conductance of the 0.1 M $MgSO_4$ separately, and to see how mistaken it would be to calculate the concentration of the dilute solution on the assumption that concentrations were proportional to conductances over this range.

The technique of measuring concentration by matching conductances has an application to the analysis of ground water (for 'hardness'), and this is taken up again in Project 9.12.

3.11 Summary

The conductance of a particular solution in a particular cell may be obtained by d.c. current and p.d. measurements, if polarization can be eliminated. Non-polarizable electrodes can be chosen to do this in some cases. A technique of wider application is the use of alternating current, and, for accurate work, the a.c. conductance bridge.

The measured conductance equals the conductivity of the solution multiplied by the effective cross-sectional area and divided by the path length. The reciprocal of this ratio, the length/area, is known as the cell constant; when it is known, the conductivity of any solution may be calculated as conductance × cell constant.

The conductivity κ varies with the nature of the solution, the temperature, and the concentration. For 'strong electrolytes' such as most salt solutions or inorganic acids, the conductivity is roughly proportional to concentration; so that the *molar conductivity* Λ, defined as conductivity/concentration is often approximately a constant with concentration. In fact molar conductivities increase slightly with decreasing concentration, to a limit symbolized Λ^0.

Kohlrausch used an empirical relationship for extrapolating Λ to Λ^0:

$$\Lambda = \Lambda^0 - \text{const.} \times \sqrt{\text{concentration}}$$

This was later given theoretical justification, for dilute solution, by the Interionic Attraction Theory of Debye and Hückel.

Kohlrausch's law provides a means of calculating Λ^0 of weak acids, which cannot be measured directly. Then the ratio Λ/Λ^0 may be used to measure the degree of dissociation, and hence the dissociation constant, of the weak acid.

It is found that ions move at different speeds, under the same potential gradient, and therefore molar ionic conductivities differ, even when calculated for the fraction of the ion bearing a single charge (e.g. $\frac{1}{2}Cu^{2+}$). The fraction of the current carried by one ion in a given solution is called its transport number, t; and $t_+ = \Lambda_+/\Lambda$. Transport numbers are determined from concentration changes (Hittorf's method) or from a moving boundary experiment.

The ionic mobilities (and transport numbers) of aqueous H^+ and OH^- are greater than those of other ions, and this fact is exploited practically in the conductimetric titration of acids and bases.

3.12 Exercises

1. Explain why the conductivity, and not the conductance nor the molar conductivity, would be the right quantity to specify as a measure of the purity of water produced by a de-ionizer. What value would you expect for domestic 'softened' water? (You may wish to test this experimentally.)

2. A conductance cell was calibrated by filling it with 0.020 mol dm^{-3} KCl solution, which has a conductivity of 0.002 768 Ω^{-1} cm^{-1}; the resistance at 25°C was 457.3 Ω. The cell was then filled with a solution containing 0.555 g dm^{-3} CaCl$_2$, and the measured resistance was 1050 Ω.

   Calculate (a) the cell constant; (b) the conductivity of the CaCl$_2$ solution; and (c) the molar conductivity of $\frac{1}{2}$CaCl$_2$ at this concentration.

3. Rewrite q. 2 in basic SI units, and re-work it.

4. When water with a conductivity of 1.12×10^{-6} Ω^{-1} cm^{-1} was saturated with

pure $BaSO_4$ at 25°C the conductivity rose to $4.63 \times 10^{-6} \, \Omega^{-1} \, cm^{-1}$. With the aid of Table 3.2, calculate the solubility of $BaSO_4$ (in units of mg dm^{-3} or g m^{-3}).

5. 1 mole NaCl was dissolved in 1 m^3 pure water at 25°C. With data from Table 3.2, calculate the approximate conductivity of the solution. If a sample were placed in a round tube 4 cm in diameter, with parallel circular Ag/AgCl electrodes 20 cm apart, what would be the current caused by a potential difference of 80 V ?

6. Plot the molar conductivities of $\frac{1}{2}Na_2SO_4$, CH_3CO_2Na and $\frac{1}{2}H_2SO_4$ against $\sqrt{c}$, and obtain the limiting values, Λ^0. Then, by use of Kohlrausch's Law, calculate Λ^0 for ethanoic acid, CH_3COOH.

(a) Λ for ethanoic acid is 5.0 Ω^{-1} cm^2 mol^{-1} at 0.10 mol dm^{-3}, and 48.8 at 0.0010 mol dm^{-3}. Calculate the degree of ionization at these concentrations, and hence the equilibrium constant.

(b)* From the conductance ratio Λ/Λ^0 for sodium ethanoate at 0.5, 0.05 and 0.005 mol dm^{-3}, test the possibility that the decrease in molar conductivity with concentration is due to an equilibrium between Na$^+$, $CH_3CO_2^-$ and undissociated CH_3CO_2Na. (Hint: calculate the 'equilibrium constant' for each concentration, and inspect its constancy.)

Data	c/mol dm^{-3}	0.50	0.10	0.05	0.01	0.005	0.001	0.0005
	$\frac{1}{2}Na_2SO_4$	—	90.0	97.8	112.4	117.2	124.2	125.7
Λ	CH_3CO_2Na	58.6	72.8	76.9	83.8	85.7	88.5	89.2
Λ^{-1} cm^2 mol^{-1}	$\frac{1}{2}H_2SO_4$	222.5	250.8	272.6	336.4	364.9	399.5	413.1

7. (a) A solution of silver nitrate(V) was electrolysed with silver electrodes in a Hittorf cell; the anode lost 0.112 g and the anolyte gained 0.555 mmol Ag$^+$. Calculate the transport number of Ag$^+$ in this solution.

(b) The molar conductivities of $AgNO_3$, $NaNO_3$ and $\frac{1}{2}Ba(NO_3)_2$ solutions (of equal concentration) are 124, 114 and 126 Ω^{-1} cm^2 mol^{-1}. Using the transport number just found, and assuming the mobility of NO_3^- remains the same in all these solutions, calculate the molar ionic conductances of Ag$^+$, Na$^+$ and $\frac{1}{2}Ba^{2+}$ at this concentration.

8. *Conductimetric titration.* 100 cm^3 aqueous HCl was titrated with 0.202 M NaOH in a conductance cell in series with a milliammeter and a constant source of alternating potential difference. From the following results find the concentration of the acid.

NaOH added, in cm^3	0.0	5.0	10.0	15.0	20.0	25.0
Current, in mA	390	284	177	124	207	294

9*. Why does Na$^+$ have a higher mobility in aqueous solution than Li$^+$ but lower than $\frac{1}{2}Mg^{2+}$, although the ionic radius of Na$^+$ is larger than that of either Li$^+$

or Mg^{2+}? What order would you expect the ionic mobilities to take in the molten chlorides?

10.* Propose one non-aqueous system in which a certain ion might have an anomolously high mobility, by virtue of a Grotthus-type mechanism.

11.* Bredig in 1893 used conductivity measurements to prove the formulas $K_2S_2O_8$ (rather than KSO_4) and $KMnO_4$ (not $K_2Mn_2O_8$). He matched the ratios Λ_1/Λ_2 (for c_1 and c_2, two widely different concentrations) for these salts with the ratios obtained for other potassium salts with accepted formulas.

Explain the basis for his method. (Hint: refer to Fig. 3.8. Does the change of Λ with concentration depend upon molecular weight, number of particles per formula, ionic charge, oxidation state, or what?)

12.* In the Debye–Hückel theory, what are the two effects, besides Brownian movement, which contribute to electrolytic resistance? Which of these will depend upon size, and what is the *effective* size in this case?

The asymmetrical ionic atmosphere will decay more quickly at higher temperature, and the viscosity of the solvent will decrease. Do these changes have more effect on the conductivity than the increase in Brownian motion as temperature increases? How do ionic mobilities change with temperature? Following this line of thought, how would you expect transport numbers to change with temperature?

13. For which of the following reactions could the rate of reaction be measured by conductimetric means?

    (a) $(CH_3)_2CO + I_2 \rightarrow CH_2ICOCH_3 + HI(aq)$

    (b) $(CH_3)_3CI + Cl^- \rightarrow (CH_3)_3Cl + I^-$

    (c) $(CH_3)_2(C_2H_5)CI + OH^- \rightarrow (CH_3)_2(C_2H_5)COH + I^-$

    (d) $H_2S(aq) + H_2O_2(aq) \rightarrow H_2SO_4(aq) + 4H_2O$

4

Galvanic Cells

4.1 Potentiometric cells

A clear distinction should be made between potentiometric cells, set up for the purpose of studying the cell reaction, and practical cells, designed to produce a useful current (§2.8).

One significant difference is that in the practical cell the internal resistance must be low, otherwise energy will be wasted as heat, and the p.d. will fall off when the cell is under load (this is discussed further in §4.8). Therefore the junction between the two half-cells will be extensive, and the electrolytes will tend to interdiffuse—though this will be restricted by some design feature such as a porous partition, or the use of gravity (the less dense solution floating on the other), or by making the electrolyte solutions into a gel or paste. In all these cases the liquid junctions will give rise to a junction potential (§5.4) which interferes with the measurement of the cell potential.

In a potentiometric cell the electrolytes of the two half-cells are usually kept apart by a salt-bridge (Appendix II) of concentrated potassium chloride solution. This eliminates the junction potential and also prevents mixing of participants by diffusion or electrophoresis. It greatly increases the internal resistance, but this is of no consequence since the potential will be measured at or near zero current.

A second difference lies in the presence or absence of the products of the cell reaction. In a practical cell there are initially no products present, and as they slowly accumulate, the p.d. falls—an effect known as 'polarization'. The soluble products diffuse away to some extent, so a cell tends to recover on standing.

In the potentiometric cell this variation of potential with the progress of the cell reaction is avoided by including known amounts of reaction products right from the start. The cell potential varies with the concentration of any soluble (or gaseous) participant (§5.1), so all reactants and products must be present in definite concentrations.

4.2 Reversible conditions

It was shown in Chapter 3 that electrolyte solutions obey Ohm's Law in a modified form. With high frequency alternating current the graph of applied potential versus current is a straight line through the origin. In this chapter however we shall be concerned only with direct current, and in this case the graph of p.d. versus current is only approximately a straight line, and one which does not pass through the origin (except in certain cases), but when extrapolated to zero current cuts the axis at a 'minimum decomposition potential', shown as E_d in Fig. 4.1(a). The only cells which have $E_d = 0$ are those such as $Cu/Cu^{2+}/Cu$, in which the reaction at the cathode is the exact reverse of the one at the anode, so that there are no net products of the electrolysis.

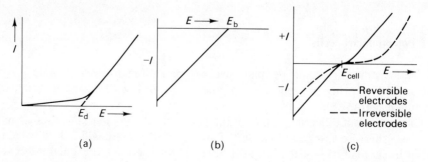

Fig. 4.1 (a) Applied current I versus applied potential E, showing minimum decomposition potential E_d. (b) The back current $-I$, as E is reduced to less than the back e.m.f. E_b. (c) The imposed current $+I$ or load $-I$ versus E

If there are products of electrolysis they are, at least in principle, capable of recombining and acting as the reactants of a galvanic cell. The cell potential of this reverse cell is known as the 'back e.m.f.', since it has a polarity opposite to that of the applied e.m.f. which was causing electrolysis. This may readily be demonstrated by setting up the circuit in Fig. 2.2, preferably with a centre-reading meter, and electrolysing dilute sulphuric acid with Pt or C electrodes for a minute or two. Then, when the driving cell is disconnected and the circuit closed, an anticlockwise deflection of the meter shows the back e.m.f., diminishing quite quickly as the oxygen and hydrogen are used up electrochemically, or diffuse away. Other systems too might involve products which remain at the electrodes and act efficiently as a 'secondary cell'.

Consider such a system after electrolysis has taken place so that products have accumulated (or this condition has been simulated by the addition of 'products'). Then, if the applied potential difference E is gradually reduced to less than the back e.m.f., the current will flow in the opposite direction to that during electrolysis, and may therefore be denoted by $-I$. The graph of this back current $-I$ versus E is shown in Fig. 4.1(b).

When graphs 4.1(a) and 4.1(b) are combined, to show the change of current with applied p.d. varying from zero, up to E_b, to E_d and higher, two different results are possible. Either the straight lines are almost continuous (full line in Fig. 4.1(c)), showing that the back e.m.f. has the same value as the minimum decomposition potential: $E_b = E_d$; or the lines do not meet, and there is a horizontal discontinuity (broken line in Fig. 4.1(c)) because E_d is greater than E_b. In the former case the electrode is said to be 'reversible', and the value of the applied p.d. for which the current is zero is the 'reversible cell potential', E_{cell}, for the back reaction.[1]

'Reversible conditions' are those such that a minute change in conditions one way or the other will bring about chemical reaction in one direction or the other; so the reaction is in a stable but sensitive equilibrium.

It has been mentioned (§2.6) that the p.d. across a galvanic cell decreases as the current drawn from it increases, that is, as the cell departs from reversible conditions. The p.d. will only equal the 'electromotive force' of the cell, that is, the reversible cell potential, when the current is reduced to zero—in other words, under 'no-load conditions'. Further understanding of the reason for this may be gained from §4.7, but for the time being let us accept it as a fact, and note that these conditions are achieved in the opposed cell circuit, to be described, or in the potentiometer (§4.3).

Practical work

Expt. 4–1.1. Set up the simple bridge circuit (Fig. 4.2) for investigating the change of current with applied p.d. The salt-bridge (Appendix II) should be of NH_4NO_3 (since KCl would react with Ag^+). The concentrations in the half-cells are chosen so that $[Ag^+]^2 = [Cu^{2+}]$, which makes the reversible cell potential the standard $E_{cell}^{\ominus}$ (§4.4).

The counter e.m.f. from the external source is variable by means of a rheostat; the value of the potential difference across the test cell is shown by the voltmeter. The value and, more important, the direction of the current through the cell are shown by the microammeter; this should preferably be centre-reading, but failing this a reversing switch or even manual connection changing will enable a uni-directional meter to be used. In order to avoid confusion about the direction of current it is helpful to invent a 'local' sign convention, namely that the current which flows when the test cell is unopposed (counter e.m.f. zero) is to be called negative, and the current forced through the cell when the counter e.m.f. is high shall be called positive. The student must work out how this applies to his own particular ammeter.

If it is found that the current direction is the same for all values of the counter e.m.f., then probably the polarity of the test cell (or perhaps the 2 V supply) has

---

[1] (a) The reversible cell potential for the *forward* reaction in electrolysis is E_b, which equals $-E_{cell}$. No confusion need arise, because while E_b (and E_d) are positive, E_{cell} is invariably negative (or zero) for an electrolytic reaction.

(b) In the case of electrodes which are irreversible or poorly reversible (as shown by the broken curve in Fig. 4.1(c)), the difference $E_d - E_b$ is known as the *overpotential* (§5.2), and one or both parts of the curve may be unobtainable or poorly reproducible. In such cases the value of E_b cannot be obtained directly, and must be calculated from the free energy change ΔG (§4.7).

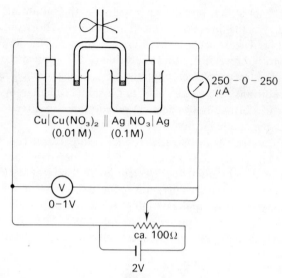

$Cu|Cu(NO_3)_2 \| Ag\ NO_3|Ag$
(0.01 M)   (0.1M)

Fig. 4.2   Bridge circuit with cell opposed by counter-e.m.f.

been wrongly deduced, so that the two sources of e.m.f. are in series rather than in opposition. Check that the negative poles of both cells are directly connected, without any intervening meter or resistor.

When the circuit is correct, take a series of readings of I and E, and plot a graph. Indicate which parts of the graph correspond to electrolysis and galvanic cell action respectively, and write the appropriate electrode reactions. From the intercept at zero current obtain the value of E_{cell} ($E_{cell}^{\ominus}$ if conditions are standard), and write the cell reaction to which this refers.

Specify the sources of error and limits on precision, and estimate the probable uncertainty in your result.

Expt. 4–1.2. As a further experiment (looking ahead to more advanced work), add about 1 cm^3 saturated NaCl solution to the silver nitrate half-cell, stir, and measure the new cell potential. Be sure to check the polarity of the cell, and to deduce correctly the cell reation to which the positive value of the cell potential refers. What has caused the change in the driving force of the reaction? (Note: this experiment may give some insight into the principle on which potentiometric titrations, §7.4, are based.)

4.3 The potentiometer

The potentiometer circuit (Fig. 4.3) retains the principle of counter e.m.f. (due to Poggendorf, 1841), but the voltmeter is omitted and the p.d. across the test cell is calculated from the proportion of the potentiometer resistance wire which is

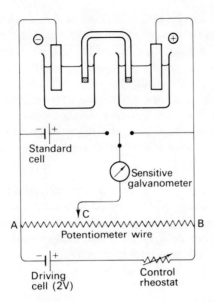

Fig. 4.3   A potentiometer circuit

included in the sub-circuit when the current is zero. In the simplest type the uniform resistance wire is mounted on a board above a metre rule, and the 'tapping' at any intermediate point is done with a square-ended metal probe, which presses the wire on to the scale, and permits length measurement to ± 1 mm.

A 2 V lead storage cell (or other stable 2 V d.c. supply) is connected permanently across the full length of the wire, with a control rheostat in series. There is therefore a uniform potential gradient along the wire.

The p.d. across the whole wire AB may be made equal to that of a Weston Cadmium Cell (or other cell of dependable cell potential) by the procedure known as 'standardizing'. The 'standard cell' is connected from its negative terminal to A (i.e. in opposition to the 2 V driving cell), and from its positive terminal, in series with a sensitive (ca. 10 μA) centre-reading galvanometer, via a tapping switch, to B. The switch is closed for an instant, and the galvanometer indicates the direction of the current; the control rheostat is adjusted until no current flows when the switch is closed. The e.m.f. of the driving cell has then been divided into a p.d. across the rheostat and a p.d. across the potentiometer wire in such a way that the latter exactly equals the e.m.f. of the standard cell.

The test cell is connected with the (supposed) negative to A and the positive, via the galvanometer, to the probe C. The probe is pressed on to the wire at different places until the point is found which results in no current through the galvanometer. The e.m.f. of the test cell is then equal to the p.d. across AC, which equals (AC/AB) × (p.d. across AB).

If no balance point can be found, and the minimum current is obtained when AC = 0, the polarity of the test cell must be reversed; but if the minimum current is when AC is its maximum, then the e.m.f. of the test cell exceeds that of the standard cell, and the potentiometer must be restandardized with the standard cell across a definite fraction (e.g. $\frac{2}{3}$) of the whole wire.

Research quality potentiometers are similar in principle, but the single wire and probe are replaced by many small fixed resistances which are brought into circuit by a dial-switch, and which localize the required potential difference to within 0.01 V; then a low resistance potentiometer wire with a sliding contact gives the null-point to within 10^{-4} V.

The electronic voltmeter (also known as the valve voltmeter) draws very little current, and hence measures a p.d. very nearly equal to the maximum (reversible) potential. It is a very convenient, though expensive, alternative to the simple potentiometer; but since each of the scale ranges starts from zero, it cannot approach the precision of a good potentiometer.

4.4 Standard cell potentials

It is often possible to obtain a rough value for a cell potential, e.g. for the purpose of constructing the electrode potential series (§2.6), simply by putting a voltmeter across the electrodes of the cell. For reproducible results, however, two features of this procedure must be improved. Firstly the electrochemical conditions must be made reversible (§4.2) by the use of a potentiometer or electronic voltmeter; and secondly the concentrations of reactants *and products* of both electrode reactions must be kept constant, as must the temperature. The effect of variation of concentration is that low reactant concentration lowers the cell potential, while low product concentration raises it (see §5.1; the effect is less than 0.2 V except for extreme deficiencies).

The cell potential of a cell which has all participants in standard concentrations is known as the standard cell potential, denoted by $E^{\ominus}_{cell}$. For elementary work, the standard concentration conditions are as follows:

solutes at 1 mole per kg solvent (or approx. 1 mol dm^{-3});

gases at 101 325 Pa ($= N\ m^{-2}$) partial pressure ('1 atmosphere').

The conventional notation for writing down a galvanic cell uses a single vertical line | or a solidus / to represent an interface between an electronic and an electrolytic conductor, and the dotted line ⋮ to represent a junction between two electrolytes (usually two liquids); but if the potential difference due to such a junction is eliminated, as by a salt bridge, this is shown by a double line ||. When an electrode consists of a metal together with some other participant, the two are shown separated by a comma, with the metal further from the interface. And when a solution contains more than one participating solute, these are shown separated

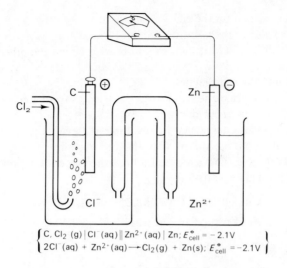

$$\left\{ \begin{array}{l} \text{C, Cl}_2 \text{ (g)} \mid \text{Cl}^- \text{(aq)} \parallel \text{Zn}^{2+} \text{(aq)} \mid \text{Zn; } E^{\ominus}_{\text{cell}} = -2.1\text{V} \\ 2\text{Cl}^- \text{(aq)} + \text{Zn}^{2+} \text{(aq)} \longrightarrow \text{Cl}_2 \text{(g)} + \text{Zn(s); } E^{\ominus}_{\text{cell}} = -2.1\text{V} \end{array} \right\}$$

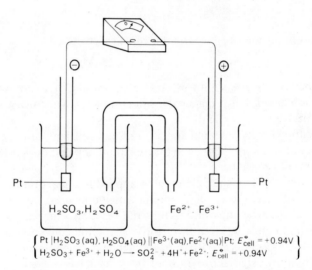

$$\left\{ \begin{array}{l} \text{Pt} \mid \text{H}_2\text{SO}_3 \text{ (aq), H}_2\text{SO}_4\text{(aq)} \parallel \text{Fe}^{3+}\text{(aq),Fe}^{2+}\text{(aq)} \mid \text{Pt; } E^{\ominus}_{\text{cell}} = +0.94\text{V} \\ \text{H}_2\text{SO}_3 + \text{Fe}^{3+} + \text{H}_2\text{O} \longrightarrow \text{SO}_4^{2-} + 4\text{H}^+ + \text{Fe}^{2+}; E^{\ominus}_{\text{cell}} = +0.94\text{V} \end{array} \right\}$$

Fig. 4.4 Two examples of cells, with conventional notation and corresponding cell reactions[2]

by commas, with the more reduced species nearest to the electrodes (see Fig. 4.4).

So far the procedure has been straightforward: the cell notation represents the cell as it can be seen on the bench, and the cell potential is the potential of one

---

[2] Note that in Fig. 4.4(b) the H^+ in the equation is also shown in the cell. Some authors (including Nuffield Adv. Sci. Book of Data, 98–100) go further, and include in the cell notation the stoichiometric coefficients from the equation, so that the equation is unambiguously implied. An objection to this practice is that the cell notation is used to show the cell as it is, and that this does not invariably imply only one reaction.

electrode—the one written on the right—compared to the other as zero. Of course the right-hand electrode in the notation need not be the one which is literally on the right of the bench: how would it look to an observer round the other side?

The cell potential and the cell reaction

It is currently believed that the e.m.f. of the cell arises from a chemical reaction, which can usually be uniquely deduced from the nature of the electrodes and electrolytes, and the observed polarity. For example in the cell: $Cu \mid Cu^{2+}(aq) \parallel Zn^{2+}$ (aq)$\mid Zn$ there is no possible doubt that the cell reaction is either $Zn + Cu^{2+} \rightarrow Cu + Zn^2$ or its reverse. The cell potential has the value 1.1 V and the observed polarity is that the zinc is negative, thus:

$$Cu \mid Cu^{2+} \parallel Zn^{2+} \mid Zn; \quad E^{\ominus} = -1.1 \text{ V}$$
$$Zn \mid Zn^{2+} \parallel Cu^{2+} \mid Cu; \quad E^{\ominus} = +1.1 \text{ V}.$$

It follows that the electrode reactions must be:

$$Zn \rightarrow Zn^{2+}(aq) + 2e^-$$
$$Cu^{2+}(aq) + 2e^- \rightarrow Cu$$

and these add up to the feasible (spontaneous) cell reaction:

$$Zn + Cu^{2+}(aq) \rightarrow Cu + Zn^{2+}(aq)$$

At this point we introduce an arbitrary convention. It is one which is often slipped in unobserved, but it makes the whole topic of sign conventions clearer if the entry point is shown explicitly.

The conventional cell potential for any written cell may also be given to the corresponding cell *reaction*[3] written in the direction such that the left-hand electrode (reduced form) is a reactant.

It follows from this that the cell potential applied to a reaction will be positive if the reaction is written in its feasible (spontaneous) direction.

For practical purposes this means that the reaction which actually occurs, to produce the e.m.f., must be given the positive E_{cell}; and conversely a negative E_{cell} indicated that the reaction as written or implied is non-spontaneous, and can only be brought about by external provision of work, as in electrolysis.

4.5 The standard hydrogen electrode

It became clear to chemists that it would be desirable to decide upon one electrode as a standard against which the potentials of other electrodes could be compared. The reference electrode would have to be (i) reversible (as defined in §4.2) and (ii) reproducible (so that there would be no p.d. between two identical electrodes).

[3] This is tantamount to attributing the cell e.m.f. entirely to the electrode reactions rather than to the contact between the metals—a defeat for Volta's 'contact theory'. But see p. 73, and Project 9.27.

Many metal/metal–ion electrodes fail to satisfy the first condition, and only Zn, Pb, Cu, Ag, Hg and a few others make reversible electrodes, which reach their true potentials in a reasonably short time. Even these are not perfectly reproducible, since their potentials vary with the purity of the metal, its history of heat treatment, hammering, bending, etc., and any strain it may be experiencing, besides surface condition and cleanness.

As a result, metal–ion electrodes had to be eliminated, and, following Nernst's proposal in 1900, the choice fell upon the *hydrogen electrode* which, although awkward to prepare and slow to reach its reversible state, is precisely reproducible by skilled workers. (It is not often used in practice as there are more convenient reference electrodes for routine work (see §7.4).

Two forms of the hydrogen electrode are shown in Fig. 4.5. The electrode is of platinized platinum, that is, platinum which has been coated with finely divided platinum (see Appendix II). Pure hydrogen is passed in slowly, at 1 atm pressure, and the solution contains hydrochloric acid of known concentration. It should be noted that the *standard* hydrogen electrode (the zero of the electrode potentials scale) is a theoretical, not a practical, electrode. This is because the specified electrolyte, namely hydrogen ion at unit *activity* (§5.3), is unavailable. In practice any hydrogen electrode will be non-standard, and the ideal must be approached by extrapolation, using the Nernst equation; but for elementary work an electrolyte with 1 mol dm^{-3} *concentration* of $H^+(aq)$ may be considered to give a sufficiently close approximation.

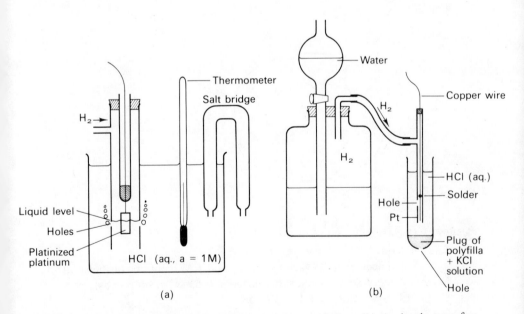

Fig. 4.5 Standard hydrogen electrodes. (a) A common design. (b) A simple type for elementary work, shown connected to a hydrogen reservoir

The conventional notation for the hydrogen half-cell and the corresponding half-reactions are as follows:

On the left: Pt, H_2(1 atm)$|H^+$(aq, 1 M)$\|$ On the right: $\|H^+$(aq, 1 M)$|H_2$, Pt
(oxidation): $H_2(g) \rightarrow 2H^+(aq) + 2e^-$ (reduction): $2H^+(aq) + 2e^- \rightarrow H_2(g)$

4.6 Reduction potentials (electrode potentials)

Every cell reaction is an oxidation–reduction (redox) reaction, and can be considered to be the sum of two half-reactions, the oxidation and the reduction, which can be made to occur in separate half-cells. It is found that if the half-cells are combined in a number of different ways, the call potentials of the resultant cells obey an additive law:

   (i) $E_{B\|C} = E_{B\|A} + E_{A\|C}$
or (ii) $E_{B\|C} = E_{A\|C} - E_{A\|B}$

(where $E_{B\|C}$ means the cell potential of the cell formed by combining electrode B on the left with electrode C on the right)

Practical work

Expt. 4–2

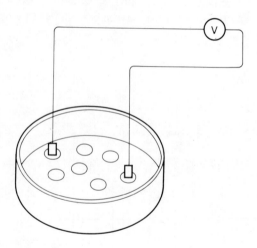

Fig. 4.6

Required   High resistance (electronic) voltmeter.
Petri-dish or other wide dish.
Small specimens of various metals and 1 M solutions of their salts.
Carbon electrode (e.g. short pencil sharpened at both ends).
$Br_2 + Br^-$ and $I_2 + I^-$ solutions.
1% Agar gel containing ca. 10% NH_4NO_3. to fill the dish to a depth of about 1 cm.

When the gel has set, cut a number of holes in it with a cork-borer. Draw a map of the holes, and label it with the half-cells which are to be used; then place 4–6 drops of the correct electrolyte into each hole, following the scheme on the map.

Take any pair of metals and hold the specimens in crocodile clips connected to the voltmeter. While touching them together, set the needle to zero. Then dip each metal into its own ionic solution. This sets up a galvanic cell, since the gel acts as a universal salt-bridge. Note the polarity and record the e.m.f.

Repeat for a number of combinations. From the results, test the validity of the additive law for electrode potentials. See §4.7 for the calculation of $\Delta G^\ominus$ from these cell potentials.

IUPAC Electrode Potential Convention

If all electrodes were paired against one reference electrode, the resultant cell potentials could be called the potentials of the various electrodes *compared to the reference electrode as zero*. The accepted convention (IUPAC, 1953) is that the standard hydrogen electrode shall be the reference electrode for this purpose, and that it shall be on the left in the conventional cell representation. The cell potential of such a cell may be referred to as the *electrode potential* of the electrode on the right.

For example,

$$\text{Pt, } H_2(1 \text{ atm}) \mid H^+(1 \text{ M}) \parallel Cu^{2+}(1 \text{ M}) \mid Cu; \ E^\ominus_{\text{cell}} = +0.34 \text{ V}$$

and
$$\text{Pt, } H_2(1 \text{ atm}) \mid H^+(1 \text{ M}) \parallel Zn^{2+}(1 \text{ M}) \mid Zn; \ E^\ominus_{\text{cell}} = -0.76 \text{ V}$$

So we may say that the electrode potential of copper is $+0.34$ V, while that of zinc is -0.76 V. The cell potential of the zinc–copper cell may be calculated from the second form (ii) of the additive law given above:

$$E_{\text{Zn}/\text{Cu}} = E_{\text{H}_2/\text{Cu}} - E_{\text{H}_2/\text{Zn}} = +0.34 \text{ V} - (-0.76 \text{ V}) = +1.10 \text{ V}$$

Reduction potentials and oxidation potentials

An alternative approach to electrode potentials, and one which is more directly useful, is through the cell reactions and half-reactions, rather than through half-cells. It is important that the results of the two approaches should be compatible, and logically consistent, and this will be so if a little care is taken over terminology.

If the cell reaction is the sum of two half-reactions (defined as reactions in which electrons are either consumed or produced), and the full balanced ionic equation is the sum of a pair of redox half-equations, then the additive law for electrode potentials may be re-expressed in terms of the reactions:

$$
\begin{array}{ccc}
\text{Full reaction} & = \text{reduction} & \text{oxidation} \\
& \text{half-reaction} \overset{+}{} & \text{half-reaction}
\end{array}
$$

$$
\begin{array}{ccc}
E_{\text{cell}} & E_{\text{red}} & E_{\text{ox}} \\
\text{Cell potential} = \text{reduction} & + & \text{oxidation} \\
\text{potential} & & \text{potential}
\end{array}
$$

For example:

$$Zn + Cl_2(aq) \rightarrow Zn^{2+}(aq) + 2Cl^-(aq); \quad E^{\ominus}_{cell} = +2.12 \text{ V}$$

$$Zn \rightarrow Zn^{2+}(aq) + 2e^-; \qquad\qquad E^{\ominus}_{ox} = x$$

$$Cl_2(aq) + 2e^- \rightarrow 2Cl^-(aq); \qquad\quad E^{\ominus}_{red} = y$$

$$x + y = +2.12 \text{ V}$$

It is not possible to discover x or y unless a value is arbitrarily given to one redox potential[4]; and the accepted convention is that the reference half-reaction should be that of the standard hydrogen electrode:

$$H_2(g) \rightarrow 2H^+(aq) + 2e^-; \; E^{\ominus}_{ox} = 0$$

$$2H^+(aq) + 2e^- \rightarrow H_2(g); \; E^{\ominus}_{red} = 0$$

Now the cell potential for the H_2/Cl_2 cell is experimentally accessible:

$$H_2(g) + Cl_2(aq) \rightarrow 2H^+(aq) + 2Cl^-(aq); \; E^{\ominus}_{cell} = +1.36 \text{ V}$$

It follows that if $E^{\ominus}_{ox}(H_2/H^+)$ is zero, then $E^{\ominus}_{red}(Cl_2/Cl^-) = +1.36$ V. Thus y in the example above is found, and $x = +2.12$ V $- (+1.36$ V$) = +0.76$ V. So every piece falls into place, and the redox potentials can be determined for all reactions which can be made to take place in an electrochemical cell (see also §4.7). A table of reduction potentials appears as Appendix I.

Note that a reactive metal such as sodium has a large negative reduction potential, since sodium ions have far less tendency to accept electrons than have hydrogen ions:

$$Na^+(aq) + e^- \rightarrow Na(s); \; E^{\ominus}_{red} = -2.71 \text{ V}$$

Why then is sodium said to be an 'electropositive element'? One should relate the term 'electropositive' to the tendency to form positive ions, and not to the sign of the electrode potential.

The equivalence of electrode potential and reduction potential

We recall that the electrode potential of metal M (assumed divalent, for convenience) is the cell potential of:

$$Pt, H_2 \,|\, H^+ \,\|\, M^{2+} \,|\, M$$

Now the associated cell reaction is the one in which metal M is the *product*:

$$H_2 + M^{2+} \rightarrow 2H^+ + M$$

So the 'electrode potential' of M is the cell potential for this reaction; and this is the sum of $E^{\ominus}_{ox}(H_2 \rightarrow 2H^+)$ and $E^{\ominus}_{red}(M^{2+} \rightarrow M)$. Since $E^{\ominus}_{ox}(H_2 \rightarrow 2H^+)$ is zero, the 'electrode potential' of M is identical with the 'reduction potential' of $M^{2+} \rightarrow M$.

---

[4] The term redox potential may be used as an indiscriminate name for reduction or oxidation potentials in general, but should not be associated with a denifite value, as the sign would then be ambiguous.

The terms are synonymous in practice. It is important to note, however, that the *oxidation* potential is NOT the electrode potential: much confusion has been caused in the past by this difference being overlooked. As oxidation potentials are listed in much U.S. literature, one must be alert.

Some electrochemists object to redox potentials on principle, and ask whether a half-equation really means anything. Since a half-reaction cannot be isolated, how can its potential be meaningful? Further, what is the physical state of the electron? It cannot correspond to any real state, such as the free gaseous electron, or the aqueous (hydrated) electron, for these are known, and their free energies are known, and are not consistent with the values of the redox potentials.

The only logical answer is that the e^- in the half-equations is a fictitious electron, not in any real state. It is no more than an abbreviation for $(\frac{1}{2}H_2 - H^+)$, that is, 'add $\frac{1}{2}$ mole H_2 where the e^- is, and add 1 mole $H^+(aq)$ to the other side'. This may seem arbitrary, but it works, and in practice nobody is worried by it. While we are questioning the real meaning of half-equations and redox potentials, it ought to be mentioned that a cell potential is not derived completely from the two electrode interactions between metal and solution, even when there is no liquid-junction potential (§5.4), because there is inevitably a contribution from the metal–metal contact. If we consider the cell which defined the electrode potential of M at the start of this section, as soon as it is put in circuit with a potentiometer it becomes:

$$\text{Pt, } H_2 \,|\, H^+ \,||\, M^{2+} \,|\, M - - - \text{Pt}$$

where $- - -$ represents any sequence of electronic conductors. Thus the M–Pt contact potential is surreptitiously hidden in the reduction potential for a chemical half-reaction. Nevertheless, the calculations 'come right'.

Chemists find half-reactions and reduction potentials very useful devices, and more convenient to apply to ordinary (non-electro-) chemistry than are half-cells and electrode potentials. Reduction potentials can be calculated even for half-reactions which cannot be made to function reversibly in a cell, since the relationship with free energy (see next section) allows them to be calculated from non-electrochemical sources. From tables of reduction potentials the cell potential of any reaction can be found (§4.9), and the sign of this predicts the feasibility of the reaction—an application amply illustrated in Chapter 5.

4.7 Potentials and free energy

We have seen that the driving force of a chemical reaction is measured by its cell potential. To summarize, if the cell potential for a reaction is negative there will be no tendency for the reaction to occur unless energy is supplied in some potent form such as electricity (as in electrolysis) or radiation (as in photochemical reactions). If, however, the cell potential is positive there will be a *tendency* for the reaction to occur, although the *rate* is unspecified, and may in fact be extremely slow.

It appears, then, that a reaction tends to occur if it is capable of producing energy in some universally convertible form (i.e. most forms of energy except heat)—and the most easily harnessed and measured form is electricity.

The relationship between potential difference and electrical energy (work) is that the work done equals the amount of electricity multiplied by the p.d. across which it flows. The SI units for these quantities are the joule, coulomb and volt respectively: so 1 C of electricity at a potential of 1 V above some 'earth' possesses an energy of 1 J.

In electrochemistry we are considering the energy which can be obtained from a galvanic cell. From Faraday's Laws, or the stoichiometry of the cell reaction (§2.2), it follows that the *amount* of electricity which must flow if one mole of reaction[5] occurs can be deduced from the equation, since it equals z moles of electrons where z is the number of electrons in the component half-equations.

Electrical work obtainable per mole reaction $= (z$ mol electrons$) \times E$

(where E is the actual p.d. developed by the cell under the current conditions specified, and not necessarily E_{cell}, the reversible cell potential).

The convention used for the enthalpy change (heat) of reaction ΔH is that energy lost by the system to the surroundings (as in an exothermic reaction) is represented by a negative sign, e.g.:

$$2H_2(g) + O_2(g) \to 2H_2O(l); \Delta H_{298} = -286 \text{ kJ mol}^{-1}$$

(where mol^{-1} means 'per mole of reaction as shown by the equation', and not 'per mole of product', as in this case H_2O).

In accordance with this convention, we shall use the symbol $+w$ to represent work put into the system, and $-w$ for work produced by the system:[6]

$$-w = zE$$

As it stands, this equation would lead to the electrical work having the units 'molar electron-volts'; and so in order that the work should be in SI units, the charge, z mol electrons, is multiplied by the factor F, the Faraday constant, so that it is in the SI unit coulombs. Experimentally F is found to have the value 6.949×10^4 C per mol electrons.

Thus we have:

$$-w = zFE$$

This is true whether the cell is under load, with E less than E_{cell}, or under no-load 'reversible' conditions. Depending upon the experimental conditions (see §4.8), the value of the current can vary from extremely high (short-circuit) to zero, and the p.d. from zero up to a maximum, the reversible cell potential E_{cell}. In the latter case the work will be a maximum, even though it can only be obtained infinitely slowly:

$$w_{max} = -zFE_{cell} \text{ (reversible conditions)}$$

[5] Also known as one gramme-equation.
[6] In the past the opposite sign convention was often used for w.

One of the most fruitful postulates of chemical thermodynamics is that this maximum work equals the *free energy change* ΔG for the cell reaction:

$$w_{max} = -zFE_{cell} = \Delta G \text{ (reversible conditions)}$$

The free energy change for any process is independent of the *mechanism* or route by which the process occurs, and depends only upon the initial and final states. It is not the energy difference, which for constant pressure conditions is the enthalpy change ΔH (heat of reaction), but as the name implies it is that part of the energy which could potentially be harnessed as electricity or any useful work (as distinct from heat).

The relationship between free energy change and enthalpy change is given by the Gibbs equation:

$$\Delta G = \Delta H - T\Delta S$$

where ΔS is the entropy change[7] and T is the thermodynamic ('absolute)' temperature. Since T is not large in aqueous electrochemical systems, ΔG generally has the same sign as ΔH, and indeed in some cells, such as the Daniell cell, ΔS is so small that ΔG was formerly believed to be equal to the heat of reaction, within experimental error. That this is not so may be shown in the Cu/Ag cell (Expt. 4-3).

The free energy in the Universe cannot be increased (this is a way of stating the Second Law of Thermodynamics) and any increase in the free energy of the one system on which our attention may be directed (ΔG positive) must have been the result of work put in (mechanical, electrical, radiant etc.) or a transfer of chemical energy from a simultaneous free energy losing reaction. Free energy is thus not necessarily conserved. It is in fact only conserved under the practically unattainable conditions of infinitely slow change at equilibrium (when $\Delta G = 0$) or under reversible conditions such as in a galvanic cell in a balanced potentiometer circuit ($\Delta G = w_{max}$). When the process is allowed to run freely and spontaneously, free energy is invariably lost (see §4.8).

This view of a process provides a useful criterion for predicting whether the change will be spontaneous (i.e. feasible without requiring the supply of work). The spontaneous reaction has negative ΔG and therefore positive E_{cell}. This is the point with which this section began, but the theory now covers *all* physical and chemical changes, not merely those which can occur in electrochemical cells.

Note that ΔG and E_{cell} both vary with temperature and concentration. The temperature may be specified thus ΔG_{293}, but is generally taken to be 298 K if not otherwise shown. If the concentrations are standard (§4.4) the sign $\ominus$ is added:

$$\Delta G^{\ominus} = -zFE^{\ominus}_{cell}$$

Practical work

Expt. 4–3. To measure ΔH *and* ΔG *for the same reaction.* The reaction chosen for this reaction must be a redox reaction which can take place in a cell consisting of

[7] For a further account of free energy and entropy, see the author's *Chemical Energetics*, ch. 5, Edward Arnold (1971).

two reversible electrodes (§4.2) so that the standard cell potential can be measured, giving $\Delta G^{\ominus}$; it must also take place rapidly, so that the heat of reaction ΔH can be measured in a simple calorimeter; and thirdly, ΔH and $\Delta G^{\ominus}$ should be sufficiently different in value, so that experimental errors do not obscure the result.

The reaction between $Zn(s)$ and $Cu^{2+}(aq)$ satisfies the first two requirements, but not the third, since the replacement of one metal ion by another of the same charge and size will have $\Delta G^{\ominus}$ very close to ΔH.

A reaction which works well is:

$$Cu(s) + 2Ag^{+}(aq) \rightarrow Cu^{2+}(aq) + 2Ag(s).$$

The cell is easily set up, and its potential difference measured by methods described above (§4.4). Moreover copper powder (excess) will readily react with a measured quantity of silver(I) nitrate(V) solution in a simple polythene bottle calorimeter. Details are given elsewhere (see Appendix II). The calorimetric measurement may be compared with the electrochemical determination of ΔH from the temperature dependence of the cell potential (Expt. 4–4, §4.10).

A promising alternative is the reaction:

$$Zn(s) + Br_2(aq) \rightarrow Zn^{2+}(aq) + 2Br^{-}(aq)$$

since the cell potential is easily measured, and zinc powder rapidly reduces saturated bromine solution, with a convenient temperature rise. The concentration of bromine should be determined iodimetrically. The reaction between zinc and iodine is also suitable, but there is the complication arising from the complexing of I_2 with I^{-}.

4.8 Thermodynamics of cells

The inter-relations between cell potentials, free energy, work and heat transfer are a little confusing on first acquaintance. To understand them one must be clear about reversible and irreversible transfer of work, and the First Law of thermodynamics.

Energy takes many forms, those in which we shall be interested being potential energy (which arises from the position of a body in a gravitational or electric field), kinetic energy (from ordered motion), thermal energy or heat (random molecular motion) and chemical energy. There is also the energy possessed by a gas by virtue of its pressure.

The various forms of energy are interconvertible, by means of suitable devices, and in theory (from the First Law) energy of type A could be converted to type B, then to C and so on, and eventually back to the original amount of type A. There is an important exception to this: none of the forms of energy in the chain must be *heat*, otherwise the rule will not hold. Any energy can be completely converted into heat, but heat cannot be *completely* converted into any other form. To emphasize this difference, the conversion of energy to any form other than heat is referred to as 'work'.

The symbols q and w represent heat and work respectively, and positive values indicate energy gained by the system under consideration.

The internal energy U of a system is the energy it possesses due to its chemical nature, temperature and pressure, and clearly if any energy is put into the system, its energy will increase by an amount equal to $(q + w)$. This is the First Law:

$$U_{final} - U_{initial} = \Delta U = q + w$$

If the pressure is kept constant (as is usually the case in electrochemistry) it is more convenient to consider a quantity equal to the internal energy *plus PV* energy, known as the enthalpy H:

$$H = U + PV$$

If pressure P is constant, $\Delta H = \Delta U + P\Delta V$

Now $P\Delta V$ represents work which must be transferred to maintain constant pressure, and so it is a portion of the work which is not available for conversion to other forms such as electricity. Let us, following Halliwell, call it 'obligatory work', w_{obl}. The remaining work is 'optional work', w_{opt}, since it can, at the option of the experimenter, be harnessed as some useful form.

So the relationship between enthalpy change, heat transfer and optional work may be derived thus:

$$\Delta U = q + w_{obl} + w_{opt}$$
$$-w_{obl} = P\Delta V \quad \text{(work is done } by \text{ the system if } V \text{ increases)}$$
$$\Delta U + P\Delta V = \Delta H = q + w_{opt}$$

This is the First Law of thermodynamics as applied to reacting systems at constant pressure. If no attempt is made to harness work, w_{opt} will be zero. So when reactants are simply mixed, in an open vessel, the heat of reaction will equal the enthalpy change; it follows that ΔH can be measured by calorimetry.

But if the reaction takes place in an electrochemical cell, the heat transfer will be less than ΔH, because the First Law must be obeyed:

$$\Delta H = H_{final} - H_{initial} = \text{a constant (for a given amount of chemical change)}$$

$$\begin{array}{ccc} \Delta H & = q & + \quad w_{opt} \\ \text{constant} & \text{variable} & \text{variable} \end{array}$$

To understand more about the way in which electrical work may vary, for the same amount of reaction, let us consider the charging and discharging of a cell at various speeds. Take the copper–silver cell as an example:

$$Cu\,|\,Cu^{2+}(1\text{ M})\,\|\,Ag^{+}(1\text{ M})\,|\,Ag; \; E^{\ominus}_{cell} = +0.46 \text{ V}$$

The enthalpy of reaction might be found by reacting copper powder with silver nitrate solution as in §4.7, or from the variation of $E^{\ominus}_{cell}$ with temperature, as in §4.10:

$$Cu(s) + 2Ag^{+}(aq) \rightarrow 2Ag(s) + Cu^{2+}(aq); \; \Delta H = -147 \text{ J mol}^{-1}$$

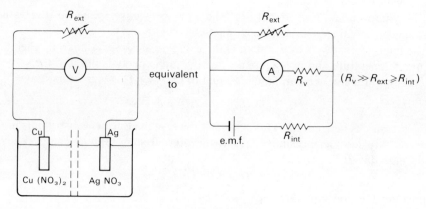

Fig. 4.7   Copper–silver cell with variable external circuit

Now if this copper–silver cell is short-circuited, e.g. by a thick copper wire, a substantial current will flow, limited only by the internal resistance of the cell, since $R_{ext} \approx 0$.

$$\text{e.m.f.} = IR_{total} = I(R_{int} + 0)$$

The thick wire will not even get hot, as the potential difference across it is zero. In fact the reaction will be completely unharnessed, and all the energy (enthalpy) of reaction will appear as heat inside the cell. If the cell is in a thermostat bath, this energy will leave the system as ambient temperature heat, which is completely incapable of doing work.

Let us assume a value of 10 Ω for the internal resistance, and since the electromotive force is 0.46 V, the current I is given by[8]:

$$I = \frac{0.46 \text{ V}}{10 \text{ } \Omega} = 0.046 \text{ A} = 46 \text{ mA}$$

Allow 1 mmole (1 mg-eqn.) of reaction to occur by the passage of 2×96.5 C (since $z = 2$ in the half-equations), and the time for this can be calculated:

amount of electricity in coulombs = current in amperes × time in seconds

$$t = \frac{2 \times 96.5}{46 \times 10^{-3}} \text{ s} = 4.2 \times 10^3 \text{ s}$$

The heat produced in this unharnessed reaction will equal the enthalpy change for the amount of reaction being considered:

$$q = -147 \text{ kJ mol}^{-1} \times 10^{-3} \text{ mol} = -147 \text{ J}$$

---

[8] For simplicity the effect of overpotential (§6.2) is omitted in this treatment and tacitly included in the 'internal resistance'; the effect of diminishing the overpotential is the same as that of decreasing the ratio of internal to external resistance.

Now in order to get some work from the cell we put a small, weak, but 100% efficient electric motor, of 20Ω resistance, in the circuit. This triples the total resistance and reduces the current to 46/3 mA ($=15.3$ mA) while tripling the time for 1 mmole of reaction (to 12.6×10^3 s). The work done by the motor can be calculated as the product of power and time (or as amount of electricity passed $\times$ p.d. across the motor):

$$-w_{opt} = (I^2 R_{ext}) \times t = It \times IR_{ext}$$
$$= 15.3 \times 10^{-3} \text{ A} \times 12.6 \times 10^3 \text{ s} \times 15.3 \times 10^{-3} \text{ A} \times 20 \text{ }\Omega$$
$$= 15.3 \times 12.6 \text{ C} \times 2 \times 15.3 \times 10^{-2} \text{ V}$$
$$= 59 \text{ J}$$

So 59 joules of electrical work is taken out of the cell, and this must be subtracted from the enthalpy change (147 J evolved per mmol) to obtain the heat evolved inside the cell:

$$-q = (147 - 59) \text{ J} = 88 \text{ J}$$

Thus 59 J of work was obtained at the cost of 88 J wasted as heat. This energy efficiency is poor, and in an attempt to increase it, the motor is changed to one with a higher resistance, say 90 Ω. Now the total resistance is 100 Ω and the current 4.6 mA, which requires 4.2×10^4 s (about 12 hours) for 1 mmole of reaction to occur.

$$-w_{opt} = (4.6 \times 10^{-3} \times 4.2 \times 10^4) \times (4.6 \times 10^{-3} \times 90) \text{ J}$$
$$= 80 \text{ J}$$

This is a better performance: 80 J of electrical work obtained (but it took 12 hours to get it!) against $(147 - 80)$, i.e. 67 J energy transferred out as heat.

Clearly the efficiency of work production is proportional to R_{ext}/R_{int}, and Table 4.1 shows how, as this ratio increases, the work harnessed increases to a maximum, equal to $zFE_{cell}^{\ominus}$. Since this is the only part of the internal energy change which is

Table 4.1 Efficiency of Harnessing Work from 1 mmole Reaction in a Copper–Silver Cell

Internal resistance (in ohms)	External resistance (in ohms)	Current (in mA)	Time period (in s $\times 10^3$)	Work obtained (in J)	Heat produced (in J)
10	0	46	4.2	0	147
10	5	30.6	6.3	30	117
10	20	15.3	12.6	59	88
10	90	4.6	42	80	67
10	990	0.46	420	87.8	59
10	∞	0	∞	88.7	58

'free' or 'available', it has been called the free energy change, $\Delta G^{\ominus}$. Since the system loses this free energy when electricity is produced, the sign is negative:

$$\Delta G^{\ominus} = -zFE^{\ominus}_{\text{cell}}$$

So far this discussion has been concerned only with galvanic cell action, and not electrolysis. So the 'limiting conditions' have not yet been shown to be 'reversible'. This may be done quite easily by drawing up a table (Table 4.2) of efficiencies of recharging the copper–silver cell with various currents. The apparatus might be as in Fig. 4.8.

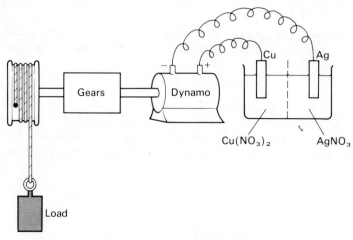

Fig. 4.8 Re-charging the cell: conversion of electrical to chemical energy

As the mass falls through height h, it does work equal to mgh (where g = acceleration of free fall) and this is converted into d.c. electricity by an ideal (100% efficient) dynamo. The rate of fall of the mass is governed by the resistance of the dynamo and the gear system, and this in turn governs the e.m.f. of the output. When the dynamo turns fast, it causes a high p.d. across the cell, and a large charging current. But little of this energy becomes chemical energy—most is wasted as heat in the cell, as Table 4.2 shows.

If the gear ratio is changed so that the mass falls more slowly, the dynamo turns more slowly and generates a lower e.m.f., and the current (proportional to this e.m.f. minus 0.46 V) decreases. The time required to charge the cell by 1 mmol of reaction increases, but the energy efficiency rises, becoming (theoretically) 100% when the dynamo output only infinitesimally exceeds the reversible cell potential, 0.46 V.

The cell is then said to be under reversible conditions because a minute change in the conditions (i.e. a slight drop in the applied p.d.) would cause the reaction to reverse.

Table 4.2 Efficiency of Charging a Copper–Silver Cell

Dynamo e.m.f. (in V)	Excess e.m.f. (in V)	Current* (in mA)	Time required† (in s × 10³)	Gain in free energy (in kJ mol⁻¹)	Energy wasted as heat (in kJ)	Efficiency %
8.0	7.54	75.4	2.5	88.7	1470	5.7
2.0	1.54	15.4	12.6	88.7	297	23
1.0	0.54	5.4	36	88.7	104	46
0.50	0.04	0.4	483	88.7	7.7	92
0.46	0.00	0.0	∞	88.7	0	100

* Assuming total resistance $= 10\ \Omega$.
† To bring about 1 mmol reaction.

4.9 Combining redox potentials

An important reason why redox potentials are widely used for predicting reactions (§5.5) is that they are so easily combined to give cell potentials. Simple addition is all that is required:

$$E^{\ominus}_{\text{cell}} = E^{\ominus}_{\text{red}} + E^{\ominus}_{\text{ox}}$$

Since the tables of data will normally list reduction potentials (§4.6), the oxidation potential (for the oxidation half-reaction) will be obtained by changing the sign of the reduction potential.

Worked example
   From tabulated data (e.g. Appendix I) calculate the standard cell potential for the following reaction at 298 K:

$$5S_2O_8^{2-} + 2Mn^{2+} + 8H_2O \rightarrow 10\ SO_4^{2-} + 2MnO_4^- + 16H^+$$

The half-reactions are:

$$2Mn^{2+} + 8H_2O \rightarrow 2MnO_4^- + 16H^+ + 10e^- \quad \text{(ox)}$$
$$5S_2O_8^{2-} + 10e^- \rightarrow 10SO_4^{2-} \quad \text{(red)}$$

The relevant entries in the table of reduction potentials are:

$$MnO_4^- + 8H^+ + 5e^- \rightarrow Mn^{2+} + 4H_2O; \quad E^{\ominus}_{\text{red}} = +1.51\ \text{V}$$
$$S_2O_8^{2-} + 2e^- \rightarrow 2SO_4^{2-}; \quad E^{\ominus}_{\text{red}} = +2.01\ \text{V}$$
$$\therefore\ E^{\ominus}_{\text{cell}} = +2.01 - 1.51 = +0.50\ \text{V}$$

(This suggests that peroxodisulphate ion is potentially capable of oxidizing Mn(II) to Mn(VII) in acid conditions. You may like to try the experiment: but the reaction is slow unless a catalyst, such as Ag^+, is present.)

   Note that the redox potentials were used in the calculation without regard for the number of electrons in the half-equations. One might think that this procedure was over simple. In order to make the half-equations 'add up' to the full equation, the first (MnO_4^-) one has to be reversed and also multiplied by 2; while the second one is not reversed, but is multiplied by 5. The first reduction potential is indeed 'reversed' (the sign is changed), but neither potentials are multiplied. Why not?

The answer is that while it is true that the free energy change ΔG for a reaction has to be multiplied when the equation is multiplied, that is taken care of by the increase in z:

$$S_2O_8^{2-} + 2e^- \rightarrow 2SO_4^{2-}; \quad \Delta G^{\ominus} = -2 \times F \times 2.01 \text{ eV mol}^{-1}$$

$$5S_2O_8^{2-} + 10e^- \rightarrow 10SO_4^{2-}; \quad \Delta G^{\ominus} = -10 \times F \times 2.01 \text{ eV mol}^{-1}$$

If the potential were multiplied as well, that would give a *further* increase in $\Delta G^{\ominus}$. Potential is like temperature in being an 'intensive' property, independent of the size of the system. Two litres of boiling water contain twice as much heat as one litre, but the temperature is the same.

So even if the z's in the half-equations were carried through meticulously, and the free energies calculated and added, this would give the same answer for the cell potential as the simple method. For our example:

$$2Mn^{2+} + 8H_2O \rightarrow 2MnO_4^- + 16H^+ + 10e^-;$$
$$\Delta G_{\text{ox}}^{\ominus} = -10\,F(-1.51) = +15.1\,F$$

$$5S_2O_8^{2-} + 10e^- \rightarrow 10SO_4^{2-}; \quad \Delta G_{\text{red}}^{\ominus} = -10\,F(+2.01) = -20.1\,F$$

$$2Mn^{2+} + 5S_2O_8^{2-} + 8H_2O \rightarrow 2MnO_4^- + 16H^- + 10SO_4^{2-};$$
$$\Delta G_{\text{reaction}}^{\ominus} = +5.0\,F$$

$$E_{\text{cell}}^{\ominus} = \frac{\Delta G_r^{\ominus}}{zF} = \frac{+5.0\,F}{10\,F} = +0.50 \text{ V}$$

The factor 10 'cancels out' all through. But what if z is *not* equal in the half-equations to be combined? That would be the case when two redox potentials are to be combined to give a *third* redox potential. Then the simple addition would be wrong. For example:

$$Fe \rightarrow Fe^{2+} + 2e^-; \quad E_{\text{ox}}^{\ominus} = +0.44 \text{ V } (z = 2)$$

$$Fe^{2+} \rightarrow Fe^{3+} + e^-; \quad E_{\text{ox}}^{\ominus} = -0.77 \text{ V } (z = 1)$$

$$Fe \rightarrow Fe^{3+} + 3e^-; \quad E_{\text{ox}}^{\ominus} \neq -0.33 \text{ V}$$

Simple addition gives an answer of -0.33 V for the third oxidation potential, but the true value is $+0.04$ V—so even the sign was wrong. The mistake lies in the assumed cancellation of z throughout, whereas it is not a constant in this case. To simplify matters, instead of adding $\Delta G^{\ominus}$, i.e. $-zFE^{\ominus}$, we may add $zE^{\ominus}$, since $-F$ is a constant.

$$3E_3^{\ominus} = 2 \times (+0.44) + 1 \times (-0.77)$$
$$= +0.88 - 0.77 = +0.11 \text{ V}$$

$$E_3^{\ominus} = +0.11/3 = +0.04 \text{ V}$$

One further warning. The procedure for calculating $E_{cell}^{\ominus}$ from $\Delta G^{\ominus}$ involves the assumption of a value for z. In most cases there is one obvious choice, but sometimes, particularly for disproportionation reactions (involving three oxidation states of an element), z may be ambiguous, and must be stated along with $E_{cell}^{\ominus}$. It is even conceivable that two cells might be set up having exactly the same cell reaction but different potentials! No real instance of this has yet been reported.

4.10 Variation of cell potential with temperature

The working potential of a practical cell, especially a partly rundown one, usually rises with increase in temperature. But this effect is mainly a result of the increase in conductivity of the cell electrolyte, and faster diffusion of the products of cell action. It is a kinetic effect, not a thermodynamic one.

Of more theoretical importance is the variation of *reversible* cell potential with temperature; for, with different cells, both increases and decreases are found, for an increase in temperature. Under reversible conditions the internal resistance of the cell becomes irrelevant, and the effect is entirely due to the variation of free energy change:

$$\Delta G = -zFE$$
$$E = \frac{-\Delta G}{zF} = \frac{-\Delta H}{zF} + \frac{T\Delta S}{zF}$$

$$\therefore \frac{dE}{dT} = \frac{\Delta S}{zF} \quad \text{or} \quad E_T = E_{298} + \frac{(T - 298)\Delta S}{zF}$$

One practical consequence of this is that a reference cell, which should be as temperature-independent as possible, should have a cell reaction with only a small entropy change. For this reason the Weston cell, $Cd \,|\, CdSO_4(sat) \,|\, CdSO_4(s) + Hg_2SO_4(s) \,|\, Hg$ superseded the Clark cell, which had zinc in place of cadmium.

The second important consequence is that the accurate measurement of E_{cell} at different temperatures enables ΔH to be determined, either by algebra (simultaneous equations) or graphically (by extrapolation to $T = 0$). An experiment of this kind using the lead–acid accumulator has been described by Johnson and Crawford in *J. Chem. Educ.*, **46**, 52 (1969); their specially prepared cell gives a linear E/T graph from 0 to 45°C, and leads to a ΔH in good agreement with the literature. In some cases the actual cell reaction may not be known for certain, and such a determination of ΔH and ΔS may help to identify the reaction.

Expt. 4–4. To measure the variation of cell potential with temperature. Set up the cell: $Cu \,|\, Cu(NO_3)_2(aq, 0.01 \text{ M}) \,\|\, AgNO_3(aq, 0.1 \text{ M}) \,|\, Ag$ in a compact form capable of immersion in a water-bath (see Appendix II). Measure the cell potential, by a potentiometer or electronic voltmeter, over a range of temperatures (at 5 or 10 K intervals), allowing time for thermal equilibrium to be established each time. Plot a graph of E against T, and obtain ΔH, $\Delta S^{\ominus}$ and $\Delta G_{298}^{\ominus}$.

4.11 Summary

Potentiometry is the measurement of the electromotive force of cells. The potential difference across a cell under load (i.e. producing electricity) or under charge will differ from the no-load or limiting e.m.f. Potentiometric cells differ in design from practical cells, since their purpose is not to give a useful current, but to offer a reproducible e.m.f. for measurement or comparison.

Reversible conditions obtain when the cell is opposed by an external source of e.m.f. (the counter e.m.f.) so precisely balanced that no current flows through the cell. Then the measured potential difference across the cell is known as the reversible cell potential, E_{cell}. If concentrations in the cell are standard, this is denoted by the symbol $^\ominus$.

Two circuits for the measurement of E_{cell} are described: the counter e.m.f. circuit using a voltmeter, and the potentiometer using a reference cell. An alternative measuring device is the electronic voltmeter, which draws so little current that conditions are virtually reversible.

For the discussion of cell potentials, it is necessary to be familiar with (i) the conventional cell notation; (ii) the relation between the polarity of the cell and the direction of the implied cell reaction; (iii) the definition of electrode potential, by reference to the standard hydrogen electrode; (iv) the concept of oxidation and reduction potentials, and the calculation of cell potentials from them; (v) the Nernst equation for correcting for concentrations other than standard; and (vi) the variation of cell potential with temperature.

The enthalpy change ΔH and the free energy change ΔG are both functions which depend only upon the initial and final states, and not upon the manner in which the change comes about. In a galvanic cell, part of the enthalpy change may take the form of heat evolution (or, more rarely, absorption), and part as electrical work. The First Law states that the sum of these must be a constant, for a given amount of change; and at constant temperature and pressure: $\Delta H = q + w_{opt}$. The optional (electrical) work may vary from zero to a maximum, which is ΔG. The maximum work is obtainable only under conditions approximating to reversible, when the current drawn from the cell is infinitesimal. It follows that there is a direct relation between the cell potential and the free energy change: $\Delta G = -zFE_{cell}$. A feasible reaction has ΔG negative and E_{cell} positive (for the conditions under consideration). The use of cell potentials to predict the spontaneous direction of reaction is considered in more detail in Chapter 5.

4.12 Exercises

1. Give the conventional notation for the cells shown in Fig. 4.9, including the cell potentials.

2. Use data from Appendix I to calculate potentials for the following reactions or half-reactions:

   (i) $Cu(s) + 2H^+(aq) \rightarrow Cu^{2+}(aq) + H_2(g)$

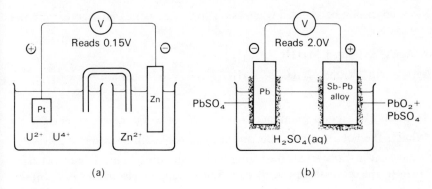

(a)   (b)

Fig. 4.9

(ii) $Cu(s) + H^+(aq) + I^-(aq) \rightarrow CuI(s) + \frac{1}{2}H_2(g)$

(iii) $Cr_2O_7^{2-}(aq) + 14H^+(aq) + 2Cr(s) \rightarrow 4Cr^{3+}(aq) + 7H_2O(l)$

(iv) $Cr_2O_7^{2-}(aq) + 14H^+(aq) + 8e^- \rightarrow 2Cr^{2+}(aq) + 7H_2O(l)$

3. Write the probable feasible cell reaction for the following cells; also state the value of z implied in your equation.

(a) $C \,|\, Br^-, Br_2 \,||\, H_2S(aq), H^+ \,|\, S, C; E^\ominus = -1.20$ V

(b) $Pt, H_2 \,|\, H^+ \,||\, Ag^+ \,|\, Ag; E^\ominus = +0.80$ V

(c) $Ti \,|\, [TiO^{2+} + 2H^+] \,||\, In^{3+} \,|\, In; E^\ominus = +0.55$ V

(d) $Pt \,|\, Fe(CN)_6^{4-}, Fe(CN)_6^{3-} \,||\, Cu(CN)_2^-, CN^- \,|\, Cu; E^\ominus = -0.79$ V

(e) $Pt \,|\, [HN_3 + H^+], [NH_4^+ + N_2] \,||\, [NO_3^- + H^+], [NH_4^+] \,|\, Pt; E^\ominus = -1.1$ V

4. Write cells in which the following reactions might occur, and calculate the standard cell potentials from the free energy changes.

(a) $Sn + Pb^{2+} \rightarrow Pb + Sn^{2+}; \Delta G^\ominus = -1.9$ kJ mol^{-1}

(b) $8HNO_3(aq, 16 \text{ M}) + 3Cu \rightarrow 3Cu(NO_3)_2(aq) + 2NO(g) + 4H_2O(l)$;
$\Delta G^\ominus = -360$ kJ mol^{-1}

(c) $H_2O_2(aq) \rightarrow H_2O(l) + \frac{1}{2}O_2(g); \Delta G^\ominus = -119$ kJ mol^{-1}

5. The Daniell cell has a cell reaction for which $\Delta G^\ominus$ and ΔH are both negative, and very close in value. (a) How would you expect the reversible cell potential to vary with temperature? (b) How would you expect the working potential of a Daniell cell, actually in use, to vary with temperature?

6. Explain the need for the minus sign in the equation: $\Delta G^\ominus = -zFE^\ominus$.

Some textbooks, as might be found in the U.S., use a convention for 'electrode potential' which is opposite to that recommended by the IUPAC; the potentials have the same values but opposite signs. Would it be correct or incorrect to omit the minus sign from the above equation in calculations based on such data?

How can confusion be avoided when using potentials expressed according to the U.S. convention?

7.* Ag, AgCl | KCl(aq, 1 M) | Hg_2Cl_2, Hg, Pt

$$2Ag(s) + Hg_2Cl_2(s) \rightarrow 2AgCl(s) + Hg(l); \; \Delta H = +10 \text{ kJ mol}^{-1}$$
$$\Delta G^{\ominus} = -9 \text{ kJ mol}^{-1}$$

(a) Is the above reaction spontaneous as written, or will it tend to reverse?

(b) What is the polarity of the cell, and the reversible cell potential at 298 K?

(c) What heat is transferred to or from the surroundings, per mole of reaction, when (i) the cell is short-circuited, and producing no electrical work; (ii) the cell is under load and is producing electricity at a potential equal to 80% of its maximum e.m.f.

5

Cell Potential and Reaction Feasibility

5.1 The variation of cell potential with concentration

Qualitatively, the variation of cell potential with changes in concentration obeys a commonsense rule: for a galvanic cell, the cell potential increases with an increase in the concentration of reactants, or a decrease in the concentration of products.

To take a simple example, the Daniell cell has a cell potential of 1.10 V when both solutions are of standard concentration:

$$Zn \,|\, ZnSO_4(aq) \,||\, CuSO_4(aq) \,|\, Cu; \; E_{cell}^{\ominus} = +1.10 \text{ V}$$

The reactants are Zn(s) and Cu^{2+}(aq); of these, the solid zinc has invariant 'concentration', but the concentration of Cu^{2+} is variable at will. If $[Cu^{2+}] > 1$ (where square brackets [ ] indicate the numerical value of concentrations in the units mol dm^{-3}) and $[Zn^{2+}] = 1$, $E_{cell} > 1.1$ V. In fact, $[Cu^{2+}]$ cannot be made much greater than unity before saturation occurs, but the converse, making $[Cu^{2+}]$ very small, is perfectly possible, and results in a lowering of E_{cell}. Similarly, a decrease in $[Zn^{2+}]$ increases E_{cell}, by diminishing the tendency which an accumulation of products has for hindering the forward reaction.

If $[Cu^{2+}]$ and $[Zn^{2+}]$ both change from 1, then it is the value of the ratio $[Cu^{2+}]/[Zn^{2+}]$ which matters: if it is greater than 1, $E_{cell} > E_{cell}^{\ominus}$, and vice-versa.

When several soluble or gaseous species participate in the cell reaction the situation becomes a little more complicated, because all the concentrations can be varied independently, by the addition of this substance or that. It becomes necessary to define a *concentration quotient*, Q_c, as the product of the concentrations of the reaction products divided by the concentrations of the reactants. For the generalized reaction:

$$v_A A + v_B B + \ldots = v_X X + v_Y Y + \ldots$$

$$Q_c = \frac{\Pi[\text{products}]}{\Pi[\text{reactants}]} = \frac{[X]^{v_X}[Y]^{v_Y} \ldots}{[A]^{v_A}[B]^{v_B} \ldots}$$

(where v_A is the stoichiometric coefficient of A, etc.; and Π is the mathematical operator 'product of'.)

You may recognize that the equilibrium constant K_c is a special case of Q_c, but while Q_c contains concentrations as actually found at any given stage of the reaction, K_c applies only to concentrations which could be found at equilibrium.

Now the simple rule, that reactants assist a reaction while products hinder it, becomes more precise when rewritten thus: *The tendency for forward reaction is related to a low value of Q_c.* In fact it can be shown (from concentration cells, §5.2) that the forward tendency is a function of log $(1/Q_c)$, that is, $-\log Q_c$. Experiment shows that the cell potential at 298 K is given by the following simplified form of the Nernst equation:

$$E_{cell} = E_{cell}^{\ominus} - \frac{0.059 \text{ V}}{z} \lg Q_c$$

where z is the number of electrons transferred per mole of reaction according to the stated equation.

A derivation of this equation, and the coefficient 0.059, will be given in the next section. It should be noted that the form of the equation may be adapted in several ways for particular purposes. Two will be considered here, while a third, for the variation of E_{cell} with pH, will be used in §5.6.

For reduction potentials the half-equation has the form:

$$\text{oxidized species} + z\,e^- \rightarrow \text{reduced species}$$

The electrons are considered to be at standard concentration (see p. 73), so Q_c becomes [Reductants]/[Oxidants], thus:

$$E_{red} = E_{red}^{\ominus} - \frac{0.059 \text{ V}}{z} \lg \frac{[\text{red}]}{[\text{ox}]}$$

Furthermore, if the electrode half-reaction is simply the reduction of a metal ion to the metal, then the 'reduced form' is the solid metal, which has unit concentration by convention:

$$M^{z+} + z\,e^- \rightarrow M(s)$$

$$E_{red} = E_{red}^{\ominus} - \frac{0.059 \text{ V}}{z} \lg \frac{1}{[M^{z+}]} = E_{red}^{\ominus} + \frac{0.059 \text{ V}}{z} \lg [M^{z+}]$$

This last form is the simplest to use, but its restriction to the electrode potentials (reduction potentials) of simple metal electrodes should be carefully observed.

Worked example

Calculate the electrode potentials for cadmium and silver in 0.01 M solutions of their salts, and hence the cell potential of the 0.01 M cadmium–silver cell.

Using data from Table 5.3 or Appendix I:

$$Cd^{2+} + 2e^- \rightarrow Cd; \; E_{red}^{\ominus} = -0.40 \text{ V}$$

$$Ag^+ + e^- \rightarrow Ag; \; E_{red}^{\ominus} = +0.80 \text{ V}$$

for Cd in 0.01 M Cd^{2+}:

$$E_{red}/V = -0.40 + \frac{0.059}{2} \lg 0.01$$

$$= -0.40 + \frac{0.059}{2} \times (-2) = -0.46$$

For Ag in 0.01 M Ag^+:

$$E_{red}/V = +0.80 + \frac{0.059}{1} \times (-2) = +0.68$$

Cell potential of $Cd\,|\,Cd^{2+}(0.01\text{ M})\,||\,Ag^+(0.01\text{ M})\,|\,Ag$

$$E_{cell} = E_{red}(\text{right}) + E_{ox}(\text{left}) \qquad . \quad . \quad . \quad \text{(see p. 81)}$$
$$= +0.68 \; - (-0.46)$$
$$= +1.14 \text{ V}$$

If the cell potential alone had been required, the general form of the Nernst equation could be used:

$$Cd + 2Ag^+ \rightarrow Cd^{2+} + 2Ag$$

$$E_{cell} = E_{cell}^{\ominus} \; - \frac{0.059}{2} \lg \frac{[Cd^{2+}]}{[Ag^+]^2}$$

$$= +1.20 - \frac{0.059}{2} \lg \frac{0.01}{0.01^2} = +1.14 \text{ V}$$

An example of the calculation of the non-standard potential for a complex reaction appears on p. 99.

5.2 Concentration cells and the Nernst equation

Practical work

Expt. 5–1. Set up two half-cells as in Fig. 5.1 and connect the two copper-foil electrodes through a sensitive millivoltmeter. Fill both half-cells with 1 M $CuSO_4$ solution, and place the salt-bridge (see Appx. II §4.2 fig A.5) in position. There should be no potential difference between the two identical half-cells, and if there is it is probably due to differences in the surface condition of the copper electrodes. These should be cleaned with dilute nitric(V) acid, rinsed, and left electrically connected in the same copper sulphate solution for a time. If a p.d. still persists it should be noted and regarded for the present purpose as a 'zero error'.

Remove and rinse the salt-bridge, and change the electrolyte in the left-hand cell (no. 1) to 0.1 M $CuSO_4$. Replace the salt-bridge and read the p.d., taking careful note of the polarity. Repeat with more dilute solutions in half-cell no. 1: these should be 10^{-2} and 10^{-3} M $CuSO_4$ made by diluting appropriate volumes of 0.1 M $CuSO_4$ with 0.1 M Na_2SO_4, to maintain the conductivity (and the ionic strength, see §5.3) of the solution.

Two further experiments (Expts. 5–2 and 5–3) could conveniently follow.

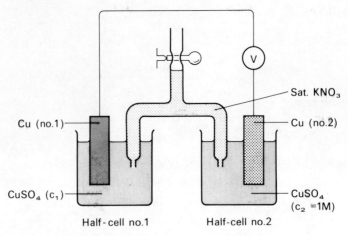

Fig. 5.1   A simple concentration cell

Discussion

In the concentration cell:

$$Cu(1) \,|\, CuSO_4(aq, c_1) \,||\, CuSO_4(aq, c_2) \,|\, Cu(2)$$

the cell potential is positive (that is, $Cu(2)$ is the more positive) if $c_2 > c_1$. Clearly then the electrode reactions are:

$$Cu(1) \rightarrow Cu^{2+}(c_1, \text{dilute}) + 2e^-$$

$$Cu^{2+}(c_2, \text{concentrated}) + 2e^- \rightarrow Cu(2)$$

The net reaction is simply[1] the spontaneous dilution of copper ion:

$$Cu^{2+}(\text{conc.}) \rightarrow Cu^{2+}(\text{dil.})$$

It can be shown that the driving force for this process is the positive entropy change of dilution, which equals $R \ln(c_2/c_1)$ for 'ideal' solutions (those for which the heat of dilution is zero). Thus the free energy change and the cell potential are as follows:

$$\Delta G = \Delta H - T\,\Delta S$$

$$= 0 \quad - RT \ln \frac{c_2}{c_1}$$

$$E_{\text{cell}} = \frac{-\Delta G}{zF} = \frac{RT}{zF} \ln \frac{c_2}{c_1} = \ln 10 \frac{RT}{zF} \cdot \lg \frac{c_2}{c_1}$$

[1] There will also be a movement of Cl^- ions from the salt-bridge into half-cell no. 1, and K^+ ions into no. 2, to maintain electrical neutrality, but since these ions have equal mobilities there is no net effect on the potential (see §5.4).

If the potentials of concentration cells of various concentration ratios (as in Expt. 5–1, or the specimen results in Table 5.1) are plotted against $\lg (c_2/c_1)$, a straight line is obtained, with a slope of approximately 0.03. This is the value of $(\ln 10) RT/zF$ at 298 K and with z, in this case, equal to 2. (In general, substituting $\ln 10 = 2.303$, $R = 8.314$ J K^{-1} mol^{-1} and $F = 9.649 \times 10^4$ C mol^{-1} gives $(\ln 10) RT/F = 0.0591$ V at 298 K)

Table 5.1 Potentials of Concentration Cells

c_1/mol dm^{-3}	Cell: $Cu\|Cu^{2+}(c_1)\|\|Cu^{2+}(c_2)\|Cu$ c_2/mol dm^{-3}	ratio (c_2/c_1)	E_{cell}/mV
1.0	1.0	1	0
0.1	0.1	1	0
0.5	1.0	2	9
0.25	1.0	4	19
0.10	1.0	10	29.5
0.05	2.0	40	48

It is now possible to derive the equation for the variation of any cell potential with concentration, since any cell can be represented as one standard cell and two concentration cells in series. For clarity, the simple Daniell cell will be used as the illustration, but the result can be made general.

Consider the non-standard cell:

$$Zn \mid Zn^{2+}(aq \mid\mid Cu^{2+}(aq) \mid Cu$$

This is effectively the same as the following three cells in series:

$$\underset{\text{cell 1}}{Zn\mid Zn^{2+}(aq)\mid\mid Zn^{2+}(1\text{ M})\mid Zn} \quad \underset{\text{cell 2}}{Zn\mid Zn^{2+}(1\text{ M})\mid\mid Cu^{2+}(1\text{ M})\mid Cu} \quad \underset{\text{cell 3}}{Cu\mid Cu^{2+}(1\text{ M})\mid\mid Cu^{2+}(aq)\mid Cu}$$

$$E_{cell} = E_{cell}(1) + E_{cell}(2) + E_{cell}(3)$$

Cell 2 is the Zn–Cu cell with standard concentrations, so $E_{cell}(2) = E_{cell}^{\ominus}$. Cells 1 and 3 are concentration cells:

$$E_{cell}(1) = \frac{RT}{2F} \ln \frac{1}{[Zn^{2+}]} \quad \text{and} \quad E_{cell}(3) = \frac{RT}{2F} \ln \frac{[Cu^{2+}]}{1}$$

$$\therefore E_{cell} = E_{cell}^{\ominus} + \frac{RT}{2F} \ln \frac{[Cu^{2+}]}{[Zn^{2+}]}$$

In general, the Nernst equation can be written:

$$E_{cell} = E_{cell}^{\ominus} + \frac{RT}{zF} \ln \frac{\Pi[\text{reactants}]}{\Pi[\text{products}]} = E_{cell}^{\ominus} - \frac{RT}{zF} \ln \frac{\Pi[\text{products}]}{\Pi[\text{reactants}]}$$

$$= E_{cell}^{\ominus} - \frac{RT}{zF} \ln Q_c$$

The equilibrium constant

The tendency for a reaction to proceed, at given temperature, is measured by the cell potential; and if the concentrations are not standard (i.e. 1 M) then it is E_{cell}, not $E_{cell}^{\ominus}$, which indicates the reaction tendency.

The Nernst equation shows that as any cell reaction proceeds, the cell potential becomes smaller. The product concentrations increase, the reactants decrease, Q_c becomes larger, and the term which is to be subtracted from $E_{cell}^{\ominus}$ increases.

A familiar example of this effect in practice is the 'running down' of the zinc–carbon 'dry cell', and the fall of the e.m.f. from about 1.5 V to perhaps half this value. However, it is not necessary to wait for the cell reaction to bring about these concentration changes. The variation of cell potential may be studied by setting up a series of cells with concentrations corresponding to successive stages of the cell reaction (see Expt. 5–2).

There could be one such cell with product and reactant concentrations in such a ratio that the value of $(RT/zF) \ln Q_c$ was exactly equal to $E_{cell}^{\ominus}$. Then E_{cell} would be zero, indicating an absence of any tendency for the reaction to proceed. Nor would there be any tendency for the reverse reaction to occur, for that would be indicated by a negative cell potential, that is, a reversed polarity. Such cells could be set up by having an even higher ratio of 'products' to 'reactants'.

So when concentrations are such as to be at equilibrium,

$$E_{cell} = 0 = E_{cell}^{\ominus} - \frac{RT}{zF} \ln Q_c$$

$$Q_c = \exp\left(zFE_{cell}^{\ominus}/RT\right) = \text{a constant}$$

Since the quotient Q_c of concentrations at equilibrium is a constant (for given temperature), it is known as the equilibrium constant, and given the symbol K_c (c for 'concentrations').

$$E_{cell}^{\ominus} = \frac{RT}{zF} \ln K_c$$

$$-\Delta G^{\ominus} = zFE_{cell}^{\ominus} = 2.303 \, RT \lg K_c$$

Expt. 5–2. Investigate the cell potential of one or both of the following cells, with varying ratios of concentrations of Fe(II) to Fe(III):

$$Pt \mid Fe(CN)_6^{4-}, Fe(CN)_6^{3-} \parallel Cu(NO_3)_2(0.1 \text{ M}) \mid Cu$$

$$Pt \mid Fe^{2+}, Fe^{3+} \parallel AgNO_3(1 \text{ M}) \mid Ag$$

A potentiometer, or a sensitive voltmeter (preferably electronic) with a full-scale deflection of about 100 mV is required. The mV range of a pH meter may be suitable.

In the case of the simple iron ions, the nitrates are to be preferred, and the solutions may be made approx. 0.5 M in KNO_3 to maintain constant ionic strength. The ratio of Fe(II) to Fe(III) should be varied from 10^{-3} by tenfold increments to 10^3.

Treatment of results. Write the equation for the cell reaction conventionally associated with the cells as written above, and calculate Q_c for the concentrations used. Record the observed cell potentials, indicating the polarity.

Plot a graph of E_{cell} versus $\lg Q_c$, and if E_{cell} passes through zero, note the value of the equilibrium constant, K. Also note the value of $E_{cell}^{\ominus}$ when $Q_c = 1$.

From the equation relating $E_{cell}^{\ominus}$ with K, calculate z, the number of electrons transferred per mole of reaction.

Note: This investigation may be extended by finding the equilibrium constant for the reaction $Ag^+(aq) + Fe^{2+}(aq) \rightleftharpoons Fe^{3+}(aq) + Ag(s)$ by thiocyanate titration for Ag^+ and by manganate(VII) titration for Fe^{2+}. Details are given in Nuffield Advanced Science: Chemistry, Experiment 17.3c.

5.3 Activity coefficients

Expt. 5–3. Using the same apparatus as for Expt. 5–1, investigate the following cells:

A $Cu \,|\, CuSO_4(1\ M) \,\|\, Cu(NO_3)_2(1\ M) \,|\, Cu$

B $Cu \,|\, CuSO_4(0.01\ M) \,\|\, Cu(NO_3)_2(0.01\ M) \,|\, Cu$

C $Cu \,|\, Cu(NO_3)_2(0.01\ M) \,\|\, Cu(NO_3)_2(0.01\ M) + MgSO_4(1\ M) \,|\, Cu$

Discussion. Cell A acts as a concentration cell even though the copper(II) ion is nominally at the same concentration in each half-cell. The reason is that the doubly-charged sulphate ions create a strong negative 'atmosphere' around each copper ion, with the result that the 'activity', or effective concentration, is considerably less than the actual concentration; whereas the nitrate ions have a much smaller interfering effect. The interionic attraction theory has been discussed in connection with conductivity, in §3.8.

It is convenient to define the activity coefficient f, thus:

$$a = fc$$

where f is not a constant, but a coefficient which depends upon the concentration of *all* ions present in the solution.

In pure solutions (i.e. of a single electrolyte) the activity coefficient approaches unity in dilute solution; as the concentration increases to around 1 M, f decreases (to about 0.7 for singly-charged ions, and to about 0.04 for doubly-charged ions), but it may increase again in very concentrated solutions (especially in the case of highly hydrated ions, which diminish the amount of free solvent). These variations are shown in Fig. 5.2 and Table 5.2.

In dilute solution the relation between activity coefficient and ionic strength μ (see p. 50) is given by:

$$\lg f = -0.51\, z_+ z_- \sqrt{\mu}.$$

where z_+ and z_- are the charges on cation and anion.

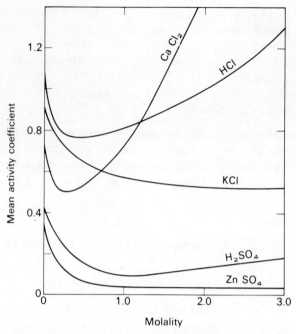

Fig. 5.2 Variation of activity coefficients with concentration

Table 5.2 Mean Activity Coefficients in Aqueous Solution at 298 K

concentration mol (kg H_2O)$^{-1}$	0.001	0.005	0.01	0.05	0.10	0.50	1.00	2.00	5.00
Debye–Hückel theory (1 +, 1 −)	0.965	0.920	0.890	0.770					
HCl	0.965	0.929	0.905	0.830	0.794	0.757	0.809	1.01	2.38
NaCl	0.965	0.927	0.902	0.819	0.778	0.681	0.657	0.67	0.87
NaOH			0.899	0.818	0.766	0.693	0.679	0.70	1.08
D–H (2 +, 1 − or 1 +, 2 −)	0.880	0.750	0.667						
H_2SO_4	0.830	0.639	0.544	0.340	0.265	0.154	0.130	0.12	0.21
D–H (2 +, 2 −)	0.744	0.515							
$ZnSO_4$*	0.700	0.477	0.387	0.202	0.150	0.063	0.043	0.035	

* Ni, Cd and $CuSO_4$ almost the same.

In cell B above the activities are still different, as in cell A, but as the solutions are less concentrated, the activity coefficients are closer to unity, and less different from each other: so the cell potential is smaller.

In cell C the activity of Cu^{2+} in the right-hand half-cell is lowered by the presence of the magnesium sulphate, which increases the ionic strength.

Activity coefficients affect potentiometry in two ways:

(1) The standard state, to which cell and electrode potentials are referred, is not 1 mol dm^{-3} concentration, but 1 mol dm^{-3} (or sometimes 1 mole per kg water) *activity* (see note, Appendix II). This is a hypothetical state, and standard potentials are calculated by theoretical extrapolation from measurements in dilute solution. Equilibrium constants and concentration quotients are, strictly, quotients of activities, not concentrations.

(2) Calculations of ionic concentrations from electrode potentials (§7.4) should take account of the activity coefficient.

The complications of activity coefficients have been disregarded in this book so far, and will continue to be for practical purposes. Often the coefficients 'cancel out', especially in an expression with equally charged ions in both numerator and denominator. In any case, the effect on potentials is relatively slight: an activity coefficient of 0.8 would make a difference of only 6 mV in the potential of the standard hydrogen electrode, and even the coefficient of 0.04 for 1 M divalent metal sulphates makes only 40 mV difference.

5.4 The liquid junction potential

When a galvanic or electrolytic cell contains a junction or boundary between two electrolytes, an e.m.f. is created, known as the liquid junction potential. When the electrolytes are different, the potential is difficult to calculate; but when the junction is between two different concentrations of the same electrolyte, the treatment is fairly simple.

One experimental approach is via the 'concentration cell with transport'. Expt. 5–1 could be repeated, but with the salt-bridge replaced by a bridge of 1 M $CuSO_4$. The cell potentials will be different this time, because although the process is still the transfer of solute from the concentrated to the dilute solution, there is now not only the electrochemical transfer of Cu^{2+} by electrode reaction, but also the electrophoretic migration of Cu^{2+} and SO_4^{2-} ions.

Thus the passage of two moles of electrons through the cell is accompanied by the following changes:

Cu(1)		$Cu^{2+}(a_1)$	$SO_4^{2-}(a_1)$		$Cu^{2+}(a_2)$	$SO_4^{2-}(a_2)$		Cu(2)
1 mol dissolved to Cu^{2+}		t_+ mol lost	t_- mol gained		t_+ mol gained	t_- mol lost		1 mol Cu^{2+} deposited

If we note that $(1 - t_+)$ equals t_- (§3.7), it is seen that the net result is the transfer from right to left of t_- mol Cu^{2+} and t_- mol SO_4^{2-}. The free energy change ΔG for the transfer of one mole of either ion is $-RT\ln(a_2/a_1)$, so ΔG for the transfer of t_- mole of 2 ions is $-2t_-RT\ln(a_2/a_1)$, (where a_1 and a_2 are the mean activities of the ions in solutions 1 and 2 respectively). Therefore the cell potential (for electrolytes with ions of equal charge) is given by:

$$E_{cell} = 2t_- \frac{RT}{zF} \ln \frac{a_2}{a_1}$$

The liquid junction potential is obtained by subtracting the cell potential for the concentration cell with salt-bridge from that of the cell with transport, thus:

$$E_J = (2t_- - 1)\frac{RT}{zF}\ln\frac{a_2}{a_1} = (t_- - t_+)\frac{RT}{zF}\ln\frac{a_2}{a_1}$$

This expression is for cells with electrodes reversible to the cation: otherwise t_- and t_+ must be interchanged. Also, it is a little more complicated if the charges on the ions of the electrolyte are not numerically equal. It is noteworthy that the liquid junction potential is proportional to the *difference* in transport numbers, and disappears if these are very close to 0.5. This is the reason for the use of KCl and NH_4NO_3 in salt-bridges, at such high concentrations that ionic transport at the boundaries is almost entirely due to these equally mobile ions.

5.5 Use of cell potentials for predicting reactions

The most widely known application of the principle of cell potentials is certainly that of ranking the oxidants and reductants in order of 'strength', and hence predicting the feasibility of redox reactions. Some standard reduction potentials (in acid solution at 298 K) appear in Table 5.3, and a fuller list (arranged alphabetically) is in Appendix I. The half-reactions are all in the form:

oxidant + electrons ⇌ reductant

and the oxidants increase in effectiveness downwards, with F_2 as the most powerful; conversely the reductants decrease in effectiveness from Li downwards. It can readily be seen that there are only two possible ways of combining any pair of half-reactions, and the combination which gives a positive standard cell potential will include the reverse of the half-equation which appears *higher* in the table. The reactants will be the substances found in the lower left and upper right positions.

We may test this simple rule by considering the possibility of reaction between the Fe^{3+} ion and the halides. The half-equation for the reduction of Fe^{3+} to Fe^{2+} is found below that of $I_2 \rightarrow 2I^-$ from which we conclude that Fe^{3+} will oxidize I^- to I_2. (It would be more prudent to say that the oxidation of I^- by Fe^{3+} is thermodynamically feasible—see below). But the Fe^{3+}/Fe^{2+} half-equation is

Table 5.3 Selected Reduction Potentials in volts at 298 K

(A fuller table, arranged alphabetically, appears in Appendix I)

$Li^+ + e^-$	$\rightleftharpoons Li$	-3.03
$Cr^2 + 2e^-$	$\rightleftharpoons Cr$	-0.91
$Zn^{2+} + 2e^-$	$\rightleftharpoons Zn$	-0.76
$Fe^{2+} + 2e^-$	$\rightleftharpoons Fe$	-0.44
$Cr^{3+} + e^-$	$\rightleftharpoons Cr^{2+}$	-0.41
$H^+ + e^-$	$\rightleftharpoons \frac{1}{2}H_2$	0.00
$Cu^{2+} + 2e^-$	$\rightleftharpoons Cu$	$+0.34$
$I_2 + 2e^-$	$\rightleftharpoons 2I^-$	$+0.54$
$Fe^{3+} + e^-$	$\rightleftharpoons Fe^{2+}$	$+0.77$
$Ag^+ + e^-$	$\rightleftharpoons Ag$	$+0.78$
$Cr_2O_7^{2-} + 14H^+ + 6e^-$	$\rightleftharpoons 2Cr^{3+} + 7H_2O$	$+1.33$
$Cl_2 + 2e^-$	$\rightleftharpoons 2Cl^-$	$+1.36$
$F_2 + 2e^-$	$\rightleftharpoons 2F^-$	$+2.87$

placed above those for the reduction of Br_2, Cl_2 or F_2, suggesting that Fe^{3+} cannot oxidize Br^-, Cl^- or F^- to the elements. All four predictions are confirmed by experiment.

Unfortunately the rule just illustrated is an oversimplification of the truth, to the point of being misleading unless the two reduction potentials differ widely. If they are less than about 0.5 V apart, then (i) the predicted reaction will not be complete and (ii) its reverse, predicted not to occur, may occur to a measurable extent. In our examples above, Fe^{3+} will indeed be reduced by I^-, but not the point of becoming undetectable by CNS^-; and conversely, pure Fe^{2+} is sufficiently oxidized by $I_2(aq)$ to give a positive result with a sensitive test for Fe^{3+}.

The interpretation of positive or negative cell potentials as 'will go' or 'won't go' is too simplistic. It would be better to interpret the signs as meaning that the reaction can, or cannot go beyond a 'central equilibrium', with reactants and products in equal concentrations.

The direct relationship between standard cell potential and equilibrium constant, which was derived in §5.2, is useful in the present context:

$$E_{cell}^{\ominus} = \frac{RT}{zF} \ln K$$

or, at 298 K: $\lg K = \dfrac{zE_{cell}^{\ominus}}{0.059\text{ V}}$

Therefore the equilibrium constant is large if $E_{cell}^{\ominus}$ is positive; small (but greater than one) if $E_{cell}^{\ominus}$ is positive and small, say up to 0.4 V; and less than one if $E_{cell}^{\ominus}$ is negative.

Worked example

Predict the products from the action of iron on 1 M $\frac{1}{2}Cr_2(SO_4)_3$ solution.

The possibilities are: Cr^{3+}, Cr^{2+}, Cr, Fe^{3+}, Fe^{2+} and Fe. The relevant half-reactions and reduction potentials are to be found in Table 5.3. A quick consideration of these shows that (i) Fe^{2+}—Fe is above Cr^{3+}—Cr^{2+}, so iron will reduce $Cr(III)$ to (II); (ii) Fe^{2+}—Fe is below Cr^{2+}—Cr, so no chromium metal will be displaced; (iii) Fe^{3+}—Fe^{2+} is well below Cr^{3+}—Cr^{2+}, so no iron(III) will be expected.

So the expected reaction is: $Fe + 2Cr^{3+} \rightarrow Fe^{2+} + 2Cr^{2+}$.

The equilibrium concentration of each of the specimens may be calculated by means of the equation given earlier in this section:

Reaction 1

$$Fe + 2Cr^{3+} \rightarrow Fe^{2+} + 2Cr^{2+}; E_{cell}^{\ominus} = +0.03 \text{ V}$$

$$\therefore \log K = \frac{2 \times 0.03}{0.059} = 1.0$$

$$\frac{[Fe^{2+}][Cr^{2+}]^2}{[Cr^{3+}]^2} = 10$$

Let the extent of reaction to equilibrium be ξ. $[Cr^{3+}]$ will fall to $(1 - 2\xi)$, $[Cr^{2+}]$ will rise from zero to 2ξ, and $[Fe^{2+}]$ will rise to ξ. Putting these concentrations into the expression for the equilibrium constant gives:

$$\frac{\xi^3}{(1 - 2\xi)^2} = 10; \ \xi = 0.45$$

To a first approximation, $[Cr^{2+}] = 0.90$, $[Cr^{3+}] = 0.10$, $[Fe^{2+}] = 0.90$. One could say that this reaction is 90% complete. Note that Cr^{3+} would not be removed completely even by excess iron, and unlimited time.

Reaction 2

$$3Fe + 2Cr^{3+} \rightarrow 3Fe^{2+} + 2Cr; E_{cell}^{\ominus} = -0.30 \text{ V}$$

$$\log K = \frac{6 \times (-0.30)}{0.059} = -30 \quad \therefore \frac{[Fe^{3+}]^3}{[Cr^{3+}]^3} = 10^{-30}$$

The amount of Cr produced by this reaction is 2×10^{-10} mol dm^{-3}, which is undetectable.

Reaction 3

$$Cr^{3+} + Fe^{2+} \rightarrow Cr^{2+} + Fe^{3+}; E_{cell}^{\ominus} = -1.18 \text{ V}$$

$$K = 10^{-20}, [Fe^{3+}] = 10^{-21} \text{ which is undetectable.}$$

It is not always made clear that if the initial concentrations of reactants and products are not standard, then the *actual* cell potential (calculated for these concentrations) must be used for predicting the feasible direction of reaction; but the standard cell potential must still be used for calculating the equilibrium constant. However when concentrations are not excessively low, and when $E^\ominus_{cell}$ is not very small, the concentration effect is unlikely to invalidate the prediction based on the sign of the standard potential.

5.6 Variation of redox potentials with H$^+$ concentrations

An important aspect of redox reactions is that many half-equations include H$^+$ or OH$^-$ ions, and in all such cases the redox potentials and cell potentials will vary with pH. Standard reduction potentials are most usually tabulated for acid solution, at pH = 0; less frequently they are given for basic solution, at pH = 14. In the latter case, the half-equations must not include H$^+$ ions since these could not exist at standard concentration; each H$^+$ is replaced by (H$_2$O $-$ OH$^-$), that is, H$_2$O with OH$^-$ added to the other side. If the oxidized and reduced forms can exist unchanged over the whole pH range, then the cell potential for any pH can be calculated by means of the Nernst equation, and that for basic solution becomes a special case of a non-standard potential with [H$^+$] = 10^{-14}. In other reactions, the reactant species may change to another form at high pH, for example by the formation of an insoluble hydroxide. In fact there are rather few redox reactions which are unaffected by pH. The symbol $E^{\ominus\prime}_{red}$ is sometimes used to denote a cell potential for concentrations which are all standard with the exception of H$^+$ and OH$^-$.

A convenient way of presenting data for reduction potentials at different acidities is by a graph such as Fig. 5.3. Anyone working on a problem requiring this kind of information will find it worth while to draw up a graph for the relevant half-reactions. The method of calculation will be illustrated by two or three examples.

1. *Chlorine*

(1a) Cl$_2$ + 2e$^-$ $\rightleftharpoons$ 2Cl$^-$. No H$^+$ or OH$^-$ involved, so $E^\ominus_{red}$ is independent of pH, shown by a horizontal line. However, Cl$_2$ does not exist in aqueous solution at pH > 5, so the line is then hypothetical.

(1b) ClO$_3^-$ + 6H$^+$ + 5e$^-$ $\rightleftharpoons$ $\frac{1}{2}$Cl$_2$ + 3H$_2$O; $E^\ominus_{red}$ = +1.47 V

$$\frac{E_{red}}{V} = +1.47 - \frac{0.059}{5} \lg \frac{[Cl_2]^{1/2}}{[ClO_3^-][H^+]^6}$$

If [Cl$_2$] and [ClO$_3^-$] are standard:

$$\frac{E^{\ominus\prime}_{red}}{V} = +1.47 - \frac{0.059}{5} \times 6 \lg \frac{1}{[H^+]}$$

$$= +1.47 - 0.071 \text{ pH}$$

This is a straight line through +1.47 V at pH 0 and +0.48 V at pH 14.

(1c) $\qquad$ HOCl + H$^+$ + e$^-$ $\rightleftharpoons$ H$_2$O + $\frac{1}{2}$Cl$_2$ $\qquad$ (acidic)

$\qquad\qquad$ OCl$^-$ + H$_2$O + e$^-$ $\rightleftharpoons$ $\frac{1}{2}$Cl$_2$ + 2OH$^-$ $\qquad$ (basic)

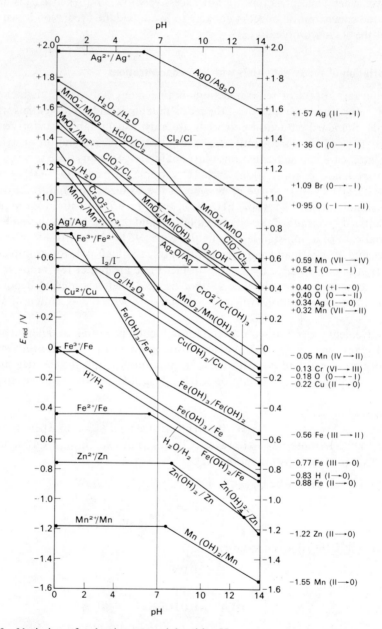

Fig. 5.3   Variation of reduction potentials with pH

Chloric(I) (hypochlorous) acid is weak ($pK_a = 7.4$) therefore the ratio $[HOCl]/[OCl^-] = [H^+] \times 10^{7.4}$, showing that the unionized species predominates at any pH below 7.4. Therefore the redox behaviour is shown by two lines, one for HOCl up to pH 7.4, and one for OCl^- in more basic solutions. The slopes are different because the former reaction consumes one H^+ per electron, while the latter produces $2OH^-$ (or consumes $2H^+$) per electron. Otherwise the calculations are the same as for ClO_3^-/Cl_2.

(2) *Iron*

(2a) Fe(II)–Fe(O). $\begin{cases} Fe^{2+}(aq) + 2e^- \rightleftharpoons Fe(s); E^{\ominus}_{red} = -0.44 \text{ V} \\ Fe(OH)_2(s) + 2e^- \rightleftharpoons Fe(s) + 2OH^-(aq); E^{\ominus}_{red} = -0.89 \text{ V} \end{cases}$

The solubility product of $Fe(OH)_2$ is 8×10^{-16}, so $[Fe^{2+}] = 1$ when $[OH^-] = \sqrt{(8 \times 10^{-16})} = 10^{-7.5}$. This corresponds to pH 6.5, and Fe^{2+} cannot be at standard concentration at higher pH than this. The line for Fe^{2+} is horizontal, but that for $Fe(OH)_2$ slopes downwards since, as OH^- is a product, $E^{\ominus'}_{red}$ will decrease as $[OH^-]$ increases.

(2b) Fe(III)–Fe(II). This line contains three distinct sections:

$$Fe^{3+}(aq) + e^- \rightleftharpoons Fe^{2+}(aq) \qquad (pH < 1)$$

$$Fe(OH)_3(s) + 3H^+ + e^- \rightleftharpoons Fe^{2+}(aq) + 3H_2O \quad (1 < pH < 6.5)$$

$$Fe(OH)_3(s) + e^- \rightleftharpoons Fe(OH)_2(s) + OH^- \quad (6.5 < pH)$$

Predictions from the potential–pH diagram

In Fig. 5.3 each line shows the variation of a standard reduction potential with pH. The thermodynamically favoured direction of any redox reaction at any given pH can be found simply by noting which half-reaction is the higher, for this will be the reduction. (The graph has the reduction potentials increasing upwards, unlike Table 5.3.) The lower half-reaction will be reversed, to become the oxidation. The reservations concerning partial reaction (p. 97) still apply.

Another way of presenting reduction potential data for elements with a number of oxidation states is the *potential diagram*, which serves as a concise summary of the redox chemistry of the element. For a description and examples of one- and two-dimensional potential diagrams the reader is referred to §§8.8 and 8.9 of the author's *Chemical Energetics* (Edward Arnold 1971).

5.7 Kinetic considerations

Calculation of the cell potential, or its estimation from potential diagrams, only permits a prediction of the thermodynamic feasibility of the reaction. Whether a feasible reaction will or will not occur at a measurable rate is a question in the domain of kinetics, and the answer cannot be predicted from potentials. However, a few general rules may be given.

(1) Temperature

Reactions are faster at higher temperatures, so a feasible reaction which does not occur in the cold *may* occur on heating. Well known examples are the reaction between acidified manganate(VII) and ethandioic (oxalic) acid, and, in the 'silver mirror test', the reduction of $Ag(NH_3)_2^+$ by aldehydes.

(2) Covalent bonds

The energy barrier (energy of activation) is likely to be high if covalent bonds have to be broken in a reaction step. This may explain the slow reaction of per-oxodisulphate, chlorate(VII), chlorate(V), hydrogen peroxide, and many other oxidants, and also ammonia, hydrocarbons, and other covalently bonded re-ductants. It is also the reason why the SO_4^{2-} ion resists attack even by reductants more powerful than SO_3^{2-}

(3) Insoluble layers

There may be a kinetic hindrance due to the purely mechanical effect of an in-soluble layer covering the reactant surface. Thus magnesium metal reacts only very slowly with water even though $E_{cell}^{\ominus} = +1.97$ V; but if the surface is amal-gamated (by momentary immersion in a mercury salt solution), this prevents cohesion of the oxide layer, and reaction is rapid. Similarly, aluminium liberates hydrogen far more readily from basic solutions than from neutral or acidic, even though there is no thermodynamic advantage; presumably because the aluminium oxide is removed as the soluble complex $Al(OH)_4^-$.

(4) Catalysts

The presence of a catalyst is essential for many redox reactions. Ionic Mn^{2+} acts catalytically in the manganate(VII)–oxalate reaction; ionic Ag^+ is necessary if $S_2O_8^{2-}$ is to oxidize Mn^{2+} to MnO_4^-; a transition metal ion such as Cu^{2+} is required for the oxidation of SO_3^{2-} by O_2; and arsenic(II) reacts only slowly with cerium(IV) if both are pure, although $E_{cell}^{\ominus} = +0.9$ V (in 1 M H_2SO_4), but the reaction is rapid in the presence of a trace of I^- as catalyst. The reason behind the last example is the unequal numbers of electrons in the half-reactions: $Ce(IV) - e^- \rightarrow Ce(III)$, but $As(III) + 2e^- \rightarrow As(V)$. So the reaction cannot occur by a single bimolecular step, but only by a rare termolecular collision. For a similar reason H_2 does not reduce MnO_4^- to MnO_4^{2-} (in neutral solution) unless Ag^+ is present as catalyst.

In biochemical systems, the process of respiration necessarily involves at some stage the energy producing reduction of elemental oxygen, O_2, to the -2 oxidation state as in H_2O. This is brought about in a controlled manner by one of several enzymes known as oxidoreductases, of which one group, the cuproprotein enzymes, contain copper atoms which may alternate between the $+1$ and $+2$ oxidation states. The reactions are complex, and probably consist of four successive single-electron transfers.

The metabolic reduction of elemental nitrogen ('nitrogen fixation') is most remarkable, in that it is a reaction with a high energy barrier, and cannot be brought about by any non-biochemical catalyst at anywhere near ambient temperature. Even so, only the blue–green algae and a few bacteria are able to bring about this vital reaction (vital because without it, the combined nitrogen essential for life would gradually be lost to the atmosphere), and it appears that they all require the elements iron and molybdenum. Why molybdenum, a comparatively rare element, and therefore not very likely to be involved in an evolutionary change? Well, a look at the data for nitrogen (Appendix I) shows that the only thermodynamically favoured reduction of N_2 is to the -3 state as in NH_3 or the amino group. The intermediate oxidation states as in NH_3OH and N_2H_4 are unlikely to be formed, and in fact analysis of nitrogen-fixing systems has failed to detect them. Therefore the three-electron reduction step from $N(O)$ to $N(-III)$ will require the provision of three electrons from a single oxidation step, which seems to rule out the usual iron- or copper-containing enzymes. It has been suggested that the role of molybdenum is to provide the three electrons by the change $Mo(III)$ to $Mo(VI)$.

(5) *Nascent hydrogen?*

The rate of reaction may depend on conditions in an unexpected way. It is thermodynamically feasible to reduce Fe^{3+} to Fe^{2+} by Cu ($E_{cell}^{\ominus} = +0.42$ V) or Zn ($+1.53$ V), but the reaction with copper does not proceed at all, while that with zinc is slow unless the solution is quite strongly acidic (although $E_{cell}^{\ominus}$ is hardly affected by pH, and not at all so below pH 1). It was at one time believed that the actual reductant was 'nascent hydrogen', possibly H atoms or energy-rich H_2^* molecules, since reduction took place only when hydrogen was being produced (though gaseous hydrogen itself is ineffective). However, cathodic reduction of Fe^{3+} is observed at potentials too low to produce H_2; and further evidence comes from the observation that Fe^{3+} is reduced by I^-, quite rapidly even though $E_{cell}^{\ominus}$ is only $+0.15$ V.

The present opinion is that the advantage of simultaneous production of hydrogen when a metal is the reductant is that it maintains a clean metal surface which is effective as a catalyst.

(6) *Overpotential?*

The redox half-reactions which involve gaseous H_2 or O_2 are kinetically hindered to a considerable extent, and only become measurably fast if the cell potential is more positive than a certain value, estimated at about 0.6 V. This is possibly connected with the *overpotential* (§6.2), which varies according to the catalytic properties of the metal surface in contact with the solution, and is particularly high at smooth or soft surfaces such as those of mercury or lead. Thus reactions such as the following do not in fact occur at 298 K:

$$E_{cell}^{\ominus}$$

$$Pb(s) + 2H^+(aq) \rightarrow Pb^{2+}(aq) + H_2(g) \qquad +0.13 \text{ V}$$

$$Zn(s, \text{amalgamated}) + 2H^+(aq) \rightarrow Zn(aq) + H_2(g) \qquad +0.77 \text{ V}$$

$$E^{\ominus}_{cell}$$

$$Cu^{2+} + H_2(g) \rightleftharpoons Cu(s) + 2H^+(aq) \qquad\qquad +0.34 \ V^1$$
$$2MnO_4^-(aq) + H_2O \rightarrow 2MnO_2(s) + 2OH^- + \tfrac{3}{2}O_2(g) \ +0.28 \ V$$
$$\tfrac{1}{2}O_2(g) + 2Br^-(aq) + 2H^+(aq) \rightarrow Br_2(aq) + H_2O \qquad +0.14 \ V$$
$$Cl_2(aq) + H_2O \rightarrow 2H^+(aq) + 2Cl^-(aq) + \tfrac{1}{2}O_2(g) \qquad +0.13 \ V$$

(This last reaction is observed in bright sunlight, however, in chlorine solution at about pH 4, for which $E^{\ominus} = +0.35$ V).

While overpotential is a precisely measurable property of an electrode, the excess cell potential required before a reaction becomes noticeably rapid is fairly vague. The two are certainly not identical, and the connection between them is not well understood. However the analogy is useful in that it brings together certain common features of electron transfer reactions in solution or at electrodes.

While the hindrance to reactions involving H_2 or O_2 is large, that for N_2 is almost insuperable (the N_2 electrode, if it could be set up, would have an enormous overpotential). No reactions of molecular nitrogen are known at ambient temperatures (other than the enzyme catalysed ones mentioned above), and N_2 is rarely a product of any redox reaction, even though it is thermodynamically a very stable oxidation state. On the other hand, chlorine exhibits only a small overpotential, and the oxidation of Cl^- occurs in reactions with only a small positive cell potential.

The deposition of metals is also in some cases subject to an overpotential, which varies with the nature of the metal deposit and that of the underlying surface. The high overpotential for iron on zinc is probably a direct reason for the failure of zinc to reduce Fe(II) to the element.

Despite all these reservations, prediction of reason feasibility from the cell potential is generally useful, because very many redox reactions in solution are rapid, and, if none of the limitations listed above apply, the reactions may be expected to occur in the direction predicted.

5.8 Practical investigations (reaction feasibility)

Expt. 5–4. Simple redox reactions.

Prepare the following solutions; the concentrations need only be approximate. 0.05 M $KMnO_4^*$, 0.05 M $MnSO_4$, 0.1 M Br_2, 0.1 M KBr, 0 1 M I_2 (in 0.5 M KI), 0.1 M KI, 0.2 M $Fe_2(SO_4)_3^*$, 0.5 M $FeSO_4^*$ or $(NH_4)_2Fe(SO_4)_2$, 0.1 M Na_2SO_4, 0.1 M $NaHSO_3$ or H_2SO_3 (SO_2 soln.)   *acidified with dilute H_2SO_4.

Also, for the analysis of reaction products, have solutions of KCNS, $K_3Fe(CN)_6$ and $BaCl_2$.

Test the $NaHSO_3$ or H_2SO_3 for the presence of SO_4^{2-} by adding to a portion some $BaCl_2$ and dil. HCl. If necessary, remove sulphate(VI) from the solutions by adding $BaCl_2$ and filtering.

Test the Fe^{3+} solution for Fe^{2+} by mixing a little with $Fe(CN)_6^{3-}$. If necessary, boil the solution with H_2O_2 to complete the oxidation to Fe^{3+}.

[1] See Appendix II under 2.6.

Test the Fe^{2+} for Fe^{3+} (CNS^- test); the solution tends to be oxidized by air unless kept acid, and with some iron wool in the bottle.

Systematically, examine the reactivity of each of the oxidized species with each of the reduced species. Where appropriate, test portions of the mixture with the sensitive detecting reagents. Present your results in the form of a grid. Make a vertical table of oxidants in decreasing order of oxidizing power (as judged by the number of reductants with which they reacted). By the side, make a table of reductants, but in increasing order of reducing power.

What is the relationship between the two tables?

For every cell on the grid, representing one direction of a redox reaction, compare the result shown with that for the reverse direction. Note any cases in which reaction was seen to occur in (i) both directions, or (ii) neither direction.

Expt. 5–5. Calculate the standard cell potentials for the following reactions, and predict the preferred direction:

$$Fe^{2+} + \tfrac{1}{2}I_2 \rightleftharpoons Fe^{3+} + I^-$$

$$Fe^{2+} + Ag^+ \rightleftharpoons Fe^{2+} + Ag(s)$$

(a) Use Fe^{2+} and Fe^{3+} solutions uncontaminated by each other (see remarks above).

Add a little I_2 solution to 5–8 cm^3 acidified Fe^{2+} solution; note any decolorization of the I_2 (compare with a dil. H_2SO_4 blank), and test for Fe^{3+}.

Add a little I^- to Fe^{3+}; note any formation of I_2 (use starch on a portion) and test for Fe^{2+}.

Add a little Fe^{3+} to excess I^-; warm the solution to hasten the completion of reaction, then cool well. Shake with a water-immiscible solvent of iodine (e.g. toluene) to remove most of the I_2; then test for residual Fe^{3+}.

Is the reaction demonstrably reversible? . . . incomplete at equilibrium?

(b) (i) Mix equal volumes of $FeSO_4$ and $AgNO_3$ solutions, acidified with a little dilute sulphuric acid, and allow the mixture to stand. Test for Fe^{3+}, and carry out suitable tests on any precipitate which forms. (Could it be Ag_2SO_4?)

   (ii) *Either* prepare a silver mirror, or obtain a black-and-white photographic negative or print (these have a black image of finely divided silver).

To make a silver mirror, use a new or grease-free test-tube, and add ammonia solution by drops to about 10 cm^3 silver(I) nitrate(V) solution until the initial precipitate of silver(I) oxide has redissolved. Add a little dilute solution of glucose or methanal, then place the test-tube in a beaker of hot water.

Then investigate the reactivity of silver metal with Fe^{3+} (see also Expt. 5–2).

(c) A mixture of $K_3Fe(CN)_6$ and $Na_2S_2O_3$ solutions is used for making over-exposed photographic prints or negatives less dark. It is known as Farmer's Reducer. Is the name appropriate, in the chemical sense? Which is the active silver-removing reagent, and what is the purpose of the other?

Expt. 5–6. Calculate $E^\ominus_{cell}$ for the following reactions and test the predictions by experiment. Be alert for partial or slow reaction.

    (i) $Fe^{2+} + \frac{1}{2}S_2O_8^{2-} \rightarrow Fe^{3+} + SO_4^{2-}$ (you may add KCNS immediately)

    (ii) $I^- + \frac{1}{2}S_2O_8^{2-} \rightarrow \frac{1}{2}I_2 + SO_4^{2-}$

    (iii) $8Fe^{2+} + ClO_4^- + 8H^+ \rightarrow 8Fe^{3+} + Cl^- + 4H_2O$

    (iv) $H_2SO_3 + ClO_4^- + H^+ \rightarrow SO_4^{2-} + Cl^- + H_2O$ (balance this)

  (v), (vi) Fe^{2+}, H_2SO_3 with ClO_3^-

    (vii) $Sn^{2+} + Fe^{3+}$

Expt. 5–7. More advanced investigations. Consider the possibilities, then try the experiments. Is the observed reaction always the one with the highest $E^\ominus_{cell}$?

  (i) $HNO_2 + Fe^{3+}$ (iii) $NO_2^- + NH_4^+$

  (ii) $HNO_2 + Fe^{2+}$ (iv) $ClO_3^- + H^+ + I^-$

Try first with excess ClO_3^-; then deduce the stoichiometry from a 'titration'.

5.9 Summary

Cell potentials and redox potentials vary with the concentrations of dissolved or gaseous participants, according to the rule that potentials (which are positive for thermodynamically favoured processes) decrease with an increase in the concentration ratio products:reactants. Very simply, an accumulation of reaction products is a hindrance to further reaction. The relationship between the cell potential, the standard cell potential and the concentrations of participants is given by the Nernst equation. The equation may be derived from a consideration of concentration cells. In precise work, activity coefficients and liquid junction potentials are of importance.

From tabulated reduction potentials, cell potentials for very many reactions may be calculated. The sign of the cell potential is an immediate indication of the preferred direction: reactions with appreciably negative cell potentials cannot occur spontaneously, while reactions with positive potentials *may* occur, unless hindered kinetically. In the case of two or more possible reactions, the one with the most positive cell potential is expected to occur, though again, kinetic considerations may invalidate the prediction.

5.10 Exercises

(Unless otherwise stated, concentrations may be taken to be equal to activities.)
1. (a) Write, in conventional notation, the cell which could generate an e.m.f. by means of the following reaction:

$$Cu(s) + Fe^{3+}(aq, 1\ M) \rightarrow Cu^{2+}(aq, 1\ M) + Fe^{2+}(aq, 1\ M)$$

(b) What would be the effect on the cell potential of the following changes, in turn?

(i) Increasing the size of the copper electrode.

(ii) Increasing the concentration of Fe^{3+} (aq).

(iii) Increasing the concentration of Cu^{2+}(aq).

(iv) Decreasing the concentrations of the three ions to 0.01 M.

2. (a) AgX is a sparingly soluble silver(I) salt. Calculate the concentration of Ag^+ in a saturated solution of AgX from the following information:

$$Ag, AgX(s) \,|\, AgX(aq, satd.) \,\|\, AgNO_3(aq, 1\ M) \,|\, Ag; \ E_{cell} = +0.40\ V$$

(b) What would be the effect of adding to the left-hand half-cell enough KX to make $[X^-] = 0.1$?

3. (a) Write cells in which the following reactions could occur:

(i) $Cu(s) + Sn^{4+}(aq) \rightleftharpoons Cu^{2+}(aq) + Sn^{2+}(aq)$

(ii) $Sn(s) + Sn^{4+}(aq) \rightleftharpoons 2Sn^{2+}(aq)$

What would be the polarity of each cell if all concentrations were standard (1 M)?
(b)* If cell (i) were set up with equal volumes of solution in each half-cell, and with all electrolytes at 1 M concentration, and if this cell were then short-circuited and left until no further current flowed, what would be the final concentrations?

4. From the half-reactions which appear in Appendix I, devise cells with cell potentials which would, respectively:

(i) be unchanged by equal dilution of both half-cells

(ii) be unchanged by the addition of a little acid to each side. (Effects due to non-ideality may be ignored.)

5. Calculate the equilibrium constant K for the following reactions:

$$Fe^{3+} + I^- \rightleftharpoons Fe^{2+} + \tfrac{1}{2}I_2(aq)$$

$$2Fe^{3+} + 2I^- \rightleftharpoons 2Fe^{2+} + I_2$$

$$H_2(g) + Cl_2(aq) \rightleftharpoons 2HCl(aq)$$

6. Calculate the effect of very slowly increasing the potential difference between platinum electrodes in a solution which is 0.1 M in both Ni^{2+} and Co^{2+}. Assume that the overpotential at the large cathode is negligible. Which metal will be deposited first, and to what value will the concentration fall before the other metal begins to be deposited simultaneously? Would this method seem to be a practical basis for the analysis of a mixture of cobalt and nickel salts?

7.* Assuming no overpotential or amalgamation effects, calculate the effect of very slowly increasing the p.d. between platinum electrodes in a solution which is 0.01 M in both Hg^{2+} and Ag^+. The possibility of the intermediate formation of the mercury(I) ion, Hg_2^{2+}, should be considered. What is the composition of the solution from which both metals begin to be deposited simultaneously?

6

Electrolysis

6.1 Minimum decomposition potentials

In Chapter 4 the distinction was made between the reversible cell potential and the actual potential difference maintained by a galvanic cell in use; and similarly the difference between the theoretical potential difference needed to bring about electrolysis at infinitesimal rate (this is the reversible cell potential of the galvanic cell which is formed by the products of electrolysis) and the practical potential difference required for electrolysis at a finite rate. Having made these distinctions, Chapter 4 went on to examine the reversible cell potential. The present section will be more concerned with the practical p.d. for electrolysis—the decomposition potential—which is invariably greater than the reversible potential, by anything from a few millivolts (for an almost ideal system, and minute current) to several volts for heavily polarized electrodes.

At least four contributions to the working potential difference may be recognized:

(1) The reversible cell potential E_{cell} (for the actual concentrations in the cell);

(2) the p.d. required to overcome the ohmic resistance of the electrolyte;

(3) polarization by concentration changes at the electrodes;

(4) activation overpotential.

The working p.d. of a galvanic cell will be $1 - (2 + 3 + 4)$, whereas the necessary p.d. for electrolysis will be $1 + 2 + 3 + 4$. *1* is found by potentiometry (§4.3) or by calculation from redox potentials (§4.6) or free energy (§4.7). *2* may be measured with an a.c. conductance bridge (§3.3); it may be quite small, under 50 mV for 0.1 A, in a 1 M solution. *3* is due partly to the accumulation of products to a concentration higher than that allowed for in the calculation of *1*, and, more importantly, to the depletion of the solution near an electrode of the ion which is being discharged there. Concentration polarization is the only one of the four effects which is affected by stirring; it is often negligibly small at low current densities, but rises rapidly as the 'limiting current' is approached (§7.7).

Contribution *4*, the activation overpotential,[1] is never negligible in practical

---

[1] The terms 'polarization' and 'overpotential' (or 'overvoltage') have been used rather loosely and interchangeably in the past, sometimes including the 'back e.m.f.'. In this book the distinction will be made that 'polarization' is diminished by mechanical stirring while 'overpotential' is not.

electrolyses, and often exceeds *2* and *3* together. It varies greatly according to the nature of the electrode reaction and the nature of the electrode surface, and unlike effects *1* and *3*, it is not eliminated by the use of alternating current. However, the overpotential vanishes as zero current is approached, as in the 'null-point' instruments, the potentiometer and the conductance bridge.

The early workers on the variation of current with potential difference in electrolysis interpreted their results as if the relationship was of the form:

$$E = E_{mdp} + IR$$

where E_{mdp} denotes 'minimum decomposition potential', R the resistance, and I the current. The validity of this equation will be questioned later (§6.2). But first let us note the historical importance of the first accurate measurements of minimum decomposition potentials at the end of the nineteenth century, which were used by Le Blanc and others to support the 'preferential discharge theory' of electrode processes (§2.4) against Daniell's earlier 'secondary products theory'. The latter was, briefly, that the ions which carry the current are first discharged, but may then immediately react with the solvent to give the observed products. For example, the electrolysis of sodium sulphate(VI) solution with inert electrodes would, in modern terminology, be explained as follows:

At cathode: $\qquad\qquad$ $2Na^+ + 2e^- \rightarrow 2Na$

$\qquad\qquad\qquad\qquad$ $2Na + H_2O \rightarrow 2NaOH + H_2$

At anode: $\qquad\qquad\qquad$ $SO_4^{2-} \rightarrow SO_4 + 2e^-$

$\qquad\qquad\qquad\qquad$ $SO_4 + H_2O \rightarrow H_2SO_4 + \frac{1}{2}O_2$

where Na and SO_4 are the unseen intermediates. The theory had the merit of simplicity, since it predicted the products of electrolysis, including the appearance of alkali and acid at the electrodes, on the basis of the known reactivity of metals such as sodium, and a plausible assumption about the reactivity of the sulphate free radical; it was still taught in elementary chemistry courses as late as 1960. The preferential discharge theory was eventually victorious in the struggle for acceptance, supposedly on the evidence that, for all solutions (at given pH) producing only hydrogen and oxygen, the minimum decomposition potentials were equal. The minimum potentials for the initial discharge of ions such as K^+, Na^+ and Mg^{2+} would not be equal, so this mechanism of intermediate free metals cannot be correct. Whether this is logically sound is one of the points raised in Project 9.29. Let us instead look at the means of measuring these potentials, their reproducibility, and the reasons for their variation.

Practical work

Expt. 6–1. The circuit shown in Fig. 6.1 is designed to allow a variable potential, from zero to over 4 V, to be applied across the electrodes of the electrolytic cell. The variable resistor should have a resistance considerably lower than that of the solutions to be used, but not so low as to cause a large drain on the battery.

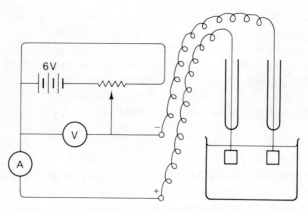

Fig. 6.1 Circuit for determining decomposition potentials

(1) With shiny platinum electrodes in 0.5 M H_2SO_4(aq) (i.e. 1.0 M $\frac{1}{2}H_2SO_4$), slowly increase the applied p.d. to 1 V, then by 0.1 V increments, until the milliammeter registers a current. Find the potential differences which give rise to selected values of the current, covering the range of the meter. Note also the lowest p.d. at which bubbles become visible on the electrodes.

When the highest measurable current has been reached, reduce the p.d. gradually, and again record the variation of current with p.d. Is the system reversible in this respect? ('Reversible' has a new meaning here: on a graph of current versus p.d., are the points obtained when the current is increasing on the same line as those for when it is decreasing?)

(2) Find also the effect of moving the electrodes, or stirring the solution. This gives an insight into one of the causes of polarization, and suggests a means for its minimization.

(3) Measure the conductance, if an a.c. bridge is available.

(4) If you have time, investigate also the effect of temperature.

(5) When you have a reliable graph for the 0.5 M H_2SO_4, repeat investigations 1 and 3 under the same conditions but with different electrolytes, one from each of the following groups in turn:

Group I: 0.05 M H_2SO_4, 1 M NaOH, 0.5 M Na_2SO_4, 1 M NH_3(aq), 1 M NH_4NO_3, 1 M KOH, 0.5 M $MgSO_4$.

Group II: 0.5 M $Cu(NO_3)_2$, 0.5 M KI, any Fe^{3+} salt, $FeBr_3$ (or any mixture to give these ions).

(6) Repeat the 0.5 M H_2SO_4 investigation, but using lead (or tin or cadmium) electrodes.

Discussion of results. Fig. 6.2 shows results which have been obtained in an investigation similar to that described above. If your own points lie on a line of different shape, consider whether this is due to a difference in the current range covered. (For example, if the maximum current had been only one-third of that shown in Fig. 6.2, there would have been much greater curvature on the graph.) As we shall see, the size of the electrodes is important also.

To obtain the 'minimum decomposition potential' (m.d.p.) from the graph, some early experimenters simply projected the apparently straight portion of the line back to the E axis to give the intercept A, while other workers read off the m.d.p. below the intersection, at B.

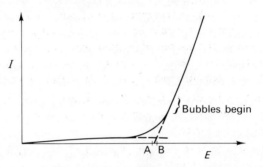

Fig. 6.2 Current–p.d. graph for electrolysis of dilute sulphuric acid with platinum electrodes

Part of the effect is due to the fact that at low currents (per unit electrode area) the product gases dissolve and diffuse away as they are formed, so that their concentration at the electrodes is low. As the current is increased their concentration rises, up to the point of incipient bubble formation; and at higher currents still the gases form bubbles and leave the electrodes, so that their concentration becomes constant. Since the adsorbed products act as a galvanic cell, with its potential in opposition to the applied p.d., and since this cell potential (or 'back e.m.f.' as it was formerly called) varies with concentration, becoming constant when bubble formation begins, the curvature is explained.

Q. If the opposing cell potential does not increase with current above the m.d.p., why is the line not *vertical* from this point? And why do the slopes differ according to the nature and concentration of the electrolyte?

Of the four factors listed at the start of this section, only *1*, the reversible cell potential, will be expected to be independent of current. *2*, the conductance effect, is a most likely cause of the slope; but this effect was estimated separately (by an a.c. measurement or by doubling the current path), and the product IR can be calculated and subtracted from each p.d. Do this now, and if the effect was substantial, redraw each graph as one of I versus $(E - IR)$.

The calculation probably showed that the conductance effect was only a minor part of the variation of current with p.d. Factor *3*, the concentration polarization, will certainly depend upon current (§7.7), but in a well stirred solution, not too dilute, and at moderately low currents, the effect is largely eliminated by the movement of the electrolyte. We are driven to the conclusion that a substantial contribution to the slope of the I/E line is due to the *variation of overpotential with current*.

The minimum practical cell overpotential is not the overpotential at zero current (which would actually be zero, see §6.2), but the overpotential at *low* current, the current at which decomposition becomes noticeable. It is loosely defined, but has some practical significance.

By inspection of the results for platinum and lead (or other metal) electrodes you can see that overpotentials for the decomposition of water differ widely according to the nature of the electrode. It would be natural to assume (and it can be confirmed experimentally) that the minimum practical cell overpotential is the sum of two independent electrode overpotentials. From the pooled results of the practical work, or from Table 6.1, calculate some of these cathode and anode overpotentials.

Q. How is the zero to be determined? By arbitrary convention (as with the S.H.E. for redox potentials), or empirically, by searching for a cell with zero minimum practical cell overpotential?

Treatment of pooled results. If a number of students have performed the experiment under similar conditions, and if their results for the same electrolyte (0.5 M H_2SO_4) agree, then curves for different electrolytes should be drawn on the same graph for comparison. Clearly there are almost endless possibilities for variation of conditions, such as temperature, nature and size of the electrodes, rate of stirring (if any) or movement of electrodes, presence of non-electrolyte additives, and direction of change of current (increasing or decreasing). Only if all these factors have been held constant are the results for different electrolytes comparable in a straightforward way.

For each of the runs, the following should be known: (i) the overall chemical change; (ii) the concentrations of ions, including H^+ and OH^-; (iii) the (theoretical) reversible cell potential, for the actual concentrations used.

Calculate the minimum practical cell overpotential (see Appendix II) for each electrolytic cell by subtracting the reversible cell potential from the minimum decomposition potential.[2]

6.2 Overpotential

Fig. 6.3 shows the variation of potential within an electrolytic cell. The overall potential drop is the sum of:

(i) the p.d. between the anode and the solution, made up of the oxidation potential of the anode reaction (including concentration polarization, if any), and the anodic overpotential;

[2] That is, the cell potential for the electrolytic reaction, which must be negative, is added algebraically to the m.d.p.; we shall regard overpotentials, whether of cells or of electrodes, as having no sign.

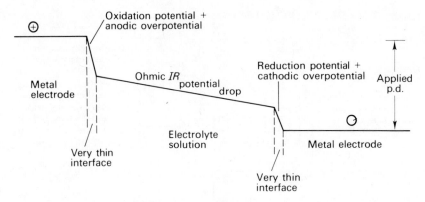

Fig. 6.3 Potential drop across an electrolytic cell

    (ii) the ohmic potential drop across the solution, equal to IR;

    (iii) the p.d. between the solution and the cathode, made up of the reduction potential and the cathodic overpotential.

The oxidation potential and the reduction potential cannot be measured absolutely, but only in relation to a reference electrode; but their sum, which is the reversible cell potential, is measurable absolutely.

The anodic and cathodic overpotentials can be measured by an ingenious combination of a current carrying electrolytic cell with a potentiometer circuit, as shown in Fig. 6.4. The potentiometer measures the p.d. between C, one of the cell's electrodes, and a reference electrode D, which makes contact with the cell electrolyte through a salt bridge in the form of a narrow tube (called a Luggin capillary) which is usually placed as close as possible to the electrode being studied.

Firstly the p.d. across C and D is measured with no current flowing between electrodes B and C; this gives the redox (electrode) potential of C relative to D, which will be subtracted from subsequent readings. Then a potential difference is applied across BC until the required current is flowing, and the potential of C is measured again. Since no current flows in the potentiometer circuit, the resistance of the solution has no effect on the measurement (i.e. no part of that IR drop is included)[3]; but the measured p.d. *does* include the overpotential, because electrode C *is* experiencing a current flow, across to B.

Practical work

    Expt. 6–2. Polarization. Set up the apparatus shown in Fig. 6.4. The ammeter should read to 50 or 100 mA d.c.; the potentiometer or high-resistance voltmeter should read to about 1.5 V. The reference electrode D may be a calomel or a silver/silver chloride electrode. The salt bridge should be shaped so that the capillary tip can be placed in contact with electrode C, on the side away from B. The salt

---

[3] The effect of the resistance of any surface layer (e.g. of oxide), however, is included.

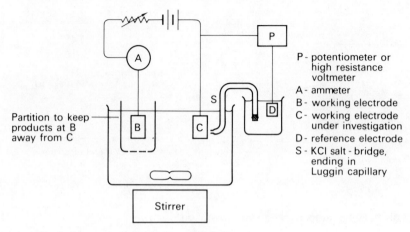

P - potentiometer or
   high resistance
   voltmeter
A - ammeter
B - working electrode
C - working electrode
   under investigation
D - reference electrode
S - KCl salt - bridge,
   ending in
   Luggin capillary

Partition to keep
products at B
away from C

Stirrer

Fig. 6.4   Circuit for measurement of overpotential

bridge can be filled with concentrated potassium chloride solution from the wider end, and then closed with a cork (not too tightly) with a slip of filter paper between the glass and the cork. The partition around B could be a wide test-tube with a hole blown in the base.

Expt. 6–2.1. Preliminaries: the IR drop. Use 0.05 M H_2SO_4 as the electrolyte in the cell, and shiny platinum electrodes. Before any current has passed between B and C, measure E_C^0, the potential of C with reference to D, at zero current to or from C.

Connect up the d.c. supply to the cell, and pass about 20 mA, with C positive. Measure the potential of C, now E_C. Then, by moving the capillary away from C and towards B, demonstrate the existence of the ohmic potential drop (as shown in Fig. 6.3). With the capillary touching B, measure E_B. Calculate the resistance of the solution, as $(E_C - E_B)/I$. If an a.c. conductance bridge is available, compare the results of the two methods of measuring resistance.

Expt. 6–2.2. The 'back e.m.f.' or 'fuel cell effect'. With the capillary secure in place at C, read E_C: disconnect the cathode B and note the change of E_C with time. How long does it take for E_C to fall to E_C^0? Pass the current again, and again break the circuit, but quickly connect B to C through A without including the external source of e.m.f. Note the galvanic cell action of the oxygen and hydrogen (products of the earlier electrolysis) still present on the electrodes. Does the reversion of E_C to E_C^0 take place more quickly when B and C are connected?

Expt. 6–2.3. The decomposition potential. Establish efficient stirring of the solution, particularly around C. Connect the external e.m.f. across B and C (again with C positive), but either with the variable resistor at maximum, or (if the source of e.m.f. is variable) at low e.m.f. Gradually increase the p.d. across BC until the ammeter A registers a small steady current. Note the values of current I and potential E_C for this and a series of increasing currents.

Reverse the polarity of the external source of e.m.f. Take a series of readings of I and E_C, with C as a cathode.

Expt. 6–2.4. Overpotential. Repeat the last investigation, but with a cathode C' of lead or tin (but still with a platinum anode B).

Finally, repeat the investigation, but with C being either a small platinum-wire anode, or a lead cathode painted so that only a small area is exposed.

Treatment of results. Interpret parts 1 and 2 of Expt. 6–2 in terms of the 'back e.m.f.' or 'secondary cell' theory. For parts 3 and 4 of the investigation, calculate the overpotential E', where $E'_C = E_C - E^0_C$, and plot graphs of E'_C versus I, E'_C versus $\log I$, and $\log E'_C$, versus I. (Log graph paper may be used.)

Which of the following equations most closely describes your results? (a, b and R are constants)

$E \times I = \text{constant}$

$E = I \times R$

$E = a + RI$

$E = a + b \log I$

$E \log I = \text{constant}$

$I \log E = \text{constant}$

$\log E = a + bI$

Evaluate the constant(s) of the equation you have selected. Finally, draw conclusions about the effect of electrode area on overpotential.

Progress towards an understanding of overpotential was historically slower than that of the reversible electrode potential. One reason was the sheer difficulty of maintaining the constant conditions necessary for reproducible results: the cleanliness, roughness and previous treatment of the electrodes can have a profound effect on the value of the overpotential. But beyond this was the apparent lack of theoretical basis for much of the research, as revealed in the frequent publication of tables of overpotentials with no mention of the current density at which they were measured, implying that they were constants. Other measurements were made at the minimum current density for bubble formation—which would have been meaningful except for the large subjective element in the observation of bubbles, and the fact that the rate of dissolution of the gases can, at low currents, equal the rate of their formation.

With hindsight, we now recognize the achievement of Tafel who, in 1905, published his famous equation:

$$\eta = a + b \lg |i|$$

where η (Greek 'eta') is the overpotential, $|i|$ is the magnitude (without sign) of the current density, and *a* and *b* are constants. This logarithmic relationship has been repeatedly confirmed, and has subsequently been given theoretical foundation. Why then did some electrochemists (particularly in the technical field) continue for 40 years to ignore it, and to treat η as a constant?

Perhaps the answer lies in an understandable liking for simple linear relationships, and a tendency to interpret a graph as a straight line whenever possible. The plot of $a + b \lg i$ (with $a = 1.0$ V and $b = 0.1$ V) is shown in Fig. 6.5, and so is a plot of $E = \eta + IR$ ($R = 2\Omega$, $I = i$), which is a rather idealized version of the graphs from which 'minimum decomposition potentials' were obtained. The right-hand line (X—X) shows points up to 100 mA cm^{-2}, and suggests a m.d.p.

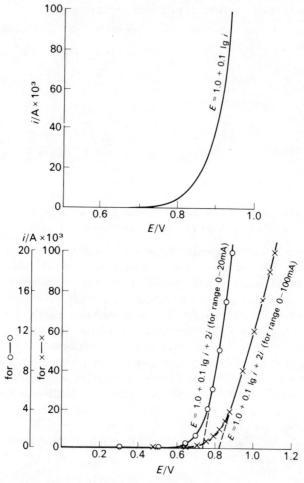

Fig. 6.5 Calculated logarithmic plot and suggested origin of 'minimum decomposition overpotential'

of about 0.82 V, while the left-hand line (O—O) is a plot of the *same function*, but showing points only up to 20 mA cm^{-2}, on an appropriately expanded scale. This time the m.d.p. appears to be 0.72 V; a change of 12% arising merely from the different mode of presentation of the same results.

The temptation to make pseudo-extrapolations of the apparently 'straight' portions must have been even greater when the data were experimental results, with inevitable errors from diffusion effects etc. Of course a graph of current versus potential difference, could be a useful way of presenting information relevant to, for instance, a plating bath. And the pseudo-extrapolation to obtain a 'minimum decomposition potential' (as was done in §6.1) might give meaningful information about the 'minimum practical cell overpotential' for the range of current shown on the graph. But since the 'corner' of the curve can be moved at will, simply by changing the scales of the graph, these intercepts cannot have any theoretical significance.

Current density and the roughness factor

The Tafel equation relates overpotential to current density, not simply to current. An indication of this could be seen in the results of Expt. 6–2.4. Current density can be defined as current per unit area of electrodes, but in fact the *effective* area may be greater than the geometrical area by a considerable factor, due to the roughness of the surface.

If i is the effective current density while i' is current/geometrical area,

$$\lg i = \lg i' - \lg r$$

where r is the 'roughness factor'. Thus the effect of the roughness factor is to alter the Tafel constant a, and to make no difference to the coefficient b (the 'Tafel slope'). In fact, b is found to be related to the mechanism of the electrode reaction (which is unlikely to be affected by the roughness, though it may well depend upon the nature of the electrode), while constant a is more a measure of the catalytic power of the electrode surface (being large for a poor catalyst).

6.3 Overpotential and activation energy

The dependence of overpotential upon the nature of the 'inert' electrode emphasizes that it is a kinetic and not a thermodynamic phenomenon. The simplest view of any electrode reaction must include at least three stages:

(1) diffusion of reactant to electrode surface,

(2) electron transfer between reactant species and electrode,

(3) diffusion of product away from electrode.

The rates of these three steps are necessarily equal, but in any given case, one of the steps will be rate-determining—that is, it will be *unable* to go any faster. If the slowness is due to (1) or (3), it gives rise to 'concentration polarization', which is the increase in applied potential necessary to keep the current (that is, the rate of the whole process) up to a given value. This is so even though the slow step does not involve electron transfer. When a sequence of reaction steps is in the 'steady state' condition, the acceleration of one step, even if it is not the rate-determining one, can accelerate all the others.

If the slowness is due to stage (2)—the electron transfer step *or* any other step occurring on the electrode surface—the necessary potential increase is called the 'activation overpotential'.

The energy required for an electron to leave the electrode and become attached to a cation, or vice versa, is not simply the difference in energy level between the two states: that would be the *reversible* potential. Yet it is not as great as the energy required to pull an electron from the electrode into a vacuum (the 'work function'). It is some intermediate state of affairs, analogous to an energy barrier (see Fig. 6.6).

Reactions which take place by molecular collision obey the Arrhenius equation:

$$k = A \, e^{-E_a/RT}$$

where k = rate constant, i.e. rate of reaction/concentration terms; A = a temperature constant; E_a = energy of activation; RT = mean thermal energy. However, studies of the kinetics of electrode reactions have shown that they do *not* obey this equation in a straightforward way. The situation is that the effective height of the energy barrier varies with the current, that is, with the rate of reaction. The barrier must be at least equal to the reversible work of reaction (not measurable absolutely for a single electrode, but equal to zFE_{cell} for both electrodes together, see §4.7), so it is the excess of the energy barrier over this that will be affected by the overpotential.

As we have seen, the overpotential varies logarithmically with current density for appreciable currents but clearly this could not be the case right down to zero current, since $\lg 0 = -\infty$. In fact the relationship becomes linear at very low currents and at zero current the overpotential is zero.

The explanation for the change in the effective height of the energy barrier comes from the recognition that, in quantum mechanics, the electron can 'tunnel'

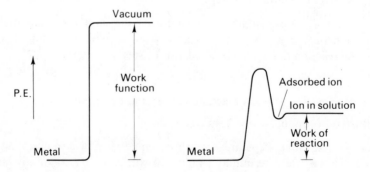

Fig. 6.6   Potential energy diagram for electron transfer

through the barrier, rather than having to surmount it; but that the longer the tunnel, the less frequent the transfer. This is illustrated in Fig. 6.7.

With certain reservations, the Arrhenius equation may be applied to the electrode reaction. As with molecular reactions, the equation must only be applied to one direction at a time, that is, to pure forward or reverse reaction, not to the net reaction which is the difference between them. The height of the undisturbed

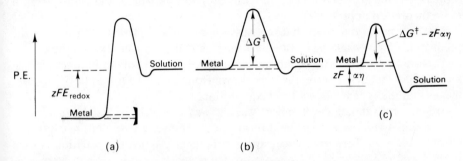

(a) (b) (c)

Fig. 6.7 Effect of raising potential energy of electrons in an electrode

(a) No applied potential; negligible forward reaction

(b) Reversible conditions; small 'exchange currents' both ways

(c) Applied overpotential; forward reaction via tunnelling

energy barrier (at zero net current and zero overpotential) is the free energy of activation $\Delta G^{\ddagger}$. For given concentrations, rate constant is proportional to rate, i.e. current; and for given electrodes, current is also proportional to current density. Hence for reaction in one direction, let us say the cathodic discharge of a metal ion, the current density is related to the free energy of activation by the modified Arrhenius equation:

$$i_0 = C\,e^{-\Delta G^{\ddagger}/RT}$$

(Naturally at zero net current the rate of cathodic discharge of a metal ion must equal the rate of anodic production of the same metal ion, so that each equals the 'exchange current', i_0.)

Now if an overpotential η is applied to the electrode, a fraction α has the effect of lowering $\Delta G^{\ddagger}$ for the forward reaction to $(\Delta G^{\ddagger} - zF\alpha\eta)$ (where α is usually about $\frac{1}{2}$), while the rest affects $\Delta G^{\ddagger}$ for the reverse direction. And if we consider the case of an appreciable net current (implying negligible 'reverse' current):

$$i = C\,e^{-(\Delta G^{\ddagger} - zF\alpha\eta)/RT}$$
$$= C\,e^{-\Delta G^{\ddagger}/RT}\,.\,e^{zF\alpha\eta/RT}$$
$$= i_0\,e^{zF\alpha\eta/RT}$$

Simplifying: $i = A\,e^{\beta\eta}$.

So the variation of current with overpotential is exponential, which explains why quite a small increase in applied potential can result in a large increase in the current (see Figs. 6.2, 6.5).

The student should satisfy himself (see §6.9, q. 8) that the equation just derived can be rearranged to give the traditional form of the Tafel equation.

Electrode kinetics is an underdeveloped subject, and has been relatively neglected in the past. Much of our electrochemical technology was derived from unconceptualized practical experience, and will probably benefit in the future from a more theoretical approach.

Bockris[4] makes the point that the early success of the Nernst equation for the prediction of reversible cell potentials may actually have hindered progress on fuel cells and the like. The equation is applicable only to equilibrium conditions, and the very fact that a current is to be drawn from the cell (if it is to be of any use) means that the system will *not* be at equilibrium.

Another unfortunate development was the way in which the Tafel equation, in its traditional and more convenient form, led to an inverted view of the cause and effect relationship between current and overpotential. When the equation is used in the form $\eta = a + b \lg i$, the question which is being asked is: 'What overpotential is caused by current density i?' It begins to seem that the current has to battle through against a reactionary force—which is almost the exact opposite of the truth. Yet when the same equation is used in its 'current-centric form' (Bockris's term):

$$i = A\,e^{\beta \eta}$$

the question is completely changed, to something like: 'If we apply an overpotential η, what current will it bring about?'

Scientists who regarded the overpotential in the first way, as an undesirable nuisance or even fault, were too readily discouraged when it proved impossible to eliminate it; whereas if the *essential* nature of overpotential had been recognized, the early expectations of 100% power efficiency would have been modified more cheerfully, and research on fuel cells need not have stopped for 40 years.

6.4 Simultaneous electrode processes

In its simple form, the theory of preferential discharge predicts that, of a number of possible electrode reactions, the one which will occur will be that which requires the lowest potential $(E + \eta)$. However, since the overpotential for a given reaction varies with the rate of that reaction, there is no precise 'minimum decomposition potential', above which the reaction can occur. For convenience, a 'minimum practical current density' can be arbitrarily chosen (perhaps 10^{-4} A cm^{-2}), below which the reaction is considered to be negligible, and the reactions can be ranked

[4] J. O'M. Bockris, 'Overpotential: a lacuna in scientific knowledge', *J. Chem. Educ.* **48**, 352–8 (June 1971).

Table 6.1 Hydrogen and Oxygen Overpotentials

Activation overpotentials vary somewhat with the nature and concentration of the electrolyte, and the temperature. The following are mainly for 1 M or 0.1 M solutions, at 25C°.

Product	Electrode	Electrolyte	Overpotential η/V at 1 A cm^{-2}	10^{-3} A cm^{-2}	Tafel slope b/V
H_2	Hg	H_2SO_4	1.41	1.05	0.12
	Pb	H_2SO_4	1.40	1.00	0.13
	Pb	HCl	1.34	0.67	0.22
	Sn	HCl	1.06	0.85	0.07
	Al	H_2SO_4	1.00	0.70	0.10
	Cu	H_2SO_4	0.80	0.44	0.12
	Ag	HCl	0.92	0.44	0.16
	Fe	HCl	0.75	0.40	0.12
	Pt	HCl	0.55	0.09	0.15
	Pt	H_2SO_4	0.47	0.09	0.12
	Pd	HCl	0.11	0.02	0.03
H_2	Hg	NaOH	1.45	1.15	0.10
	Cu	NaOH	0.69	0.33	0.12
	Pd	KOH	0.52	0.13	0.13
O_2	Pt	H_2SO_4	1.06	0.70	0.12
O_2	Ni, Ag	NaOH	1.05	0.60	0.15
O_2	Pt	NaOH	0.70	0.55	0.05
O_2	Fe	NaOH	0.58	0.40	0.06

in order of increasing 'minimum practical decomposition potential' at the particular electrode in question. But if two competing reactions have m.p.d.p's which differ only slightly, the potential required for the more favoured to proceed rapidly will be high enough for an appreciable amount of the less favoured to proceed simultaneously.

When A, one of two possible reactions, has a lower reversible discharge potential than the other, B, but a large enough overpotential (at the operative current density) to make its practical potential the higher, then a mixture of products is bound to result. For since the overpotential for process A varies with the current density *for electrode process A*, it follows that A will occur to just that extent which makes its practical potential equal to that of B. (An example is the H_2/Na competition at the mercury cathode, §6.6. See also Projects 9.1 and 9.20.)

The selection of the right material or shape for the electrode can make a distinction between two simultaneous processes. The catalytic properties of the electrode are reflected in the factor A of the equation derived in §6.2:

$$|i| = A\,e^{\beta\eta}$$

A change to a different electrode material may reduce, for perhaps one of two competing reactions, the overpotential necessary to maintain a given current density. In other cases, concentration polarization may be deliberately induced by use of a small electrode, or minimized by use of a large one (see Expt. 6–3).

In considering the possible products of electrolysis, two common misconceptions should be avoided. One is the confusion between the ions which carry the current and the ions which are discharged: *all* ions present contribute to the conductivity, but do not necessarily take part in the electrode reactions. The other erroneous idea is that only cations can react at a cathode (and anions at an anode) since the negative electrode must 'attract' positive ions, and vice-versa: in fact neutral molecules, or even anions, can be driven by thermal motion into contact with the cathode, and may be reduced there if that should be the reaction with the lowest decomposition potential.

An important instance of this is the production of hydrogen from neutral or alkaline solutions, which cannot occur through the discharge of $H^+(aq)$ since the rate is higher than would be in accordance with the low concentration of these ions. It is significant that the water in the hydration sphere (p. 3) of the current carrying electrolyte ions is 'pre-conditioned' for reaction at the appropriate electrode, both sterically and, by the inductive effect, electrostatically. Project 9.29 is concerned with the extended debate on the mechanism of the 'electrolysis of water'.

Current efficiency

Apart from a minute initial current needed to charge the electrodes in the manner of a condenser, the only way that charge can flow into or from an electrode is by an electrode process involving electron transfer with the electrolyte—that is, by a chemical reaction at the electrode. Therefore it follows from the principles of stoichiometry (§2.2) that the amount of electricity which passes through an electrolytic or a galvanic cell must equal the sum of the amounts of all the reduction reactions which occur at the cathode, which in turn must equal the sum of the amounts of all the oxidation reactions at the anode. The *total* current efficiency must be 100%.

However, the term current efficiency normally refers to *one* electrode reaction of interest, and could be defined thus:

$$\text{current efficiency} = \frac{\text{electricity used in one selected reaction}}{\text{total electricity passed}} \times 100\%$$

In a coulometer designed so that the amount of electricity passed can be measured by the amount of a certain product (e.g. silver, or iodine) the current efficiency must be known to be 100%. In other cells the efficiency may be less than this, for three principal reasons: (i) competing electrode reactions, with loss of electricity on an unwanted product; (ii) diffusion of the required product to the other electrode, and its destruction there (e.g. diffusion of iodine to the cathode); (iii) secondary reaction of the product (decomposition, or reaction with other products, air, electrode material, etc.).

Current efficiency should not be confused with energy efficiency, which may be defined as the free energy increase of the desired product relative to the electrical energy used. Energy efficiency is necessarily less than 100% since for any electrolysis the practical decomposition potential must exceed the reversible cell potential (§6.1).

6.5 Anodic oxidations

The principal large-scale technical electrolyses which centre on the anodic process are the production of fluorine and chlorine, and the production of peroxodisulphuric acid for the purpose of hydrolysis to hydrogen peroxide. Certain organic electrolyses are described in a later section (§6.7), and those anodic processes which are for the purpose of changing the shape of materials (e.g. electromachining) are left until Chapter 8.

Fluorine

Electrolysis is the only known method of producing fluorine, and this fact emphasizes the point that an anode, at sufficient potential, is the strongest 'oxidizing agent'.

When in 1888 Moissan announced his discovery of fluorine (for which he received the Nobel Prize in 1906) it was the outcome of many years struggle to restrain the active element which attacked almost everything with which it came into contact. Fluorine reacts with water, so the electrolyte must be anhydrous: a solution of potassium fluoride in hydrofluoric acid is suitable. Surprisingly, a copper vessel may be used, because it is soon protected by a layer of copper(II) fluoride. The electrodes are made of steel (cathode) and nickel or carbon (anode).

Recently much interest has developed in the chemistry of organic fluorine compounds. Hydrocarbons can be fluorinated by fluorine generated *in situ* by electrolysis (see §6.7).

Chlorine and chlorates

The electrolysis of aqueous sodium chloride solution produces, initially, sodium hydroxide, hydrogen and chlorine. If the sodium hydroxide is required pure, a mercury cathode may be used; otherwise the cheaper 'diaphragm cell' is sufficient. These cells are described in §6.6, and both are designed to keep the chlorine well away from the sodium hydroxide.

If, in contrast, there is no diaphragm, and the solution is well stirred, the chlorine produced at the anode immediately reacts with hydroxide ions from the cathode (see §5.6). The product is sodium chlorate(V) or chlorate(I),[5] depending upon the conditions. For chlorate(V), hot saturated sodium chloride solution is electrolysed with a graphite anode and an iron cathode, with the addition of a little dichromate to modify the cathode behaviour. If the solution is kept cold, and if the electrolysis is stopped at an earlier point, the main product is sodium chlorate(I).

---

[5] Formerly known as hypochlorite.

An interesting feature of the cell design is the use of additional graphite electrodes positioned as in Fig. 6.8, but not connected to the source of potential difference. If there are n additional electrodes, the cell behaves as $(n + 1)$ cells in series, and if the applied p.d. is increased by a factor of $(n + 1)$, each intermediate electrode becomes a cathode on one side and an anode on the other. The product is marketed, without further purification, as 'liquid bleach'.

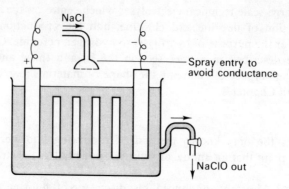

Fig. 6.8   Cell for the electrolytic manufacture of sodium chlorate(I) solution

There have been proposals for the electrolytic purification of sewage, especially in coastal towns where hitherto it has simply been piped into the sea. If the sewage were mixed with sea-water and electrolysed, the chlorate(I) ion formed would destroy bacteria, and render the waste material harmless.

Peroxo compounds

When dilute sulphuric(VI) acid is electrolysed, with platinum electrodes, hydrogen and oxygen are formed in the ratio 2:1 by volume; but with more concentrated acid the ratio increases, reaching 3.5:1. This 'loss of oxygen' was first noticed by Michael Faraday, and in 1878 Berthelot put forward the correct explanation, that the competing anode reaction is the formation of peroxodi-sulphuric acid, $H_2S_2O_8$:

$$2HSO_4^-(aq) \rightarrow 2H^+(aq) + S_2O_8^{2-}(aq) + 2e^-$$

This reaction is the basis of the Weissenstein process for the manufacture of hydrogen peroxide, since the peroxodisulphuric acid is hydrolysed on heating:

$$H_2S_2O_8 + 2H_2O \rightarrow 2H_2SO_4 + H_2O_2$$

The oxidation of sulphate(VI) is favoured by conditions which hinder the competing reaction, $2H_2O \rightarrow 4H^+ + O_2 + 4e^-$: low pH (which increases the oxidation potential), low temperature and high anodic current density (which raise the overpotential). Practical details are given at the end of this section.

In neutral or weakly acid solutions an alternative anode reaction is the formation of the peroxosulphate ion SO_5^{2-}; this is undesirable in the Weissenstein process, since on heating this compound decomposes, producing oxygen, not hydrogen peroxide.

The anode reaction steps have not yet been fully elucidated, but in acid solution the initial step is probably the discharge of HSO_4^-, while in neutral solution it is the discharge or perhaps semi-discharge of SO_4^{2-}:

$$\left. \begin{array}{l} 2HSO_4^- \rightarrow 2HSO_4 + 2e^- \\ 2HSO_4 \rightarrow S_2O_8^{2-} + 2H^+ \end{array} \right\}$$

acid

neutral

or

$$\left. \begin{array}{l} SO_4^{2-} \rightarrow SO_4 \text{ (adsorbed)} + 2e^- \\ SO_4 + SO_4^{2-} \rightarrow S_2O_8^{2-} \\ SO_4 + H_2O \rightarrow H_2SO_5 \end{array} \right\} \quad or \quad \left. \begin{array}{l} SO_4^{2-} \rightarrow SO_4^- \text{ (ads.)} + e^- \\ 2SO_4^- \rightarrow S_2O_8^{2-} \\ or\ SO_4^- + H_2O \rightarrow H_2SO_5 + e^- \end{array} \right\}$$

A similar reaction is the anodic oxidation of cold K_2HPO_4 solution to $K_4P_2O_8$, peroxodiphosphate.

Practical work. Electrolytic oxidation and reduction

Expt. 6–3. Electrolytic preparation of potassium peroxodisulphate(VI). Electrolyse cold (0°C) saturated potassium hydrogen sulphate(VI) solution, with a small platinum anode and a large platinum cathode, at 12 V and about 1.5 A, for at least

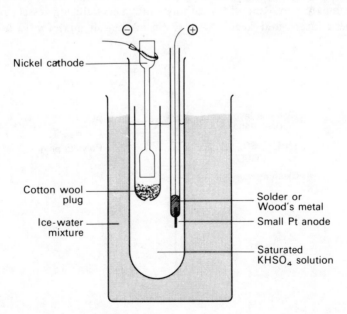

Nickel cathode

Cotton wool plug

Ice-water mixture

Solder or Wood's metal

Small Pt anode

Saturated $KHSO_4$ solution

Fig. 6.9 Preparation of potassium peroxodisulphate

30 minutes. Crystals of potassium peroxodisulphate appear. They may be collected in a sintered glass crucible, or on a porous tile, washed with a little cold distilled water followed by a little ethanol, then dried. The product is stable.

In acid solution peroxodisulphate slowly oxidizes iodide, and this provides a method of quantitative analysis. Find either (a) the $S_2O_8^{2-}$ content of the crystals, or (b) the solubility of $K_2S_2O_8$ from the concentration of the residual liquor. (The 'dead-stop' end-point method, p. 158, is suitable for the iodine–thiosulphate titration.)

Also investigate the oxidizing powers of $S_2O_8^{2-}$ on (i) Mn^{2+}, with trace Ag^+; (ii) Ag^+ in ammoniacal solution.

Expt. 6–4. Electrolytic reduction of vanadate to vanadium(II) or (III). The first stage in the reduction of ammonium vanadate(V) in sulphuric acid solution may be carried out electrolytically, but to save time, sulphur dioxide or, better, ammonium sulphate(IV) may be used (see Appendix II). Further reduction at a cathode occurs readily, giving a green solution of vanadium(III) and ammonium sulphates(VI), which crystallize on standing to give 'vanadium alum', $NH_4V(SO_4)_2 . 12H_2O$.

The preparation of the vanadium(II) state requires more care, and the apparatus shown in Fig. 6.10 is required. Place a hot mixed solution of ammonium sulphate(VI) and oxovanadium(IV) (formerly vanadyl) sulphate(VI), prepared as above, in the tap funnel electrolytic cell, and heat to 90°C; electrolyse at 12 V for about 2 hours, until the intermediate green colour of V(III) has become grey-blue. Discontinue the current, and cool the whole cell in an ice-bath; then add about 5 cm³ toluene to form an air excluding layer. Electrolyse for one further hour, then remove the anode compartment. Run off the catholyte into a crystallizing vessel (together with the toluene layer), and keep at −5°C (in an ice-salt mix) for 12 hours. Violet

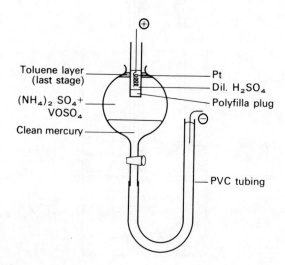

Fig. 6.10 Preparation of vanadium(II) and (III) states

crystals of the double salt vanadium(II) ammonium sulphate(VI) appear, and may be filtered off, washed in ethanol, and dried (and bottled) in nitrogen. Investigate the reactions of the vanadium(II) compound with (a) air; (b) cold dilute HNO_3; hot dilute HCl.

The investigation of the anodic oxidation of V(II) appears as Project 9.18.

6.6 Cathodic reductions

The discharge of metal ions at a cathode and the formation of the free metal, often in the form of a coherent plating, is one of the greatest technical uses of electrochemistry. Metals which can be deposited from aqueous solution include Cu, Ag, Au, Ni, Co, Mn, Cr, Zn, Cd, Sn, and several mixtures (alloys) of these. Electroplating will be described later, in §8.2, but it may be noted here that under chosen conditions (high current density) the metals can be deposited in the form of loose powders (especially Cu, Zn, Fe and W).

The production of the base metals (K, Na, Ca, Mg, Al) by the electrolysis of molten salts will be described in §8.1. However, these metals, and others like them, can be discharged from aqueous solution if a mercury cathode is used. The Castner–Kellner cell (described below) makes use of this. For small-scale preparation of the elements, the amalgam may be distilled in an inert atmosphere. In 1910 Mme Curie isolated radium by the electrolysis of a small quantity of $RaCl_2$ solution, using a mercury cathode.

An oddity which was discovered over 150 years ago, and which is still imperfectly understood, is "ammonium amalgam'. When concentrated ammonium chloride or sulphate solution is electrolysed with a cooled mercury cathode, no hydrogen is produced, and the mercury becomes stiff and buttery. It is apparently a solution of the free ammonium radical in mercury. If it is allowed to warm up, it swells, and bubbles of hydrogen and ammonia appear. Project 9.18 is concerned with ammonium and other amalgams.

The electrolysis of water to produce pure hydrogen (e.g. for margarine manufacture) is carried out technically using nickel electrodes and 20% sodium hydroxide solution. Some cells are built to operate under pressure, which keeps the gas bubbles smaller, and thus less of an obstruction to the current.

Prolonged electrolysis of any aqueous solution gradually enriches the heavy water (D_2O) content, since the decomposition potential for the liberation of H_2 is slightly less than that for D_2. In Norway and at the Niagara Falls, where hydroelectric power is generated, surplus electricity is used to manufacture heavy water for the nuclear power industry and other scientific purposes. Almost 100% D_2O is available, and if free deuterium gas is required, it can be made from this by electrolysis; of course the electrolyte must then be one, as for example K_2SO_4, which contains no 'light' hydrogen.

Another 'laboratory' use of preparative electrolysis is the controlled reduction of compounds to an unusual lower oxidation state. The preparation of vanadium(III) and (II) compounds has been described above (Expt. *6–4*).

Electrolysis of sodium chloride solution

The electrolysis of sodium chloride solution, to give sodium hydroxide, chlorine and hydrogen, is a major industry. In the U.K. alone, over 1 million tonnes each of Cl_2 and NaOH are produced each year, representing a power consumption of about 400 MW.

Cells of many different designs are in use, but all are basically one of two types: the mercury cell and the diaphragm cell. The former predominates in Britain, and has the advantages of greater production capacity, slightly higher current efficiency, and a very pure product. However, the capital invested in the expensive mercury is large, and makes the mercury cell the less economic in times of high interest rates. Furthermore, the small unavoidable loss of mercury in the waste brine effluent is now recognized as an environmental pollution hazard.

The modern form of the mercury cell is essentially two long cells, either side by side or one above the other (Fig. 6.11). The upper, or electrolytic, cell slopes slightly, so that both the mercury and the saturated brine (25 %NaCl) run along its length. Graphite anodes are set a short distance above the cathodic mercury

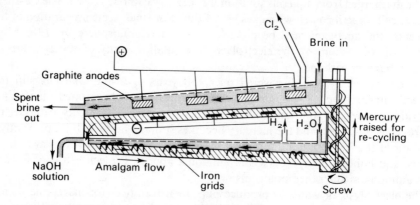

Fig. 6.11   The flowing mercury (Castner-Kellner) cell[6]

surface, and the electrolysis produces chlorine (which is led off at the top of the cell) and dilute sodium amalgam (see §6.9, q. 12). The combined effect of the low activity of sodium in the amalgam, and the high overpotential of hydrogen liberation at the smooth mercury surface is sufficient to make sodium the predominant cathode product. The flow rate is such that when the mercury reaches the lower end of the cell, the concentration of sodium is about 0.2% by mass: an amalgam of higher concentration would be too viscous to flow easily, and would be susceptible to attack by dissolved chlorine. In the lower cell, the amalgam flows below a counter-current of water, and a number of stationary iron (or graphite) grids are placed so as to be in contact with both liquids. The overpotential of hydrogen is

[6] After D. W. F. Hardie, *Electrolytic Manufacture of Chemicals from Salt*, O.U.P.

relatively low at an iron surface (see Table 6.1, p. 122), so the sodium is now able to react with water; the arrangement is equivalent to a short-circuited cell, thus:

at mercury surface: $Na(amalgam) \rightarrow Na^+(aq) + e^-$

at iron surface: $H_2O + e^- \rightarrow OH^-(aq) + \frac{1}{2}H_2(g)$

The mercury, depleted of sodium, is pumped (often by an Archimedian screw) back up to the start of the cycle.

The principle of the diaphragm cell (Fig. 6.12) is that the brine is held in a porous container made of perforated steel lined inside with asbestos paper. A

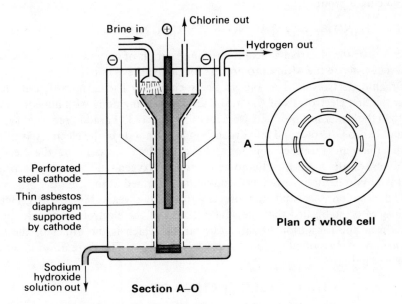

Fig. 6.12 Gibbs diaphragm cell (after Hardie, *op. cit.*)

graphite anode is set in the centre of the solution, and the steel container is made the cathode. The whole is enclosed within a large tank. It is arranged that the sodium chloride solution seeps through the asbestos diaphragm at a rate equal to that of the electrolysis, so that the solution dripping off into the collecting trough is almost pure sodium hydroxide, with very little chloride. To avoid electrical leakage to the brine inlet, the stream of brine is made into a non-conducting spray.

6.7 Organic electrolysis

The use of preparative electrolysis has been relatively neglected in organic chemistry, both on the industrial and the laboratory scale. The reasons for this are not clear, for there are a wealth of reactions, particularly anodic oxidations and couplings, which are known to occur, often with purer products or better yield than with the alternative non-electrochemical methods. It may be that until recently potentiostatic equipment was not readily available, so that it was difficult to maintain a steady potential difference across the electrodes when temperature or concentration changed—an important requirement in technical electrolysis.

An example of an electrochemical process which has become obsolescent for economic reasons is the cathodic reduction of glucose to mannitol and sorbitol, which was practised on a large scale in 1936, but which has now virtually ceased. Another electrolytic reaction which was formerly widespread is Haber's electroreduction of nitrobenzene, which gives aniline or, under controlled conditions, intermediate products:

$$C_6H_5NO_2 \xrightarrow{+2e^-} C_6H_5NO \xrightarrow{+2e^-} C_6H_5NHOH \xrightarrow{+2e^-} C_6H_5NH_2$$

In contrast, the electrochemical hydrodimerization of acronitrile to adiponitrile is now a key step in the Monsanto process for the synthesis of nylon.

Organic electrolysis is as old as electrochemistry itself. In 1801, only months after the first electrolysis of water, the same was being done with aqueous alcohol. In 1830 the oxidation products were identified. In 1833 Faraday reported the formtion of carbon dioxide and a hydrocarbon at the anode in the electrolysis of potassium ethanoate (acetate) solution[7]; he considered these to be the 'secondary products' of attack on the ethanoate by anodic oxygen, and was very surprised to find the hydrocarbon—a reduced compound—formed at the anode.

This reaction was studied more closely, in the years 1848–50, by Hermann Kolbe, who established that the general effect of the electrolysis of salts of 'fatty acids' was the formation of the hydrocarbon which is the dimer of the radical formed by the loss of CO_2 from the discharged anion. These are now known as the Kolbe reactions:

$$\text{e.g.} \quad 2CH_3CO_2^- \rightarrow 2CO_2 + C_2H_6 + 2e^-$$

$$2C_nH_mCO_2^- \rightarrow 2CO_2 + C_{2n}H_{2m} + 2e^- \quad (m \text{ usually} = 2n + 1)$$

It is generally accepted that free alkyl radicals are intermediates in these reactions (Kolbe had hoped to prepare free radicals). The anode is usually of platinum, and fairly small, so that the current density (and hence the concentration of radicals) is high:

$$CH_3CO_2^- \xrightarrow{-e^-} CH_3CO_2^{\cdot} \longrightarrow CH_3^{\cdot} + CO_2$$

$$2CH_3^{\cdot} \longrightarrow C_2H_6$$

At low current densities other products are often formed by reaction of the radical $C_nH_m^{\cdot}$ with the solvent, to give the lower hydrocarbons C_nH_{m+1} or C_nH_{m-1} (unsaturated), or alcohols C_nH_mOH. Substituents, particularly on the α–C atom, may also interfere with the Kolbe coupling.

[7] See *Experimental Researches in Electricity*, Everyman Edn., para. 484.

The evidence for the radical mechanism is reviewed by K. M. Johnston in the first of two papers on organic electrochemistry (*Educ. in Chem.* **4**, 299–303), It is noteworthy that the initiation of the polymerization of styrene—behaviour typical of radicals—can be brought about by electrolysis of ethanoate.

Substitution of hydrogen by halogens can be carried out electrolytically, and this is likely to become a process of great industrial importance. In the case of chlorination, the advantage is that no chlorine is wasted as HCl, as when Cl_2 is used directly:

$$C_6H_6 + HCl \rightarrow C_6H_5Cl \text{ (at anode)} + H_2 \text{ (at cathode)}$$

cf. $\quad C_6H_6 + Cl_2 \rightarrow C_6H_5Cl + HCl$

Continued electrolysis gives further substitution, right up to C_6Cl_6.

Fluorination is easily brought about by electrolysis in liquid hydrogen fluoride, and this is very much more convenient (and controllable) than direct reaction with fluorine. An example of this 'Simons process' is the electrolysis of a mixture of butanoic acid and hydrogen fluoride, in an iron cell, with nickel anode and steel cathode, at about 6 V:

$$C_3H_7COOH + HF \xrightarrow{\text{at anode}} [C_3F_8 + C_3F_7COF]$$

subsequently: $C_3F_7COF + H_2O \rightarrow C_3F_7COOH + HF$.

Practical work

Expt. 6–5. Preparation of ethane by the Kolbe reaction. Prepare an electrolytic cell by winding about 2 m bare copper wire around a porous pot, fitted with a two-holed bung carrying (1) a platinum electrode sealed into a glass tube, and (2) an exit tube for the gases produced. Stand the porous pot in a tall-form beaker, and add a suitable volume of electrolyte solution, both inside and around the pot, made up in the proportion 50 g hydrated sodium ethanoate and 50 cm^3 pure ethanoic acid to 50 cm^3 water.

The exercise is to investigate the current yield of ethane and carbon dioxide at the platinum anode, at different currents. The cell should first be allowed to run for a time to displace air. Then one procedure might be to pass a steady, measured current for a definite time, and to collect the gases in a graduated tube, over very dilute acid (to inhibit dissolution of CO_2). After measurement, the gas could be shaken with sodium hydroxide solution, and the final volume, presumably due to ethane, noted. This CO_2-free gas could be analysed by chromatography if desired, or tests for the presence of ethene could be applied.

The effect of varying the applied potential should be investigated. Any change in the ratio of 'hydrocarbon' to carbon dioxide should be noted, and an explanation suggested. The effect of temperature could also be studied, using a larger container around the electrolytic cell, filled with hot or iced water.

If the cell is to be used for preparative purposes, the gases from the anode compartment should be passed through a U-tube of soda-lime, to remove carbon dioxide. 12 V should produce ethane at a suitable rate.

6.8 Summary

The minimum practical decomposition potential for an electrolytic reaction is obtained by the extrapolation of the apparently straight line portion of a current/applied potential graph. The m.p.d.p. is never less than the magnitude of the (negative) cell potential of the reaction, and often exceeds it considerably because of effects due to the electrode kinetics. One of these effects, concentration polarization, is only important at low concentrations of reactant, or at very high current density. The other effect, activation overpotential, is often a major contributor to the m.p.d.p., especially in reactions involving gas evolution. The variation of overpotential with current density, and with the nature of the electrodes, must often be considered in connection with predictions concerning competing or simultaneous reactions.

These principles are illustrated, in the second half of the chapter, by examples of preparative electrolyses from inorganic and organic chemistry, both on the industrial and the laboratory scale.

6.9 Exercises

1. Draw sketch graphs of the variation of current (up to about 1 A) with p.d. for the following electrolytes with smooth platinum electrodes. No exact current scale need be shown.
    (i) 1 M KOH (minimum practical decomposition potential = 1.67 V)
    (ii) 0.01 M KOH
    (iii) 0.01 M NH_3(aq) (m.p.d.p. = 1.74 V)

2. Consider the minimum practical decomposition potentials for 1 M solutions:

HCl	1.34 V	HNO_3	1.69 V
HBr	0.94 V	H_2SO_4	1.69 V
HI	0.52 V	H_3PO_4	1.70 V

If the hydrogen overpotential is assumed to be the same in all cases, (i) what value does it have? (ii) What is the anode product in each case, and what overpotential does each require (assuming standard product concentrations)?

3. If you have not performed the practical work in §6.2, measuring the change of potential of a single electrode with current, treat the following results (to part 3) according to the instructions given on page 115.

Electrolyte: dilute sodium sulphate (VI) solution;

Electrodes: smooth platinum, each 1 cm^2 in area.

Reference electrode: Hg, $Hg_2Cl_2|1.0$ M KCl ($E_{red}^{\ominus} = +0.281$ V)

Potential of electrode C = $-E_C$; at zero current $-E_C^0 = 0.700$ V

$-E_C$/V	0.70	0.80	0.85	0.90	0.93	0.97	1.00	1.05
i/mA	0.0	0	2	5	10	21	37	100

4. In the electrolysis of a dilute solution of copper sulphate, with copper electrodes, the current–p.d. graph was as shown in Fig. 6.13. The part of the curve between A and B is almost a straight line. Why is this, and what is the significance of the slope of AB?

Why does the curve pass through the origin O, although BA projected does not touch O?

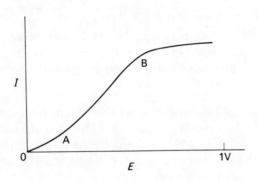

Fig. 6.13

Why does the curve level off at B? What is the significance of the value of I corresponding to the horizontal part of the curve?

Which aspect of the curve—A, B, or the slope AB—would be most altered by a change in the rate of stirring?

5. What product(s) would you expect at the cathode in the following cases? No calculations need be attempted. 'Dilute' refers here to about 0.01 M.

  (i) high current, small cathode, dilute neutral copper sulphate;

 (ii) high current, small cathode, dilute acidified copper sulphate;

(iii) moderate current, large cathode, dilute acidified copper sulphate;

(iv) low current, large cathode, concentrated neutral copper sulphate;

 (v) low current, large cathode, concentrated neutral zinc sulphate;

(vi) high current, small cathode, concentrated neutral zinc sulphate;

(vii) high current, small cathode, dilute acidified zinc sulphate.

6. During nickel-plating, a current of 2.5 A was passed for 1.0 hour, and the cathode gained 2.55 g in mass. Calculate the current efficiency.

7. In the electrolysis of sodium hydroxide solution, for the production of hydrogen, the p.d. across the nickel electrodes was 2.60 V and the current was 2.0 kA. Assuming 100% current efficiency, calculate the energy efficiency (§6.4).

Use the Tafel equation and Table 6.1 to calculate the cell overpotential at 2 kA, given that the effective electrode area is 10 m² each. What is the maximum energy efficiency attainable at this current density, if electrolytic resistance were made negligible?

8. Show that the two forms of the Tafel equation, given in §§6.2 and 6.3 respectively, are equivalent; and show the connection between the constants A, β, a and b.

9. A solution of HBr and HI, both initially 1 M, is electrolysed with Pt electrodes. What will be the concentration of I^- when Br_2 begins to be liberated, to the extent of 1% of the anode products? (Assume the overpotentials of Br_2 and I_2 to be equally small.)

10. The minimum practical decomposition potential of 1 M $AgNO_3$ with smooth Pt electrodes is 0.70 V. Assuming that the oxygen overpotential is the same as it was for HNO_3 in q. 2, and that the overpotential for the deposition of silver is negligible, calculate the pH of the anolyte solution from the apparent oxidation potential for the evolution of oxygen.

Similarly calculate the pH of 1 M $Cd(NO_3)_2$ from the m.p.d.p., 1.98 V.

11. It is known that the reaction of $Br_2(aq)$ with $I^-(aq)$ is rapid and virtually complete:

$$Br_2(aq) + 2I^-(aq) \rightarrow I_2(aq, \text{ as } I_3^-) + 2Br^-(aq); \lg K = 18$$

Calculate the concentration of Br_2 that could exist in a solution which was 1 M in I^-, Br^- and I_2. It is suggested that during the electrolysis of this solution, some of the iodine produced at the anode is a 'secondary product' resulting from the initial discharge of Br^- ion. Neglecting overpotential, what is the oxidation potential for the production of Br_2 at the low concentration calculated above? How does this compare with that for the production of I_2 at 1 M concentration?

12.* In the Castner process for the manufacture of sodium hydroxide by the electrolysis of hot concentrated sodium chloride solution (§6.6), ionic sodium is reduced at the mercury cathode in preference to the reduction of hydrogen ion or water. In practice the cathodic discharge potential is about 1.83 V, and the pH of the solution at the mercury surface is about 13.

(i) What is the reversible potential for the reduction of Na^+ to $Na(s)$ (assume $c_{Na+} = 6 \text{ mol dm}^{-3}$)?

(ii) What lowering of the actual discharge potential for sodium is due to amalgam formation? It is sometimes said that this effect is due to the low concentration of sodium in solution in mercury. Test this supposition by calculating the activity of sodium in the amalgam, and comparing it with the mole fraction.

(iii) What must be the actual overpotential for the competing hydrogen process?

(iv) The total current density is 0.3 A cm^{-2}, and 0.3% H$_2$ is found in the Cl$_2$. Refer to Table 6.1 for the hydrogen overpotential at 298 K. Compare this value with your answer to (iii), and comment.

13. Write half-equations for the following organic redox reactions. (The reagents most frequently used to bring them about are indicated, but should not, apart from H$^+$ or OH$^-$, appear in the equations.) Which of the reactions might be brought about by electrolysis?

(i) $RCH{=}CH_2$ $\xrightarrow{\text{(H}_2\text{O}_2.\text{ trace OsO}_4)}$ $\begin{array}{c} RCH{-}CH_2 \\ |\quad\ | \\ OH\ \ OH \end{array}$

(ii) $RCH{=}CH_2$ $\xrightarrow{\text{Zn, HCl(aq)}}$ RCH_2RCH_3

(iii)

naphthalene $\xrightarrow{(Cr_2O_7^{2-},\ H^+)}$ phthalic anhydride

(iv)

$\xrightarrow{(MnO_4^-,\ OH^-)}$

(v) methanal, CH_2O $\xrightarrow{(Ag(NH_3)_2^+)}$ CO_2

(vi) CH_3CH_2OH $\xrightarrow{(Cr_2O_7^{2-},\ H^+)}$ CH_3CHO

(vii) $\begin{array}{c} |\quad\ | \\ {-}C{-}{-}C{-} \\ |\quad\ | \\ OH\ \ OH \end{array}$ $\xrightarrow{Pb(IV)}$ $\rangle C{=}O + O{=}C\langle$

14. Ketones, general formula $R_2C{=}O$, are readily converted to pinacols,

$$\begin{array}{c} R_2C{-}OH \\ | \\ R_2C{-}OH \end{array}$$

by electrolysis in acidic aqueous solution, at sufficiently high applied potential and current density. Write the half-equation for the overall electrode reaction; and also suggest a plausible reaction mechanism.

At low potential and current density a considerable amount of the alcohol R_2CHOH is formed: comment.

7

Electro-Analytical Methods

The purpose of this chapter is to survey briefly a wide range of analytical applications of electrochemistry. The emphasis will be on principles rather than practical techniques, and although enough information is given for the setting-up of an improvized demonstration of each method, specialist instruments are not generally described. For analytical purposes a reference book or manufacturer's handbook should be consulted for a full account of techniques and precautions necessary to ensure accuracy.

7.1 Electrogravimetry

The principle of electrogravimetric estimations is extremely simple. The solution containing suitable metal ions is electrolysed at a controlled potential, sufficient to cause electrodeposition of one metal but not of others. The platinum cathode is weighed before and after the electrolysis.

The potential selected for the electrolysis must be high enough to exceed the minimum practical decomposition potential (§6.1) sufficiently to cause an appreciable current; and to allow for a rise in the magnitude of the cell potential (the back e.m.f.) as the concentration of the reducible metal ion becomes low. But it must be below the value at which other metals begin to be deposited. The calculation is similar to those in qq. 6 and 7 of §5.10.

7.2 Coulometry

As an alternative to weighing the metal deposited on the cathode in an electrogravimetric estimation, a coulometer can be included in the circuit to measure the amount of electricity which passes. The electrolysis is continued, at controlled potential, until the current falls virtually to zero. The chemical coulometer (or voltammeter) could be based on the deposition of copper or silver,[1] the liberation of iodine (see below), or even the volumes of hydrogen and oxygen (see §2.2).

---

[1] The copper or silver coulometer would have an advantage over simple electrogravimetry only if these metal deposits were easier to dry and weigh than those of the metal being estimated.

The deposition of a metal is not the only kind of electrode reaction which can be measured by coulometry: the cathodic reduction of an oxidant such as dissolved chlorine could be used. Alternatively the converse of electrodeposition, anodic dissolution, can be the basis of the estimation of the thickness of a metal plating (given that the plating is attacked more readily than the substrate, in the electrolyte used).

The scope of coulometry is greatly extended by the inclusion of secondary reactions; the electrolysis generates a substance which then reacts with the substance to be estimated. This application is often called a coulometric titration (see below).

Worked example

A sample of brass (zinc + copper) weighing 0.105 g was dissolved in nitric acid, which was then diluted and partly neutralized by calcium carbonate.

The whole solution was electrolysed at a potential which was known to be insufficient for the deposition of zinc or hydrogen at the cathode. In series with the electrolytic cell was an iodine coulometer as shown in Fig. 7.1. It was initially filled

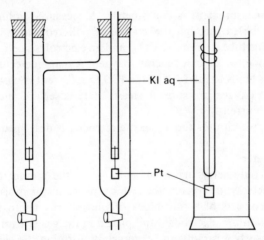

Fig. 7.1 Iodine coulometers: commercial model (left) and improvized (right)

with approx. 1 M KI solution, and at the end of the electrolysis the solution was titrated[2] against 0.10 M thiosulphate, requiring 23.1 cm.[3] What was the composition of the alloy?

$$2S_2O_3^{2-} \rightarrow S_4O_6^{2-} + 2e^-$$
$$I_2 + 2e^- \rightarrow 2I^-$$
$$0.10 \text{ M} = 0.10 \text{ mol dm}^{-3} = 0.10 \text{ mmol cm}^{-3}$$
$$23.1 \text{ cm}^3 \times 0.10 \text{ M} = 2.31 \text{ mmol S}_2O_3^{2-} \equiv 2.31 \text{ mmol I}^-$$

[2] Alternatively, a constant-current coulometric titration could have been used to estimate the iodine.

$\therefore$ 2.31 mmol electrons (2.31 F mC) passed through the coulometer, and through the electrolytic cell.

$$Cu^{2+}(aq) + 2e^- \rightarrow Cu(s)$$

$\therefore \dfrac{2.31}{2}$ mmol Cu was present in 0.105 g brass.

$$\text{Proportion of copper} = \frac{\frac{1}{2} \times 2.31 \times 63.5 \text{ mg}}{105 \text{ mg}} = 70.0\%$$

Biological oxygen demand

One characteristic of water which is polluted with sewage and other organic matter is that as bacterial decay occurs, the concentration of dissolved oxygen is reduced. When this so-called Biological Oxygen Demand (B.O.D.) exceeds the rate of replenishment by photosynthesis or aeration, the water becomes incapable of supporting animal life (including fish), and, furthermore, the products of the decay become evil smelling. A reliable measure of this kind of pollution is therefore the measurement of the B.O.D. of a sample of the water, kept in a sealed vessel, in the dark.

One method of measurement is coulometric. A measured volume of air, in a closed system, is bubbled through the sample of polluted water. Also in the air circuit are a soda-lime tube (to remove CO_2) and an electrolysis cell, such as $CuSO_4$ with a platinum anode, which can generate oxygen. A manometer measures the air pressure, and as this tends to fall (due to the B.O.D.), current is passed through the cell to maintain the oxygen pressure. A steady state is set up, and the B.O.D. is proportional to the current.

Another method, which uses the 'oxygen electrode', is described in §7.7.

Electrolytic hygrometer

An example of coulometry in instrumentation is the commercially available (e.g. Beckman) 'Electrolytic Hygrometer', which measures the moisture content of gases. Basically it consists of a thin block of phosphorus pentoxide held firmly between a pair of platinum electrodes, and placed in the gas stream or gas sample. Water vapour is absorbed rapidly and completely, forming the electrolyte, phosphoric acid. A current is then passed between the electrodes, decomposing the phosphoric acid into H_2, O_2 and P_2O_5. In the case of a steady stream of gas, the moisture content is measured by the current required to keep the conductance of the P_2O_5 at a predetermined low value; and in the case of a static sample, it is the integrated product of current and time.

This topic is taken up again in Project 9.16.

Coulometric titration

A variation of coulometry makes use of the amperostat, or steady current circuit. The electronic device maintains the current at a preselected value by automatically increasing the applied p.d. whenever necessary. In some cases the value of the applied p.d. may be recorded (perhaps automatically) and plotted against time on a graph. A *sudden* rise in p.d. indicates the end of the electrolytic reaction and the start of another. The time interval between sudden changes of p.d. is, of course, proportional to the amount of electricity used for that particular reaction. Some commercial instruments provide for variable current, and include a small computer which integrates current and time.

An advanced example of a fully automatic continuous coulometric titration apparatus designed for a particular purpose is the Philips Air Pollution Monitor, which presents a continuous record of the concentration of sulphur dioxide—an accepted indicator of air pollution.

A measured sample of air is bubbled through the electrolytic cell, which contains a solution of H_2SO_4, KBr and Br_2. Any sulphur dioxide reacts with the bromine, thus:

$$SO_2 + 2H_2O + Br_2 \rightarrow 4H^+ + SO_4^{2-} + 2Br^-$$

The decrease in Br_2 concentration is detected by a decrease in the potential of a platinum sensor electrode in the solution, and this signal, amplified, starts an electrolytic current between two other electrodes, which continues until enough Br_2 has been generated at the anode to replenish that reduced by the SO_2. The product of time and current, which is proportional to SO_2 concentration, is calculated and recorded automatically. Unattended automatic operation is possible, including periodic recalibration, and the monitor can detect as little sulphur dioxide as 0.01 parts per million.

Practical work

A simple way of maintaining an approximately constant current despite changes in electrolyte conductance is to make the cell a very small proportion of the total resistance, by putting it in series with a resistor of 200 Ω or so. The circuit then requires a driving battery of some 50 to 100 V. However, electronic constant current supply units are available at reasonably low cost (ca. £20); or one may be constructed according to one of the published circuits (Appendix II).

In certain cases the anode (B in Fig. 7.2) or cathode (C) may have to be isolated from the test solution by a porous partition (a porous pot, or a perforated test-tube with soaked filter-paper wad).

The 'end-point', or moment when the desired electrochemical reaction is complete, may be indicated visually by a colour change, in which case the resemblance to an ordinary titration is very close. The following experiment is an example. Otherwise the end-point may be detected potentiometrically, as in Expt. 7–5.

Expt. 7–1. Coulometric titration of an acid. Set up the apparatus as in Fig. 7.2, omitting electrode D and the potentiometer. The cathode C should be a small platinum-foil electrode, while anode B, which need not be isolated in this case, is of silver wire. The solution in the cell is roughly 0.1 M KCl, coloured with bromo-thymol blue indicator (or methyl red).

Add a 1.00 or 2.00 cm³ aliquot of the acid to be estimated (around 0.1 M), and ensure adequate stirring. Switch on the electrolytic current and start the stop-clock;

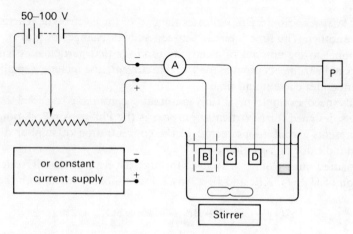

Fig. 7.2 Apparatus for constant current coulometric titration

note the current after 10 s and at subsequent intervals. When the indicator changes colour, stop the clock.

Repeat the titration with the following refinements: (i) adjust the current so that the duration of the run is about 200–250 s; and (ii) switch off the current at a pre-determined time, about 25 s before the anticipated end-point, and finish the titration using two-second bursts, estimated by switching on and off in rhythm with a ticking clock. The intermittent electrolysis allows time for stirring, and is the equivalent of 'addition by drops' near the end of a burette titration.

The cathode reaction is (as long as H^+ ions are present):

$$2H^+(aq) + 2e^- \rightarrow H_2(g)$$

Alternatively, especially near or after the end-point, it may be:

$$2H_2O + 2e^- \rightarrow 2OH^-(aq) + H_2(g)$$

At the anode: $Ag(s) + Cl^-(aq) \rightarrow AgCl(s) + e^-$.

(If a silver electrode is not available, any other may be used, if it is isolated from the test solution.)

Note that the coulometric titration eliminates the need for standard volumetric reagents. It is capable of high precision, and is particularly advantageous for estimating low concentrations.

7.3 Conductimetry and conductimetric titrations

Conductimetry—the estimation of concentration from conductivity alone—is simple if the solution contains only a single substance. Otherwise, since the conductivity depends upon *all* ions present, the measurements may be more difficult to interpret.

The variation of conductivity with concentration has been discussed in Chapter 3, and it will be recalled that for strong electrolytes conductivity κ is approximately proportional to concentration. If it were exactly proportional, then the molar conductivity Λ would be a constant, but Fig. 3.7 shows that this is not so. For conductimetry, the cell constant (which relates the measured conductance and the more general property, the conductivity) need not always be known. For if the same cell, with the same rigidly spaced electrodes, is always used, conductances may be compared instead of conductivities.

Expt. 3–7 (p. 57) was an example of conductimetry, used to find the solubility of calcium sulphate. It allowed for the non-linearity of the conductance/concentration relationship (i.e. the inconstancy of Λ) by having a solution of known concentration diluted until it exactly matched the unknown in conductance.

Conductimetric measurements are easily made, and find many applications in cases where the *total* electrolyte concentration is of interest: e.g. ground water (see Project 9.12), the purity of deionized water, the salinity of sea-water. For oceanographical purposes an operational definition of salinity is necessary, and because of the variable composition of sea-water, the older definition based on chloride ion concentration was unsatisfactory: the new UNESCO definition is conductimetric.

A typical technical application of conductimetry is a boiler feed-water monitor, which might consist of a pair of annular (ring) carbon electrodes set into a length of plastic pipe, through which the feed-water passes on its way to the boiler: if the electrolyte concentration exceeds the safe limit, the increase in conductance sets off an alarm.

Conductimetric titrations

A conductimetric titration is an ordinary burette titration, but the determination of the equivalence point is done after the event, by studying the variation of conductance with volume of titrant added. An example was given in Chapter 3 (Expt. 3–6), involving an acid–base titration. The end-point was at the minimum conductance, since H^+ and OH^- ions are more mobile (§3.9) than other cations and anions respectively.

With more delicate equipment, such as the high-frequency conductance bridge (or even an external radio-frequency impedance coil), titrations can be performed in which the equivalence point is detected by a change in the slope of the graph of conductance against titrant volume. The conductance of a solution of ethanoic acid, for example, increases as sodium hydroxide solution is added (forming ionized sodium ethanoate), but the increase becomes greater after the end-point. Even the titration of a weak acid by a weak base (which is very unsatisfactory with a visual indicator) becomes possible.

7.4 Potentiometry and potentiometric titrations

The variation of cell potential with concentration has been discussed in Chapter 5 (§§5.1, 5.2) and was shown to be expressed by the Nernst equation. The most convenient cell for the determination of the concentration (strictly, activity) of a single ion is one consisting of one electrode reversible to the ion of interest, and a *reference electrode* with a known and reproducible electrode potential. For example, if it were desired to measure the concentration of Cu^{2+} in a solution (free from more easily reduced ions), the following would be suitable:

Reference electrode $|$ KCl $|$ Cu^{2+} (unknown) $|$ Cu

$$E_{cell} = E_{red}(Cu^{2+} \mid Cu) - E_{red} \text{ (reference)}$$

$$E_{red}(Cu^{2+} \mid Cu) = E_{red}^{\ominus}(Cu^{2+} \mid Cu) + \frac{RT}{2F} \ln[Cu^{2+}] \qquad (\S5.1)$$

$$= E_{cell}^{\ominus}(Cu^{2+} \mid Cu) + \frac{0.059 \text{ V}}{2} \lg[Cu^{2+}] \text{ at 298 K}$$

It is not actually necessary to know in advance the values of $E_{red}^{\ominus}$ or E_{red} (reference), since preliminary experiments with solutions of known concentrations are easily performed. In fact, by using for calibration known concentrations of the ion to be determined, in solutions made up to a chosen ionic strength by an inert salt, the error due to the activity coefficient (§5.3) can be avoided.

Many reference electrodes are available, but only two need be described here:

(1) *The silver–silver chloride electrode*

A silver wire (fairly stout, about 10 cm long, half of it twisted into a coil) is made the anode in dilute hydrochloric acid for about 5 minutes at 0.1 A or so. The silver surface becomes partly covered by an adherent layer of almost insoluble silver chloride.

When immersed in any aqueous solution, the silver chloride dissolves to a minute extent, until the concentrations of silver and chloride ions satisfy the solubility product of AgCl:

$$[Ag^+][Cl^-] = 2 \times 10^{-10} \text{ at 298 K; thus } [Ag^+] = \frac{2 \times 10^{-10}}{[Cl^-]}$$

and since the electrode potential of Ag^+/Ag varies with $[Ag^+]$, the potential of the Ag/AgCl electrode is dependent upon the chloride concentration, $[Cl^-]$.

For use as a reference electrode, the silver–silver chloride electrode is immersed in a standard chloride solution, such as 1.0 M KCl, and contact with the test solution may be made through a salt bridge.

At 298 K: $AgCl(s) + e^- \rightarrow Ag(s) + Cl^-(aq)$; $E_{red}^{\ominus} = +0.2224 \text{ V}$

(2) *The calomel electrode*

This is the most widely used reference electrode. Calomel is an old name for mercury(I) chloride, which is an almost insoluble compound. The Hg/Hg_2Cl_2 electrode is, like the Ag/AgCl electrode, reversible to chloride ion: but it is more accurately reproducible because the mercury is not susceptible to potentials arising from strains in the metal. The chloride concentration is commonly fixed by the use of saturated KCl as the electrolyte, giving the 'saturated calomel electrode' (s.c.e.) with $E_{red} = +0.2420$ V at 298 K. But since the solubility of KCl varies with temperature, the temperature coefficient of the s.c.e. is large, and for precise work 1.0 M or 0.1 M KCl is used ($E_{red}^{\ominus} = +0.2810$ V; E_{red} (0.1 M) = $+0.3335$ V).

Commercially available calomel electrodes are convenient to use, being sealed units, often cylindrical in shape, and no thicker than a pencil (Fig. 7.3a). A calomel electrode may be incorporated into the design of a 'combined' glass electrode for a pH meter (§7.5), and it is worth remembering that even if the glass electrode is broken, the calomel reference electrode may still function.

An improvized version could take the form shown in Fig. 7.3b.

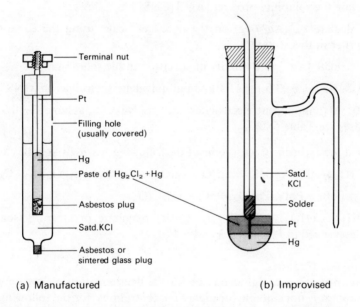

      (a) Manufactured   (b) Improvised

Fig. 7.3 Calomel electrodes: commercial model (left) and improvised (right)

Practical work

Expt. 7–2. Potentiometric determination of solubility products.

Required   Potentiometer or electronic mV meter (pH meter).

          Reference electrode.

          Silver, lead or copper electrodes.

          0.10 M $AgNO_3$, $Pb(NO_3)_2$ or $Cu(NO_3)_2$ solutions.

          0.010 M solutions of selected anions (see below).

1. Set up, and measure the cell potential of:

Reference electrode | KCl bridge | AgNO$_3$ (aq, 0.10 M) | Ag

or the corresponding Cu or Pb cell.

2.* (Optional). Similarly measure the cell potentials when the AgNO$_3$ is 0.010 M and 0.0010 M, and calculate the activity coefficients (§5.3) for the three concentrations. Then use 0.0010 M AgNO$_3$ in 0.10 M NH$_4$NO$_3$ and note that the activity coefficient is approximately the same as for 0.10 M AgNO$_3$.

3. Prepare a solution of silver thiocyanate AgCNS by adding 3 drops (approx. 0.15 cm^3) of 0.1 M AgNO$_3$ to about 30 cm^3 0.01 M KCNS. Measure the reduction potential of the silver electrode in this suspension.

ᒪalculate the solubility product [Ag$^+$] [CNS$^-$] as follows:

(a) Calculate E_{red}(Ag$^+$/Ag) on the hydrogen scale, using the equations given earlier in this section;

(b) Calculate [Ag$^+$], the activity of silver ion in the solution used;

(c) Assume $f = 0.93$ for the 0.01 M uni-univalent electrolyte, so [CNS$^-$] = 0.009

(For 0.01 M uni-divalent electrolytes such as Na$_2$CO$_3$ assume $f = 0.6$; and for other cases see Table 5.2.)

4. Repeat the experiment with some of the following sparingly soluble electrolytes:

Ag$_2$CrO$_4$, AgBr, AgOH (=Ag$_2$O), AgIO$_3$, Ag$_2$CO$_3$, Ag$_3$PO$_4$, Ag$^+$C$_6$H$_5$CO$_2^-$;

PbCl$_2$, PbBr$_2$, PbI$_2$, PbSO$_4$, PbCO$_3$, PbCrO$_4$;

Cu(OH)$_2$, Cu(IO$_3$)$_2$, Cu$_3$(PO$_4$)$_2$, Cu(II) palmitate or stearate (soaps). This topic is continued in Projects 9.3 and 9.4.

Potentiometric titrations

Potentiometry is a useful technique for the determination of low ionic concentrations, but it is not suitable for higher concentrations, for the following reasons: (1) the variation of E_{red} with concentration, being logarithmic, is not very sensitive to small differences in high concentrations (for instance, the difference in E_{red} (Cu^{2+}/Cu) in 1.00 and 1.01 M Cu^{2+} would be virtually undetectable); (2) the difference between activity (derived from the potential) and true concentration is too great.

In the case of high concentrations, then, it is preferable to titrate the ion of interest against a reagent of known concentration, and to use potentiometry to detect the equivalence point. This is usually very satisfactory, since the relatively rapid reduction in concentration at the equivalence point is reflected in a large change in electrode potential. It depends, however, upon the availability of an electrode which is 'reversible' to one of the ions being titrated, that is, one which quickly takes up its equilibrium potential.

The great variety of reactions which can be performed as potentiometric titrations may be considered in two categories: those in which the ion of interest is removed from solution by precipitation or complex formation, and those in which it is oxidized or reduced to a different oxidation state. Examples of each will be given. Acid–base titrations monitored by a pH meter would formally be included in the former category, but will not be considered until after the section on the glass electrode.

Practical work
Potentiometric titrations with silver nitrate
The silver electrode shows an unusually quick and reliable response to changes in the concentration of its ion. It is therefore suitable for monitoring the progress of the titration, by precipitation, of Cl^-, Br^-, I^-, CNS^-, SO_4^{2-}, CrO_4^{2-}, HPO_4^{2-}, etc., by silver nitrate(V) solution.

For some of these titrations it is possible to use a visual internal indicator, potassium chromate(VI): if the silver nitrate is run from the burette into, say, chloride containing a little chromate, the first permanent appearance of pink-orange Ag_2CrO_4 indicates that the chloride has virtually all been precipitated. However, the additional silver nitrate required to precipitate the chromate is a source of 'end-point error' and the method is unsatisfactory in reverse (e.g. with chloride in the burette), or for ions forming precipitates less insoluble than silver chromate.

Expt. 7–3. Titration of chloride. The following experiment enables the potentiometric and chromate equivalence points to be compared.

Set up the apparatus as in Fig. 7.4, and add 10.0 cm³ 0.1 M hydrochloric acid (partially neutralized) to sufficient water in the cell. For the purpose of the comparison, also add 0.2 cm³ of 0.1 M K_2CrO_4.

Run in the 0.1 M $AgNO_3$ by 1.0 cm³ portions, recording the potential of the silver electrode. When the expected equivalence point approaches (as known from a preliminary run if necessary), reduce the additions to 0.5 or 0.1 cm³, so that an

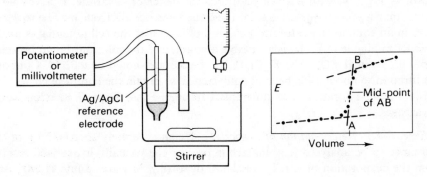

Fig. 7.4 Potentiometric titration

accurate graph can be drawn. Note also the first permanent pink colour. Read the potentiometric equivalence point from the graph, as shown in Fig. 7.4. Calculate the relative error in the chromate end-point.

Expt. 7–4. Potentiometric silver nitrate titrations. Use the apparatus shown in Fig. 7.4 to estimate: (i) chromate(VI); (ii) sulphate(VI); (iii) a mixture of chloride and iodide.

Redox titrations

Any pair of redox half-reactions can be combined to give a reaction suitable for a potentiometric redox titration, provided that both are rapid in solution, and that the reduction potentials differ by at least 0.3 V (otherwise reaction will be incomplete, and the graph difficult to interpret). In some cases no indicator is necessary: the strong purple colour of manganate(VII) makes the solution turn pink immediately after the equivalence point. For other reagents, chemical indicators are available, but these are not on the whole very easy to use. In the case of dichromate, the strong colours of the $Cr_2O_7^{2-}$ and Cr^{3+} ions make visual detection of the equivalence point difficult, and the potentiometric method is particularly valuable.

A classical titrimetric determination of copper is based on the disproportionation of CuI_2 into insoluble CuI plus free iodine:

$$Cu^{2+}(aq) + 2I^-(aq) \rightarrow CuI(s) + \tfrac{1}{2}I_2(aq)$$

Excess potassium iodide is added to the Cu^{2+} solution, and the iodine produced is then titrated against thiosulphate. Unfortunately the equivalence point is rather difficult to see, even with starch as an indicator, because some of the iodine is adsorbed on the surface of the precipitate, and does not react until the thiosulphate is in excess. Potentiometric titration can overcome this disadvantage, if time is allowed after each addition near the equivalence point, because as the thiosulphate reacts with the last traces of iodine, the situation is indicated by the cell potential.

Finally, it should not be forgotten that coulometric titrations, too, can be monitored potentiometrically.

Expt. 7–5.1. Potentiometric titration of Fe(II) by dichromate. Use the apparatus shown in Fig. 7.4, with a small platinum-foil indicator electrode. If a voltmeter (rather than a potentiometer) is to be used, the reference electrode may be replaced by Pt in an equimolar mixture of $Fe^{2+} + Fe^{3+}$, so that the cell potential is small. About 1 millimole of Fe(II) is a suitable amount, and the solution should be made about 0.2 M in H_2SO_4. The $K_2Cr_2O_7$ in the burette should be 0.02 M. Continue the titration to about 50% beyond equivalence, to obtain the complete curve.

For repeated titrations the differential technique (see Expt. 7–8) offers some advantages.

Expt. 7–5.2. Determination of copper(II). Weigh accurately about 0.25 g of the substance to be analysed (e.g. malachite ore; or the partially hydrolysed residue from the evaporation of $CuCl_2$ solution), dissolve it in warm dilute H_2SO_4 and make up to 100 cm³. Pipette a suitable volume into about 10 cm³ of 1 M KI (excess), and titrate the liberated iodine vs. 0.1 M thiosulphate (see text, above). The thiosulphate solution can be standardized if necessary by use of the iodine coulometer described in §7.2.

The apparatus is the same as for Expt. 7–5.1; the reference electrode may be Pt in a solution of 1 M KI containing a trace of I_2. Towards the equivalence point it may be necessary to allow time after each addition, until the potential becomes steady.

7.5 Electrodes reversible to the hydrogen ion

Hydrogen ion concentration, or pH, is of such importance in so many chemical and biochemical systems that untold time and effort have been spent in search for, and development of, potentiometric instruments for measuring it. The essential feature is an electrode reversible to aqueous H^+ ion; that is, an electrode which rapidly takes up a potential related (by the Nernst equation) to the H^+ concentration (activity). The four best-known are: the simple hydrogen electrode (as described in §4.5), the quinhydrone electrode, the glass electrode, and the antimony electrode. Of these four, the first two have the advantage, for electrochemical research, that their behaviour is in accordance with simple thermodynamic theory; whereas the last two have to be 'calibrated' since they show a response which cannot be deduced from first principles.

The Quinhydrone Electrode

Quinhydrone is the name for a commercially available mixed crystal of quinone and hydroquinone. When the solid dissolves in water it forms an equimolar mixture of the two compounds, which are the oxidized and reduced forms, respectively, of a redox pair, thus:

$$+ \ 2H^+(aq) + 2e^- \rightleftharpoons$$

quinone   hydroquinone

Since H^+ ions appear in the half-equation, the reduction potential is pH dependent (in the same way as numerous other redox systems—see §5.6), and so the potential of a platinum electrode immersed in the solution, compared to that of a 'saturated calomel electrode', gives a measure of the pH. Quinhydrone is only sparingly soluble in water, so 0.1 g or so is sufficient to saturate the sample being tested.

Unfortunately the electrode cannot be used for solutions of pH > 9, because side reactions interfere.

The glass electrode

The glass electrode is the most generally useful pH indicator electrode. In 1905 Haber observed that the p.d. between two solutions separated by a thin glass membrane was dependent upon the difference in pH of the two solutions. This led to the development of special types of glass with good pH response and relatively low resistance (down to $10^7 \, \Omega$); and with the very sensitive modern electronic milli-voltmeters the membrane need not be so thin and fragile as was formerly the case.

The glass electrode, in its usual form, consists of a silver–silver chloride electrode in 0.1 M HCl solution, within a glass tube terminating in a thin-walled bulb about 8 mm in diameter. The bulb is immersed in the test solution, which is also in contact, through a porous plug, with a calomel reference electrode. The glass electrode and the calomel electrode are often combined in a single unit (Fig. 7.5).

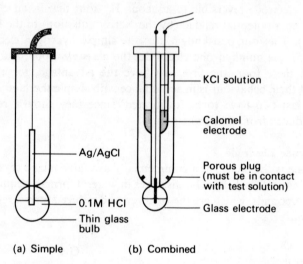

(a) Simple   (b) Combined

Fig. 7.5   Glass electrode

The mechanism by which the potential of the glass electrode depends upon the pH of the external solution is not thoroughly understood, for it cannot involve any redox reaction at the glass surface. It seems that, by incorporation of H^+ ions within the lattice structure of the glass, there is a slight permeability to these ions, and hence a tendency for migration of H^+ from the solution which has the lower pH (higher H^+ concentration). This is similar to a liquid junction potential, or to the potential set up across a semi-permeable membrane (permeable to water).

The potential difference which would just prevent this current of H^+ ions would be, on this analogy, the liquid junction potential (§5.4) for transference numbers $t_+ = 1$ and $t_- = 0$:

$$E = \frac{RT}{F} \ln \frac{a_2}{a_1}$$

In practice the potential includes an unexplained constant (which differs from one electrode to another), which must be allowed for by calibration or standardization, using buffer solutions of known pH:

$$E_{\text{glass}} = \text{const.} + \frac{RT}{F} \ln a_{\text{H}^+}$$

where a_{H^+} is the activity of H^+ in the test solution, and the constant includes the potential of the calomel electrode.

Since the glass electrode is not a redox electrode, it can be used in solutions which contain oxidants or reductants (which would interfere with the hydrogen or quinhydrone electrodes); secondly, since no platinum surface is exposed to the solution, there is no danger of 'poisoning' by cyanides, sulphides, arsenic etc.; the solution may be deeply coloured, or contain organic matter; and the electrode does not interfere with or contaminate the test liquid, and so is suitable for bio-chemical applications. Some glass electrodes can measure the pH of a single drop of liquid.

The antimony electrode

If antimony (as powder or small pieces) is melted in a small hard-glass test-tube and then cooled, it forms a rod of the metal with a coating of antimony(III) oxide; the potential of this rod is found to be dependent upon the pH of the solution in which it is placed:

$$E_{\text{Sb}} = a + b \lg[\text{H}^+]$$

where a and b are rather variable, but usually about 0.14 V and 0.06 V respectively. The electrode needs to be standardized before use, but is very robust, and is dependable, to a fair degree of accuracy, within the pH range 2–7.

The need for a pH electrode for alkaline solutions is met by the silver–silver oxide electrode.

Operational definition of pH

The formal definition of pH:

$$\text{pH} = -\lg[\text{H}^+(\text{aq})] \qquad \text{(where [X] denotes activity of X)}$$

is unsatisfactory in practice, since a single electrode potential cannot be measured, and so $\lg[\text{H}^+]$ cannot be obtained from potentiometry without assumptions as to the reference electrode. Attempts to measure $[\text{H}^+]$ by other means (e.g. vapour pressure) also fail, because these give the mean activity of the electrolyte as a whole, not the activity of a single ionic constituent.

An operational definition of pH has therefore been adopted: that is, one based on measurements which can actually be made. These are E_x, the electrode potential of the hydrogen electrode (or, less accurately, the glass electrode) in the unknown solution X, and E_s, the potential of the same electrode in the standard pH solution S. The same reference electrode is, of course, used in each case. Then:

$$pH(X) = pH(S) + \frac{E_x - E_s}{(RT \ln 10)/F}$$

Standard solutions have been defined, which between them cover the pH range 3.5 to 9.

Commercial pH meters are designed so that after two simple adjustments (one for temperature, the other to match the pointer reading to the known pH of the standard solution) the pH of any other solution into which the glass electrode is placed is shown directly.

pH Titration curves

The change in pH in the course of an acid–base titration is shown by the 'titration curve', or graph of pH against volume of titrant (Fig. 7.6). The characteristic feature is that the curve has maximum slope at the equivalence point. For example, in the titration of 10 cm³ 0.1 M HCl by 0.1 M NaOH, the pH changes from 5.3 to 8.7 with the addition of only four drops of titrant, that is, from 9.9 to 10.1 cm³. For weaker electrolytes the rate of change is less, and makes the use of visual indicators unsatisfactory if both acid and base are weak.

The interpretation of the curves in terms of equilibrium constants and buffer action will not be pursued here, but may be found in standard texts on titrimetric analysis.

When a polybasic acid (e.g. H_2SO_3) is titrated by a strong monoacidic base (e.g. NaOH); or when a polyacidic base (e.g. Na_2CO_3) is titrated by a strong monobasic acid, a curve with multiple inflections is obtained, each point of maximum slope representing the equivalence point for a single proton transfer step. In

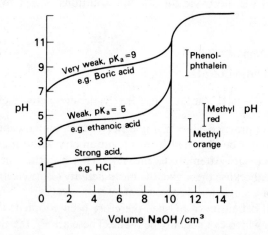

Fig. 7.6   Titration curves for 10 cm³ of various 0.1 M acids, against 0.1 M NaOH

the case of Na_2CO_3 and HCl (Fig. 7.7) the two equivalence points are at the completion of the following reactions:

(i) $CO_3^{2-} + H^+ \rightarrow HCO_3^-$

(ii) $HCO_3^- + H^+ \rightarrow H_2O + CO_2$

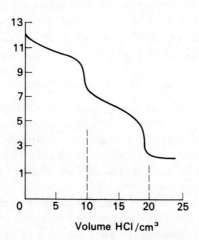

Fig. 7.7   Titration curve for 10 cm³ 0.1 M Na_2CO_3 against 0.1 M HCl

Practical work

Expt. 7–6.1. Calibration of an antimony electrode.

Required   Antimony rod, with copper wire soldered on (see Appendix II).

Electronic voltmeter, or potentiometer.

KCl salt bridge.

Silver–silver chloride electrode, or other reference electrode.

Set up the cell:

$$Sb, Sb_2O_3 \mid H^+(aq) \parallel KCl(aq) \mid AgCl, Ag.$$

The H^+ concentration must be insensitive to small additions of impurities, so buffer solutions are used for the calibration. These may be made up from commercially obtainable sachets of powder, or according to the following recipes.

pH2.   10.6 cm³ 1.0 M HCl + 50 mmol KCl made up to 1 dm³.

pH4.   80 cm³ 2.0 M ethanoic acid + 18 mmol sodium ethanoate, in 1 dm³.

pH7.   0.1 M ammonium ethanoate solution.

pH10. 10 mmol $NaHCO_3$ + 10 mmol Na_2CO_3 per dm³.

Plot a graph of pH versus cell potential.

Expt. 7–6.2. Measure the pH of the following solutions:

1 M HCl; 10^{-3} M HCl; 1 M CH_3COOH; 10^{-3} M CH_3COOH; 1 M NH_3; $FeCl_3$(aq); Na_3PO_4(aq); other liquids of interest (biological, household, etc.).

Expt. 7–7.·pH titration curves. Set up the apparatus as in Fig. 7.7, with an antimony electrode (Appendix II). Pipette 20 cm³ 0.1 M HCl into the 100 cm³ beaker, add water until the electrodes make adequate contact, then measure the pH. Run in 0.1 M NaOH from the burette, stopping to measure the pH after the following volumes: 4, 8, 12, 16, 18, 19, 19.4, 19.8, 20.0, 20.2, 20.6, 21, 22, 24, 28 cm³. Plot the graph. (A visual indicator such as methyl orange may be included for comparison.)

Titrate ethanoic acid with ammonia solution, in the same way.

Expt. 7–8. Differential titration curves. Since the equivalence point of pH or any potentiometric titration is shown by the point of maximum slope, it would be logical to measure not the potential for any particular volume of titrant, but the *change* in potential for a given small addition of titrant, at various total volumes. A graph of this kind could be made by plotting the slope of the ordinary titration curve (dE/dV), against V.

It is also possible to measure the differential potential directly, by means of the apparatus shown in Fig. 7.8. Two identical electrodes are used, but one is placed in a 'backwater', where it does not sense the addition of titrant until the solution there is flushed out and readmitted, by the syringe arrangement. The approximate equivalence point must be known, or found by a direct titration, since dE/dV, the

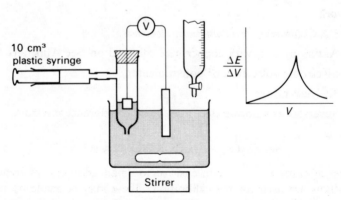

Fig. 7.8 The differential potentiometric titration

rate of change of potential with volume, is very small until that point is approached. Additions of 0.1 or 0.2 cm³ (2 or 4 drops) are suitable for the differential measurements, but of course larger volumes may be run in *between* measurements.

Another variation, sometimes known as the 'bottled end-point' method, is to have one electrode in a separate half-cell linked by salt bridge or porous plug, containing a solution known to be of the composition obtained at the equivalence point. This solution may be made up artificially, or obtained from a preliminary potentiometric titration.

7.6 Ion-selective electrodes

Until about 1965 the only ion-selective electrodes commercially available were the glass electrode for hydrogen ion (§7.5) and another kind of glass electrode sensitive to sodium ion. Now there are specific-ion electrodes for more than 20 ions, including Cl^-, F^-, Br^-, I^-, CN^-, HS^-, HPO_4^{2-}, Ca^{2+}, Mg^{2+}, Cu^{2+} and NH_4^+. Some of these have, as the essential selective membrane, a thin crystal of a solid state electrolyte such as silver chloride (see p. 30) or lanthanum fluoride. In these membranes, one of the ions is free to move, and if the activity of this ion differs in the solutions on each side of the membrane, there will be some migration towards the more dilute side, and hence the development of a potential difference. In other cases a liquid organic ion-exchange agent, held on an inert porous support, forms the membrane. The design and use of both these types of electrode are very similar to those of the glass pH electrode described above.

In some cases (including Na^+ and Cl^-) combination electrodes are manufactured which combine a solid state ion-selective electrode and the reference electrode into a single sensor unit, capable of operating in as little as 10^{-5} dm^3 solution. These have important medical and biochemical applications.

Besides direct estimation of ions, specific-ion electrodes can be used for the detection of the equivalence point in the titration of many other ions. For example, the lead-sensitive electrode is used in the titration of sulphate (for which no ion-selective electrode is yet available) with lead nitrate solution. One contribution of these electrodes to pure electrochemistry, rather than to analytical chemistry, is that they allow the construction of many more cells without liquid junctions (see Appendix II).

7.7 Polarography and polarographic (amperometric) titrations

When electrolysis takes place with inert electrodes and at a controlled potential, the continuation of the current depends upon the continuous supply of the reactive species to the electrodes. If the concentration of one of the electrode reactants is low, then at potentials below that required for electrolysis of the solvent, the current may fall rapidly to a value—known as the limiting diffusion current—determined by the rate of diffusion of this reactant species to the electrode. This effect, known as concentration polarization, has been mentioned earlier (§6.1).

If there is a high concentration of other, non-reacting ions present (from a 'supporting electrolyte'), the current will be virtually independent both of the conductance of the solution, and of the applied potential. Consider for example the electrolysis of a solution of sodium sulphate containing a trace of copper(II) sulphate, at a potential sufficient to produce oxygen at the platinum anode and copper at the cathode, but below that required for the evolution of hydrogen. The current will be carried to the cathode almost entirely by the arrival of Na^+ and the departure of SO_4^{2-} ions, but the transfer of electrons there will depend upon the rate of arrival of Cu^{2+} ions by diffusion—a rate which is proportional to the concentration of Cu^{2+} in the bulk solution.

The application of this phenomenon to analytical chemistry, as developed by Heyrovsky around 1920, is known as polarography. Most commonly the cathode is a drop of mercury emerging slowly from a capillary tube, supplied from a reservoir of pure mercury. The advantage of this rather awkward arrangement is that the metal surface is constantly renewed, and kept free of reaction products, and of other adsorbed substances which would alter its characteristics.

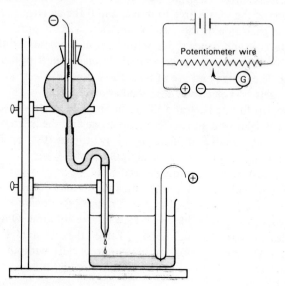

Fig. 7.9 A simple polarograph

The shape of the current/applied potential difference graph for a solution containing cadmium(II) is shown in Fig. 7.10. Curve A is for a solution containing 1.5 times as much Cd^{2+} as that which gave curve B. Below about 0.38 V the current is the very small 'residual current'; while above about 0.42 V there is a relatively substantial current (of the order of 10 μA). The rise in current as the potential rises past that at which Cd^{2+} can be discharged gives rise to the 'wave'. The height of the wave is the 'diffusion current', and is an almost direct measure of the concentration (e.g. $h_A = 1.5\ h_B$); while the 'half-wave potential' $E_{1/2}$ is specific to (and therefore identifies) the ion or molecule giving rise to the wave. $E_{1/2}$ is closely related to the reduction potential for the species, after allowance for the low concentration in solution, but also the low concentration of the product (e.g. the metal amalgam).

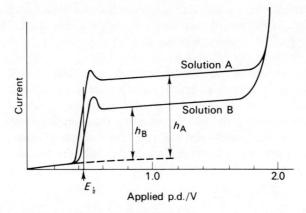

Fig. 7.10 Polarogram for two Cd^{2+} solutions

At about 1.8 V Na^+ ions begin to be reduced at the mercury cathode, and the current rises to a very large value. The reduction of the solvent water to hydrogen also commences, and this sets an upper limit to the usable potential range.

If two or more reducible species are present, the polarographic curve will show successive waves, and so long as the half-wave potentials are not too close, the separate heights will estimate the various species. Concentrations of 10^{-3} to 10^{-4} M of the reducible species are most easily measured, but the range 10^{-2} to 10^{-8} M is possible. Dissolved oxygen is reduced at the cathode, and this provides one of the most accurate ways of estimating its concentration (see below). The interpretation of the polarogram also provides information on the mechanism of the electrode reaction (see Fig. 7.11). The oxygen waves may obscure waves due to other species of interest, so oxygen is commonly removed before polarographic analysis, either by bubbling pure nitrogen through the solution, or by adding sodium sulphate(IV), Na_2SO_3.

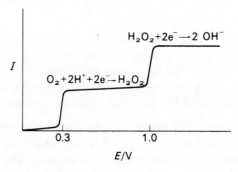

Fig. 7.11 Polarogram for dissolved oxygen

A complication which is not well understood is the appearance of a 'peak', or false maximum, at the top of each wave, as shown in Fig. 7.10. These peaks can usually be suppressed, without altering $E_{1/2}$ or wave height, by the addition of a little gelatin, or two drops of methyl red.

The increase in size of the mercury cathode area, and its sudden decrease as each drop falls away, causes a vertical zig-zag to be superimposed on the curves: but as long as the scanning rate (change of E with time) is not too great, there is no difficulty in obtaining the line representing the average current (Fig. 7.12). It is also possible to use a small solid electrode, for example of lead, but this must be cleaned before every run by being made an anode for a few minutes.

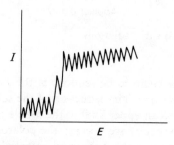

Fig. 7.12   Unsmoothed polarogram showing effect of drop-size changes

Practical work

Expt. 7–9. Set up a simple polarograph as shown in Fig. 7.9. The mercury reservoir is a thistle funnel connected by flexible PVC tubing to a length of capillary tube drawn out to a jet (see Appendix II). A drop rate of about 1 every 4 s is recommended, and adjustment of the reservoir height should be made accordingly. The screw clip should not be used to regulate the flow—it is too erratic—but simply as an on/off valve. Alternatively the flow may be stopped by clamping the capillary, inverted, just above the reservoir level. Note that a bubble in the mercury column— even an almost invisible one—may break the electrical circuit.

(1) To calibrate the polarograph for Cd^{2+}.

Take a suitable volume of 10^{-2} M $CdSO_4$ solution (made up from $CdSO_4 \cdot \frac{8}{3}H_2O$) and mix with an equal volume of a solution containing 0.1 M KCl, 0.05 M Na_2SO_3, and either 0.01 mass % gelatin, or 5 cm³ 0.1% methyl red solution per dm³. Allow the mixed solutions to stand for at least 15 minutes, while the dissolved oxygen is removed.

Then, with the solution in the cell, and the mercury dropping, set the galvano-meter at its least sensitive, apply about 1.2 V, and switch the sensitivity up to the range which gives almost full-scale deflection. Then move the potentiometer probe to zero, and slowly increase the p.d., recording the galvanometer reading (arbitrary units are sufficient). At the end of the run do not stop the mercury flow. Repeat with 1:2 and 1:10 dilutions of the known Cd^{2+} solution, and then with the unknown supplied by the supervisor. (Cadmium salts are poisonous).

(2) Make up a solution containing 0.005 M each of $CdSO_4$ and $ZnSO_4$. Mix with the carrier solution as before, and plot the polarogram of the mixed solution.

Investigate an unknown solution, containing two metal ions, to discover whether it contains Zn or Cd, and if so, how much.

Other suitable ions are Cu^{2+}, Pb^{2+}, Mn^{2+}, Ni^{2+}, Sn^{2+} and Fe^{2+}. Some organic molecules are reduced at the mercury cathode, and can be investigated polarographically.

The 'oxygen electrode'
The special need for a portable electrochemical oxygen analyser (for biological and ecological investigations) has led to the development of solid polarographic electrodes responsive to dissolved oxygen. The key feature is that the electrodes are protected by a semi-permeable membrane, which allows oxygen (along with other small molecular solutes) to diffuse through, but which acts as a barrier to cyanides, sulphides and other ions which might 'poison' the electrode surface, and reducible metal ions which would interfere. The membrane also enables the electrodes to be surrounded by a high concentration of 'support electrolyte', without allowing this to enter the bulk solution being tested.

Some commercial oxygen analysers are available (see Appendix II), one of which is claimed to measure oxygen down to 1 part in 10^7; but these are rather expensive.

A relatively simple device is the polarized galvanic cell known as the Mancy electrode (Fig. 7.13). This consists of two electrodes, of lead and silver, set close together, in an alkaline electrolyte (e.g. 1 M KOH). The lead acts as the anode:

$$Pb(s) + 4OH^-(aq) \rightarrow PbO_2^{2-}(aq) + 2H_2O + 2e^-$$

The product, potassium plumbate(II), is soluble in the alkaline solution. The silver electrode is inert as a cathode, and in the absence of any heavy metal ions the only possible reaction there is the reduction of dissolved oxygen:

$$O_2(aq) + 4e^- + 2H_2O \rightarrow 4OH^-(aq)$$

The current is therefore limited by the rate of diffusion of oxygen to the electrode surface, which is in turn proportional to the concentration of dissolved oxygen.

This cell is very easily set up and operated if no membrane is required, but the solution used must then be pure. The concentration of oxygen in a gas stream could be measured by passing this gas, after purification, through a sintered glass disc into the alkaline electrolyte solution in which the electrodes are immersed.

For more general usefulness the electrodes and electrolyte must be enclosed in the thin polyethylene membrane, but this creates a minor engineering problem, since the membrane must fit tightly, without leakage, and be very close to the flat

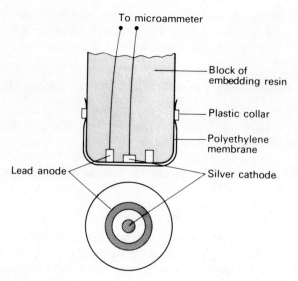

To microammeter

Block of
embedding resin

Plastic collar

Polyethylene
membrane

Lead anode

Silver cathode

Fig. 7.13   The 'Mancy electrode'

surface of the electrode assembly. Unless the volume of electrolyte within the unit
is small, too much oxygen has to diffuse through before steady conditions are
reached, and so the response time is inconveniently long. The setting-up and
calibrating of such an electrode unit is the subject of Project 9.25.

Polarographic (amperometric) titrations

The volumetric titration of a reducible species by a precipitating or complexing
reagent may be followed polarographically. The equivalence point detection by
this method is more sensitive than with visual indicators, and more dilute solutions
(down to 10^{-4} M) can be used. All that is necessary is that the species to be titrated
should give a substantial diffusion current at a chosen applied potential, but that
neither the titrant nor the reaction products should do so. Then the fall of the
diffusion current to zero indicates the equivalence point. A few measurements near
to this point will allow it to be found by extrapolation.

One example would be the titration of lead (at say 0.01 M) by 0.10 M $K_2C_2O_4$
(ethanoate). Similarly, a known Pb^{2+} solution could be used to titrate sulphate(VI),
in slightly acid solution.[3]

The polarized electrode ('dead stop') titration

This technique, a special kind of amperometric titration, is used for any redox
reaction in which one of the reactants is part of a reversible redox system, while the
other constitutes an irreversible one.

[3] D. R. Browning (*Sch. Sci. Rev.* **47**, 158) suggests the addition of an equal volume of
ethanol, to reduce the solubility of $PbSO_4$.

Consider the case of the iodine–thiosulphate reaction. If the iodine solution, with excess iodide, is placed in a breaker with a dip-type pair of bright platinum electrodes (as for conductivity measurements), and about 0.5 V d.c. is applied, a current will flow, since at both electrodes an electrode reaction occurs readily:

$$\text{at the anode:} \qquad 2I^- \rightarrow I_2 + 2e^-$$

$$\text{at the cathode:} \quad I_2 + 2e^- \rightarrow 2I^-$$

Thiosulphate is run in from the burette, and the current is watched. As the equivalence point approaches, the concentration of iodine becomes low, and the cathodic current falls. The other possible cathode reaction: $S_4O_6^{2-} + 2e^- \rightarrow 2S_2O_3^{2-}$ does not occur, for kinetic reasons (high overpotential). When the concentration of iodine has been reduced virtually to zero, the current ceases (the 'dead stop').

If the *titrant* forms the reversible redox system, then the current will suddenly begin to flow at the equivalence point (? 'lively start').

7.8 Summary

Electro-analytical methods might be divided into two categories: (1) truly electro-chemical techniques, and (2) electrochemical end-point indicators. The first group could be sub-divided into: (1A) potentiometric measurements, based on the variation in reversible electrode potential with concentration (these include the hydrogen electrode, the glass electrode and the ion-specific electrodes); (1B) coulometric measurements, based on Faraday's Laws; (1C) simple conductimetry —of rather limited applicability; and (1D) polarographic measurements—one of the most versatile tools for analysis of dilute solutions.

The methods in the second group involve the use of electrochemical techniques for the detection of the equivalence point or 'end-point' of a titration, during which a solution of one reactant is added, in increasing amount, to a fixed amount of the other reactant. A property such as conductivity, or the potential of an electrode, is monitored, and a sudden change in that property indicates that the original reagent has been consumed, and that the titrant is now in excess. When used to compare solutions of similar concentration (one being a known 'standard'), titrimetric methods may exceed the accuracy of the methods listed as category (1).

7.9 Exercises

1. The thickness of nickel plating on a plastic object was measured coulometrically. All but 2 cm² was masked off with wax, and this exposed area was made the anode in a cell with an electrolyte of slightly acidified sodium chloride solution. What potential difference should be applied so that electrolysis ceases when all the exposed nickel has dissolved? If an iodine coulometer in series produced 4.0 mmol I_2, what was the average thickness of the nickel plating?

2. In an experiment to measure the Biological Oxygen Demand of a sample of canal water (p. 138), air in a closed system was bubbled through a 250 cm^3 sample. CO_2 was removed continuously. It was found that a coulometric current of 322 mA through a Pt | $CuSO_4$(aq) | Pt cell at 298 K was just sufficient to prevent a decrease in gas pressure. Calculate the B.O.D. of the canal water in the units (cm^3 O_2) dm^{-3} min^{-1}.

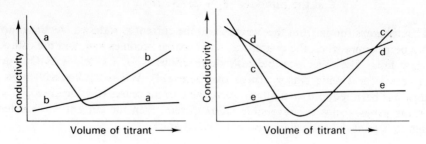

Fig. 7.14

3. Identify the conductimetric titration curves corresponding to the following titrations of aqueous reagents:
   (1) HNO_3 + KOH (from burette)
   (2) H_2SO_4 + Ba(OH)$_2$
   (3) KOH + CH_3COOH
   (4) NH_3 + HCl
   (5) CH_3COOH + NH_3

4. After the trial run of a conductimetric titration, which procedure should be adopted for the accurate run?
   (a) about twenty readings of conductivity, after equal additions of titrant, ten before and ten after the equivalence point;
   (b) about ten readings, at small volume increments, all close to the equivalence point;
   (c) well-spaced readings at first, becoming closer until the equivalence point is reached.

5. The conductivity κ of a saturated aqueous solution of silver chloride at 298 K is 3.38×10^{-4} Ω^{-1} m^{-1}, and that of the distilled water used to make the solution is 1.57×10^{-4} Ω^{-1} m^{-1}. The limiting molar ionic conductivities of Ag^+(aq) and Cl^-(aq) at 298 K are 61.9 and 76.4 Ω^{-1} cm^2 mol^{-1} respectively (see p. 49). Calculate the solubility of silver chloride in molar units.

6. A few drops of dilute silver nitrate solution were added to 100 cm^3 0.010 M KCl to produce a saturated solution of AgCl. The potential of a silver electrode in this

solution was 0.587 V relative to a saturated calomel electrode, while the potential of the same electrode in 0.010 M $AgNO_3$ was 0.925 V. Calculate the solubility of silver chloride.

Why does this value differ from that obtained from the data in q. 5? What quantity would give a truer comparison of the two methods?

7. What are the relative advantages of conductimetric and potentiometric methods of low ionic concentration determinations?

8. Calculate the pH of a solution of 0.10 M HCl after the addition of various volumes of 0.10 M NaOH, and plot the graph. Compare this with the experimentally obtained pH titration curve (Expt. 7–7).

9. The figure shows the pH titration curve for the titration of 20 cm^3 phosphoric(V) acid, H_3PO_4, by the addition of 0.5 M NaOH. Calculate the concentration of H_3PO_4.

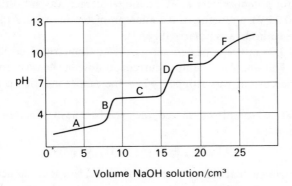

Fig. 7.15

   (i) Explain in terms of the chemical reactions occurring, the significance of the level and rising parts of the curve, marked A to F.
   (ii)* Also draw the pH titration curve for the titration of 24 cm^3 of the same NaOH solution by the same dilute H_3PO_4.

10. Which of the following statements is a satisfactory reason why polarography is often preferable to potentiometry for the measurement of low concentrations of metal ions?

   (1) polarography requires simpler and cheaper equipment;
   (2) polarography is more convenient for a single estimation of an unfamiliar ion;
   (3) polarography can detect a reducible ion in the presence of a higher concentration of inert ions;

(4) polarography can be used to measure concentrations of mixtures;

(5) polarography can measure concentrations down to lower values than can potentiometry.

11. Which of the following titrations could be followed by a simple amperometric or polarized electrode technique? Which electrode would control the current?

(a) H_3PO_4 against $NH_3(aq)$.

(b) Ca^{2+} against EDTA (complexing agent).

(c) Cu^{2+} against EDTA.

(d) $Cu^{2+} + 2I^- \rightarrow CuI(s) + \frac{1}{2}I_2(aq)$

12.* For the estimation of cyclohexane in petrol, by coulometric titration, a 2.00 cm^3 sample was taken. A mixture of ethanoic acid, methanol, 0.15 M KBr and 0.1 mass % mercury(II) ethanoate catalyst was placed in the cell of an apparatus similar to that shown in Fig. 7.2 (p. 140). The cell was covered to prevent evaporation. Instead of a potentiometer at P, an amperometer was substituted; that is, a source of p.d. (0.25 V), a resistor, and a microammeter, in series. At first no current flowed since the cathode was polarized (§7.7).

A current of 3.00 mA was passed across the coulometric electrodes, producing some bromine. This enabled a minute current to flow in the amperometric circuit. The coulometric current was stopped when the amperometric current had risen to 20.0 μA.

When the 2.00 cm^3 sample was added, the cyclohexene in it reacted with bromine, by direct addition:

$$C_6H_{10} + Br_2 \rightarrow C_6H_{10}Br_2$$

The amperometric current fell as a result of this. Then a coulometric current of 3.00 mA was passed until the amperometric current was restored to its former value: 13.2 s was required. Calculate the mass % cyclohexene in petrol (density 0.66 g cm^{-3}).

8

Some Technological Applications

8.1 Metal extraction and refining

Electrolytic extraction (electro-winning)

The principal reasons for using an electrochemical method for the extraction of a metal from its ores are that (1) the reduction with carbon is thermodynamically unfavourable at conveniently attainable temperatures; or (2) low grade ores are to be worked, initially by reaction with an aqueous reagent, giving a dilute solution of a salt of the metal. The first reason applies to sodium, magnesium, calcium, aluminium, etc. (see Table 8.1); and as these active metals cannot be deposited by electrolysis from any aqueous solution, electrolysis of molten salts is used (though research on electrodeposition from organometallic compounds in non-aqueous solution appears promising, especially for aluminium).

Table 8.1 Metals Which are Extracted or Refined by Electrolysis

Electrolyte state	Electro-winning	Refining
Molten	Al, Mg, Na, Li, K, Ca, Sr, Ba, Be, B, Th, U, Ce, Ti, Zr, Mo, Ta, Nb ...	Al
Aqueous	Cu, Zn, Co, Ni, Fe, Cr, Mn, Cd, Sb, Pb, Sn, In, Ag	Cu, Ni, Co, Sn, Pb, Hg, Ag, Sb, In

General features of fused-salt electrolyses include (1) the use of mixtures of salts to reduce the melting-points; (2) the use of the heating effect of the electric current to maintain the temperature of the melt; (3) the use of graphite anodes, at which the usual product is chlorine (aluminium electro-winning is an exception); (4) some means of protecting the molten metal from air and from the anode; (5) applied potential differences are usually 6 to 8 V, and currents may be as high as 10^5 A.

Plate 4 shows cells for the electrolytic production of aluminium.

It is noteworthy, at a time when world resources of many metals are getting alarmingly low, that there will never be a shortage of aluminium so long as there is energy to extract it, since on a molar basis it is the fourth most abundant element in the earth's crust (after O, Si and H) at 4.8 mole $\%$. However, supplies of high-grade bauxite are becoming exhausted, and the cost of obtaining aluminium oxide for the electrolytic cells will increase. Recycling of scrap aluminium will become even more important than it has been hitherto.

The extraction of metals through the electrolysis of aqueous solutions is less widely practised. Low-grade copper ores are leached by sulphuric acid, giving copper(II) sulphate solution which is electrolysed with a copper cathode (which gains mass) and a lead anode (at which oxygen is evolved, and sulphuric acid reformed). Some zinc is produced in a similar way, the low-grade ore being roasted to the oxide, then treated with sulphuric acid.

Electrolytic refining

Electrolysis of aqueous solutions is used on a large scale to refine metals produced by carbon reduction. Copper, nickel, silver, tin and lead are among the metals commonly treated in this way. Large anodes of the crude metal and thin sheets of the pure metal are set in cells containing a suitable electrolyte ($CuSO_4 + H_2SO_4$. $NiSO_4 + NiCl_2$, $PbSiF_6 + H_2SiF_6$), usually acidified to increase conductivity. As the anode dissolves, impurities with a more negative oxidation potential remain undissolved (e.g. Bi, Sb and Ag in lead), and are collected in bags hung around the anode, and later refined. Metals with a more positive oxidation potential dissolve along with the principal metal, of course, but they fail to deposit on the cathode. Current efficiencies of 90–95$\%$ are obtainable, and the energy consumption may be as low as 60 kJ mol^{-1} (e.g. 0.2 kWh kg^{-1} for Cu). This is only one-tenth of the energy required for metal *extraction* from aqueous solution.

8.2 Electroplating

Electroplating, the cathodic deposition of a thin layer of metal on the surface of an object, is most often carried out for the purpose of enhancing the appearance, or protecting against corrosion, or both. The metals commonly used for plating are copper, silver, gold, tin, zinc, nickel and chromium. Electroplate can be thinner than, and yet because of its uniformity just as effective as, metal plated mechanically, e.g. by dipping. Indeed the rising price of tin would have made tin-plate (on steel) uneconomic had it not been possible to change to the electrolytic method of manufacture: and now tin-plating is, after aluminium and caustic soda/chlorine, the most important electro-technology.

In most electroplating cells the anode is a piece of the metal being deposited, since this will dissolve at the same rate as the deposition at the cathode, and the electrolyte solution is not depleted of its metal content.[1] The plating bath is almost invariably a mixture of a current carrying but otherwise inert electrolyte and

[1] Chromium plating is an exception: an inert anode is used, and the chromic(VI) acid electrolyte has to be replenished.

a compound of the metal, in many cases a complex ion. It is essential that no local displacement of the dissolved metal by the cathode metal should occur, since the metal coating produced in this way is usually powdery and poorly adhesive. For example, silver nitrate solution would be useless as a plating bath for a copper object, since copper can displace silver by local action (see Expt. 2–2.2); the complex dicyanoargentate(I) (argentocyanide) is used instead.

A process which is very similar to electroplating is *electroforming*, which consists of the deposition of a very thick layer of metal (usually copper or nickel) which, when stripped away from the original article or 'former', reproduces in negative relief all the detail of the surface. The electroformed object then serves as a mould, for example for plastic injection moulding. Gramophone records are reproduced in this way, as are blocks for printing (electrotype).

Objects to be plated need not be of metal, since the surface can be made conducting by graphite, painted on as a suspension known as aquadag, or by silver deposited by chemical reaction (a 'silver mirror'). This procedure permits the electroplating of plaster, plastic, wax, wood etc.

The best constitution of the plating bath, its temperature, pH, and other factors are often determined by experiment, and electroplating was for a long time more a craft than a science. Thorough removal of grease, dirt and oxide films from the surface is always essential. A high current is desirable, to save time, but too high a current density may produce a loose spongy deposit, or even a metal powder. The appearance of the plate may be enhanced by 'brighteners', and other addition agents, usually colloids such as gelatin or glue, improve the adhesion. These agents encourage the formation of the metal as small crystals, but the way in which they act is still imperfectly understood.

A most important characteristic of a successful plating bath is that it should have good '*throwing power*', that is, that the plating should be of uniform thickness at points near to and far from the anode, and that plating should occur in crevices etc. where diffusion may be restricted. An introduction to throwing power will be obtained from the following experiment.

Expt. 8–1. Dependence of plating thickness on current path. For this investigation into the effect of the length of the current path on the thickness of deposited metal, the cathode is made of two parallel plates (back B and front F) held tightly together. For example, two pieces of copper foil may be used, the front one slightly larger, and bent over at the edges to produce a seal. Weigh the two parts separately before and after the plating, during which this double cathode is set parallel to an anode of about half its width (Fig. 8.1), and maintain the current at a predetermined value by adjustment of a rheostat. Record the area of cathode immersed, and the distance between the electrodes; also the current and duration. Observe the solution closely, in good light, during the electrolysis, especially around the anode.

With copper electrodes, use (1) acidified, (2) neutral and (3) ammoniacal copper(II) sulphate solutions. Use a fairly high current (say $0.2 \ A \ cm^{-2}$) and then, if time permits, repeat the series at one-tenth of this.

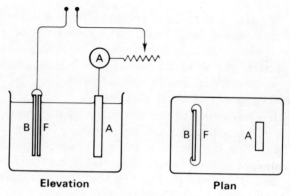

Elevation   **Plan**

Fig. 8.1   Electrolysis cell with double cathode

Calculate (a) the overall current efficiency; (b) the ratio of deposit on F to deposit on B.

In the light of your results and observations, comment upon the following accounts of the plating process:

Account A. During the electrolysis of acidified copper sulphate solution with copper electrodes, the anode dissolves to form Cu^{2+}(aq) ions which are attracted by the negative cathode, to which they travel by the shortest route. On arrival, the ions are discharged, and form a deposit of copper metal.

Account B. When a potential difference is applied between copper electrodes in acidified copper sulphate solution, the anode, being at a more positive potential than the solution, tends to ionize to Cu^{2+} ions, which would diminish or nullify the p.d. between electrode and solution were it not for the migration of Cu^{2+} and H^+ away from and SO_4^{2+} towards the anode region. Similarly, the p.d. between cathode and solution causes the discharge of Cu^{2+} to metallic Cu. Since the metal cathode is at one potential throughout, the deposition of metal should be uniform all over.

Further questions:

(i) It may be observed that, at high current densities, a dense solution falls away from the anode. Does this have any bearing on either of the above accounts?

(ii) Because the solution has an appreciable resistance, the potential of the solution at F will be more positive than that of the solution at B, when any current is flowing. How does this fact affect the above accounts? Will high or low conductivity lead to greater uniformity of deposit?

(iii) If the deposition of copper is susceptible to concentration polarization, activation overpotential, and variable current efficiency (i.e. some H_2 production at high current density), how would this affect the throwing power?

Expt. 8–2. Practical electroplating. Copper plating from acidified copper(II) sulphate solution is usually successful over a broad range of conditions. However, a coarse-grained structure, and even a flaky or spongy deposit, will result from too low a current density or too high a temperature ($>80°$), so it is important to maintain a high conductivity. It is found that a nearly saturated solution containing sulphuric acid (high mobility of H^+) at 20–40°C is suitable. If the acidity is too low there is danger of a dark-coloured deposit containing copper(I) oxide. The current density should be 2–5 A dm^{-2}, and as the throwing power is rather poor, articles should be turned frequently so that every part spends some time near to the anode.

Recipe:

$CuSO_4 . 5H_2O$	200 g (0.8 mol)	or 250 g— for electroforming
H_2SO_4	50 g (0.5 mol)	or 75 g—
molasses or dextrin	0.8 g	
wetting agent	few drops	
thiourea	0.04 g (optional brightener; not <5 mg or >80 mg)	
water to	1 dm^3	

A copper plating bath with better throwing power, which can be used to plate more electropositive metals such as iron or zinc, is described in Project 9.2, as are baths for zinc and silver plating, and the plating of non-metal objects.

8.3 Electrochemical polishing and machining

When a metal is made the anode, at fairly high current density in a suitable electrolyte, dissolution may occur in such a way as to produce a polished surface. Irregularities and scratches disappear as the higher points are dissolved preferentially. Electropolishing is often quicker than mechanical polishing, especially on an intricately shaped object; and since the process causes no stress (work-hardening) it is preferred for preparing metal specimens for laboratory tests.

Several electropolishing baths are based on phosphoric(V) acid or chloric(VII) (perchloric) acid, with oxidants such as chromic(VI) or nitric(V) acids to assist 'passivation'. The current density to be aimed at is that at which the anode becomes polarized, with no further increase in current with increased potential (until oxygen evolution commences). It is believed that under these conditions the recessed areas become passive, possibly due to the formation of a thin oxide layer, more readily than the elevated areas. A height difference of 10 μm is sufficient to produce this differential dissolution rate.

Electrochemical machining is another form of anodic dissolution, but with the purpose of modifying the shape of a piece of metal. It is often used on the very hard and strong alloys (such as those required for aircraft engines) since these are extremely difficult to cut or grind mechanically.

Usually the electrolyte solution is neutral sodium chloride or, better, chlorate(V), and the cathode reaction is the production of $H_2 + OH^-$(aq), leading to the precipitation of the hydroxide of the metal being machined. The cathode is shaped

Plate 1 Early electrolytic apparatus (Crown copyright, Science Museum, London).

Left Reproduction of a voltaic pile as used by Nicholson and Carlisle in 1800.

Centre Apparatus for the electrolytic decomposition of potash, ca. 1810.

Right Apparatus as used by Davy for demonstrating the 'electrolysis of water' (Royal Institution, 1810–1825)

Plate 2 Electrocoating a Cortina body shell in the Ford Dagenham Assembly Plant. (Courtesy Ford Motor Co. Ltd.)

Plate 3 The 'Comuta' experimental electric car. With a sodium–sulphur battery (§2.8) it has a range of 40 miles between recharges. (Courtesy Ford Motor Co. Ltd.)

Plate 4 One of the four 500 m long cell rooms at the Invergordon Smelter. On the right are replacement carbon anodes waiting to be swung into place when required. (Courtesy The British Aluminium Co. Ltd.)

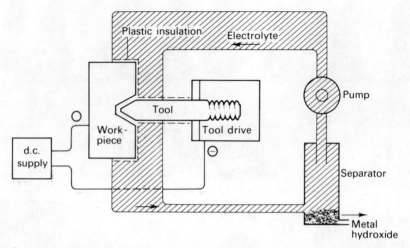

Fig. 8.2 Electrochemical machining

a little smaller than the required cavity, and the electrolyte is circulated mechanically so that the anodic metal hydroxide is swept away (to be filtered off before the electrolyte is recycled). Very high current densities are necessary—up to $1000\,A\,cm^{-2}$ —both in order for metal removal to be conveniently fast, and to exceed the passivating range; and so the gap between the cathode and the surface being cut must be kept very small. The anodic current diminishes rapidly away from the place nearest to the cathode, and enters abruptly into the current range at which the metal is made passive; this effect enables the electrochemical machining to be precise.

8.4 Anodizing

Most metals have a very thin layer of oxide over their surface, formed by reaction with air. In the case of some reactive metals this film is sufficiently tough and adhesive to give good protection against corrosion. With aluminium the natural film does not give sufficient protection for some purposes, but it can be thickened by making the aluminium article the anode for about 30 minutes at about $1\,A\,dm^{-2}$. A film about 0.02 mm in thickness develops, which gives protection, and enhances the appearance. The article is usually 'sealed' before use by immersion in boiling water, which converts the aluminium oxide to a partially hydrated form.

Expt. 8–3. Anodizing of aluminium.

(1) Choose a suitable aluminium object for treatment (e.g. a cheap manufactured article such as a brooch, or a shape cut from 2 mm aluminium sheet, or machined from aluminium rod). Twist a wire, preferably of aluminium, around the object so that it provides firm support and electrical contact, but does not touch any important area of the surface.

(2) Thoroughly de-grease the object by wiping it with a cloth moistened with trichloroethane (or proprietary 'dry-cleaner'), and then avoid any further contact with the fingers. Then ensure a uniformly clean surface by etching it in warm 1 M NaOH solution for a minute or so (vigorous evolution of hydrogen should occur), followed by neutralization in dilute nitric acid (say 0.2 M) and a rinse in clean water.

(3) Suspend the object in an electrolyte of 2 M sulphuric acid (1 vol. concentrated acid added, with stirring, to 7 vols. water), kept at 25–27°C by immersion in a large bowl of water at this temperature. Connect to the positive pole of the d.c. supply.

(4) Arrange a cathode of thin aluminium sheet (or several thicknesses of foil) in the form of a cylinder surrounding the anode. Using a variable potential control, maintain a current of 10–20 mA per cm^2 of anode. Stir the electrolyte occasionally. As the oxide layer forms, the resistance increases and so the applied potential will need to be raised, but should not exceed 15 V. Fifteen minutes will produce an anodized surface, but if it is to be dyed, at least 30 minutes is necessary. Remove and rinse.

(5) Dye at 65–75°C in solutions of about 2 g of a suitable dye per dm^3, acidified by 5 cm^3 1 M ethanoic acid if necessary. In addition to various common dyes, the Aluminium Federation (Broadway Ho., Calthorpe Rd., Birmingham 15) has recommended for this experiment the use of Black 2Y, 10 g per dm^3 acidified solution, for a deep black surface; or iron(III) ammonium oxalate solution (22 g $(NH_4)_3Fe(C_2O_4)_3.4H_2O$ per dm^3, used at 50°C) for a gold colour. The latter solution should be stored in the dark or prepared as required by mixing equal volumes of 0.1 M $FeCl_3$ and 0.3 M $(NH_4)_2C_2O_4$ solutions.

(6) When the desired intensity of colour has been reached, rinse the object and 'seal' the anodized layer by immersing it for 15 minutes in boiling water or, better, a boiling solution of 5 g nickel(II) ethanoate and 5 g boric acid per dm^3. (This treatment converts the aluminium oxide to a partially hydrated form.) Then rinse, and rub with a clean cloth.

8.5 Corrosion of iron

One of the most widespread electrochemical processes is also a most unwelcome one: in Britain alone the corrosion of iron costs an estimated £10^9 p.a. (3.5% of the gross national product), of which about one-third could be saved by improved protective measures. In the power industries an estimated £25m p.a. is saved by cathodic protection (see below).

Rusting has been known throughout history, but it was not until 1902 that a satisfactory explanation (proposed by W. R. Whitney) was available. It is now generally accepted that the principle cause of the corrosion is the establishment of a short-circuited galvanic cell, thus:

$$Fe(s) \rightarrow Fe^{2+}(aq) + 2e^-$$
$$\tfrac{1}{2}O_2(aq) + H_2O(l) + 2e^- \rightarrow 2OH^-(aq)$$

followed by two subsequent non-electrochemical steps leading to hydrated iron(III) oxide.

Rusting requires liquid water, not merely water vapour, because there must be an electrolyte solution in contact with the metal if the above cell is to be formed. Pure water is not sufficient, but it is normally impossible to exclude some electrolyte, if only dissolved CO_2; salt from sea-spray or highway ice-clearing is particularly deleterious.

It is found that if oxygen is totally excluded, or destroyed chemically (e.g. by hydrazine) rusting is prevented. The possible alternative reduction half-reaction, the production of hydrogen, does not generally occur unless the solution is very acidic. Even so, the presence of water, electrolyte, oxygen and iron together does not necessarily lead to corrosion. If conditions are uniform at all points on the metal surface, rusting is extremely slow. It appears that the oxidation and reduction half-reactions must occur at different sites. One situation which permits this separation of half-reactions is when the iron is in contact with a more noble metal (e.g. copper), for then that metal acts as the cathodic site (for the reduction of O_2), and the neighbouring iron becomes an anodic site, and is attacked.

However, even in the absence of a dissimilar metal corrosion can occur at points which are *partly* hidden from the air, such as under bolts or rivets, under specks of insoluble material, or in a corner, crack or hole. It appears that rusting, the oxidation of iron, occurs at places *furthest* from the source of dissolved oxygen; and it was to explain this strange behaviour that the theory of **differential aeration** was devised (for a fuller account see U. R. Evans, *Rusting of Iron: Causes and Control*, Edward Arnold, 1972).

Consider the conditions within a drop of impure water held in a crevice on an iron surface. Near the water–air interface there will be a plentiful supply of oxygen, but in the remoter parts of the drop there may be a much lower concentration. At the oxygen-rich site, the reduction of oxygen to hydroxide ions will tend to occur,

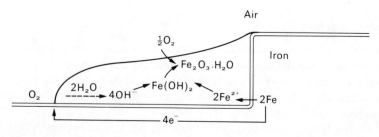

Fig. 8.3

comsuming electrons there, and making the metal positive relative to the solution. This polarity hinders the oxygen reduction, particularly at sites where oxygen concentration is low, but encourages the anodic oxidation of the iron metal. Any hole or crevice tends to deepen.

The diagram (Fig. 8.3) shows these electrochemical reactions, and also the place where the products (Fe^{2+} and OH^-), diffusing from the anodic and cathodic sites, meet and precipitate as iron(II) hydroxide, which is rapidly oxidized to the iron(III) state. The rust is thus produced away from the point of attack, and does not (except in special cases such as a small hole in an otherwise sound coat of paint) protect the metal from further attack. On the contrary, its water-holding properties promote even more rapid corrosion.

Cathodic protection

Of the various protective measures against rusting, one is very directly related to the electrochemical mechanism: namely cathodic protection, in which the iron structure is made cathodic (negative with respect to the electrolyte). There are three ways in which this can be done: (1) plating with zinc ('galvanized iron'); (2) sacrificial anodes; and (3) direct current from a generator.

In the case of galvanized iron, the zinc is constantly under attack (but fortunately the zinc oxide produced affords a degree of physical protection), but the iron underneath is thereby made cathodic.

For iron pipes or other underground structures, protection is often given by nearby buried blocks of magnesium alloy, each electrically connected to the iron. Steel ships are also protected by sacrificial anodes (following the method devised in 1824 to protect the copper bottoms of the ships of the Royal Navy). A sufficient number of these anodes must be provided, because protection ceases where the length of the current path through the electrolyte becomes too great. (Why? The iron, a good conductor, will be at almost the same potential all along its length.) In places where a generator and cable may be positioned, it is sometimes cheaper to replace the magnesium by scrap iron or carbon, and to maintain them at a small negative potential by an external source.

Practical work

Refer to the Appendix of Ref. 15 at the end of this chapter (U. R. Evans).

See also, A. H. H. Twidle, 'Corrosion of steel: a simple demonstration of differential aeration potential', *Sch. Sci. Rev.* **53**, 346–8 (December 1971).

For testing rust inhibitors by a method involving the bursting of pre-stressed ball bearings, see Ref. 16.

8.6 Fuel cells

In an earlier section on 'Practical Cells' (§2.8) some design features of good cells were mentioned: high ratio of electrical capacity to mass, low internal resistance, a steady potential difference which does not fall excessively when a current is drawn, and a long 'shelf life'. Three categories were introduced: primary cells, secondary (rechargeable) cells, and fuel cells, but these categories are not mutually exclusive, and refer to the function and design of the cell as much as to the electrochemical reactions which occur. Primary cells are portable sources of small quantities (say 1 kJ) of electrical energy, and the price is justified by the convenience rather than by the value of the electricity. Secondary cells, also, are relatively small, self-contained units, designed so that the reactants in the current producing reactions may be regenerated in position when a direct current is passed through the cell in the reverse direction. The energy which can be stored in a lead–acid cell of mass 1 kg is about 70 kJ, which is about the same as in an equal mass of torch batteries, and less than a tenth of that in some recently developed rechargeable batteries such as the sodium–sulphur battery. However, the lead–acid cell is particularly suitable for use for the starter motor of a petrol-driven car, because it can provide heavy currents (200 to 400 A) for short periods without suffering damage. As the source of power for *driving* (rather than starting) the car, lead–acid batteries are less satisfactory, for they can only provide about 100 W kg^{-1} on continuous discharge, which means that the economic top speed is equal to a brisk walking pace (e.g. milk floats, fork-lift trucks). For electrically driven vehicles to be viable, the mass and the cost per unit of power must be reduced to about one-hundredth of those of the present car battery. It now seems quite possible that the fuel cell will achieve this.

The principles of the fuel cell may be shown by considering one of the simplest systems—the hydrogen–oxygen cell. Hydrogen is supplied to one of the porous catalytic electrodes, and oxygen or air to the other. The electrolyte is a concentrated solution of an acid (e.g. phosphoric(V) acid) or, more commonly, an alkali (usually potassium hydroxide). The overall reaction, $H_2 + \frac{1}{2}O_2 \rightarrow H_2O(l)$, has $\Delta G^{\ominus} = -237$ kJ mol^{-1} and hence $E^{\ominus}_{cell} = +1.23$ V at 298 K. The enthalpy change for the combustion of H_2 to $H_2O(g)$ is -242 kJ mol^{-1}. Therefore if the fuel cell could be operated at its maximum (reversible) cell potential, an efficiency of 98 %[2] chemical energy conversion would be achieved. This may be compared with the theoretical maximum efficiency of 40–50 % for any 'heat engine' type of energy convertor, with its Carnot limitation of $(T_2 - T_1)/T_2$, where T_1 and T_2 are the temperatures of the heat sink and source respectively. This apparent doubling of conversion efficiency was like a mirage which deluded and eventually disappointed early researchers into fuel cells.

As was pointed out in §6.5, the *working* cell potential is invariably lower than the reversible (or 'no-load') potential, by an amount comprising the overpotentials at the two electrodes, together with any concentration polarization and the '*IR* drop' due to internal resistance. There can be no current without overpotential, although the size of the overpotential depends profoundly upon the catalytic properties of the electrode surface. For this reason research into cheaper and more effective catalytic electrodes is one of the principle directions that the fuel cell

[2] Various other ratios of $\Delta G^{\ominus}/\Delta H$ from the $H_2O(l)$ and $H_2O(g)$ equations are possible, but the calculation is in any case purely academic.

development programme is taking. There is little hope of finding the 'perfect catalyst' (cf. philosophers' stone), and the goal of anything like 100% efficiency has now been abandoned—in fact fuel cell technologists might well be content with the same 40% limit that applies to heat engines, in return for electrodes that were cheap, durable and easy to maintain. In this respect it appears that fuel cells will have the important advantage that they can achieve 40% energy conversion even on such a small scale as a 25 kW unit (whereas the modern gas turbine generator does not approach this unless it is capable of 10^5 kW) and so their first use may be for small domestic or vehicle units.

If the overpotential of the hydrogen–oxygen cell presents a problem at normal temperatures, that of a hydrocarbon fuel cell (e.g. CH_4–O_2) is quite impossible. The rate of reaction is negligible below about 200°C, yet hydrocarbon fuels, either natural gas or 'cracked' petroleum oil, are so much cheaper (and easier to store) than hydrogen that a considerable part of the $50m fuel cell effort has gone towards attempts to utilize them. One way is to convert the hydrocarbon to hydrogen immediately before use, by catalytic reaction with steam:

$$\text{e.g. } CH_4 + H_2O \rightarrow CO + 3H_2 \quad \text{(ca. 900°C)}$$
$$CO + H_2O \rightleftharpoons CO_2 + H_2 \quad \text{(ca. 300°C)}$$

The technical difficulties of the conversion and purification are serious but not insuperable.

The other solution to the unreactivity of hydrocarbons is to raise the temperature of the cell, to 650°C or so, by using a molten salt electrolyte such as mixed lithium and sodium carbonates. At these high temperatures the overpotentials are low, and no expensive catalytic electrodes are necessary. For this reason, high temperature hydrogen–oxygen cells have also been designed, either using molten carbonates, or a very concentrated potassium hydroxide solution under pressure (as in the first practical fuel cell, built by Bacon and Frost at Cambridge in 1959). In all such cells, corrosion is one of the most serious obstacles, and most of the construction materials of the most advanced Pratt and Whitney cell have been developed specially for the purpose, in the last 7 years.

A heavy duty fuel cell which consumes carbon monoxide at 1000°C is being designed by Westinghouse, and uses a solid state electrolyte of ZrO_2 containing a little Y_2O_3 (which gives it an O^{2-} deficiency). To avoid corrosion troubles at this high temperature, the air electrode is made of a solid state conductor (SnO_2) rather than a metal.

It must not be thought that low temperature aqueous cells are being neglected, however. Esso in the U.K. and Exxon–Alsthom (U.S.A./France) are developing methanol fuel cells which will require electrodes of high specific catalytic power and large surface to volume ratio. That a low temperature fuel cell is possible was proved in the General Electric Company's hydrogen–oxygen cell which provided the electric power in the Gemini spacecraft; but this, using an ion-exchange resin electrolyte and platinum-coated PTFE electrodes, was far too expensive for terrestrial use. Fuel cell technology is part science, part economics.

Expt. 8–4. A methanol fuel cell. Prepare the fuel cell anode by platinizing a piece of fine nickel gauze, about 6 × 10 cm, by making it the cathode (negative) in chloroplatinic acid solution, as described in Appendix II. A cheaper alternative plating solution is 0.5 % palladium chloride in 1 M hydrochloric acid. Curve the gauze around the outside of a porous pot.

Prepare the cathode by silver plating a similar piece of nickel gauze, simply by letting it stand in dilute silver nitrate solution for an hour or so. Curve the gauze so that it fits inside the porous pot, and arrange for oxygen or air bubbles to pass upwards over it (O_2 bubbled through a sintered glass disk is best, but air from a cheap aquarium aerator will suffice).

An alternative arrangement, described by K. R. Williams in Ref. 9 below, consists of a porous carbon rod with a blind hole drilled along its axis, to which oxygen is supplied via a plastic tube. The rod should be activated by heating to redness followed by quenching in water, and it may be silver plated for extra efficiency.

When the cell is assembled, with 6 M KOH electrolyte (CARE—caustic, wear goggles) but without fuel, check that no spurious potential is arising from galvanic action of the nickel. Then add methanol (or hydrazine) to the outer part of the cell to give a concentration of about 2 % by volume. Mechanical stirring is desirable.

Measure the cell potential with a high-resistance voltmeter, both on open circuit and when various currents are being drawn. How steadily is the cell able to supply 1 mA?

For an extension of this work see Projects 9.8, 9.34 and 9.38.

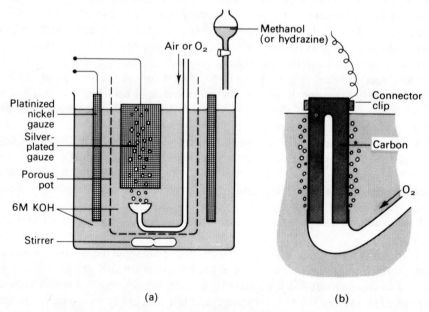

(a)   (b)

Fig. 8.4 (a) Methanol–oxygen fuel cell (demonstration). (b) Alternative version of cathode

Further reading

1. Hampel, C. A. (Ed.). *The Encyclopedia of Electrochemistry.* Reinhold, New York, 1964.

2. Mantell, C. L. *Electrochemical Engineering.* McGraw-Hill, New York, 1960 (for §8.1).

3. Brimi, M. A. and Luck, J. R. *Electrofinishing.* Elsevier, New York, 1965 (§§8.2, 8.3).

4. Milazzo, G. *Electrochemistry,* 505–13. Elsevier, New York, 1963 (§8.4).

5. Palin, G. R. *Electrochemistry for Technologists.* Pergamon, Oxford, 1959.

6. Potter, E. C. *Electrochemistry.* Cleaver Hume, London, 1956.

7. Reference electrodes for fused salts *see* (a) Janz, G. J. *J. Chem. Educ.* **39**, 59 (1962); (b) Laity, R. W. *ibid.* **39**, 67 (1962).

8. Gregory, D. P. *Fuel Cells.* Mills and Boon, London, 1972.

9. Williams, K. R. Fuel Cells. *Sch. Sci. Rev.* **45**, 521–6 (1964).

10. (a) Maugh, T. H. Fuel Cells: Dispersed Generation of Electricity. *Science,* **178**, 1273–1274B (1972); (b) *ibid.* **180**, 542 (1973); (c) Austin, L. G. *Sci. American* (October 1959); (d) Vijh, A. K. Electrochemical principles in a Fuel Cell. *J. Chem. Educ.* **47**, 680–2 (1970); (e) Hawkins, M. D. *Educ. Chem.* **10**, 217–8 (1973).

11. (a) Meleka, A. H. Electrochemical Machining. *Science J.* **3**(1), 51–55 (January 1967); (b) Hoare, J. P. and LaBoda, M. A. *Sci. American,* **230**, 30–37 (January 1974).

12. (Na–Sn alloy cell): *New Scientist,* **308**, 93 (October 1962).

13. Lee, M. Electric Vehicles, *Science J.* **3**(3), 35–40 (March 1967).

14. Klein, H. Arthur. *Fuel Cells,* Univ. London Press, 1966. (A very readable book at an elementary level. See especially p. 108 for a description of the G.E.C. H_2–O_2 cell.)

15. Evans, U. R. *The Rusting of Iron: Causes and Control.* Edward Arnold, London, 1972.

16. Slabaugh, W. H. Corrosion, *J. Chem. Educ.* **51**, 218–20 (1974).

9

Projects in Electrochemistry

Introduction

It seems educationally sound to distinguish between the shorter experiments which have appeared in the earlier chapters of this book, and the extended investigations which follow. Both have among their objectives the development of skills in observation and in manipulation of equipment; awareness of accuracy and precision, and the limitations of measurements; critical evaluation of evidence; the handling and representation of data; and the drawing of valid conclusions. However, the shorter experiments also had the didactic purpose of teaching certain specific facts, laws and principles: for this reason they were placed at chosen points in the text, and were intended to be worked through in sequence, and in conjunction with the text and the exercises, so that the knowledge gained through them could become the foundation for subsequent sections.

The extended experiments, or Projects, serve a different purpose. They allow a fuller involvement on the part of the student, and a truer participation in the act of discovery. There was undoubtedly some element of enquiry in the practical work referred to above, but since it was essential that the 'discoveries' should be on the whole the 'right' (i.e. currently accepted) ones, these discoveries had to be 'guided', and the student had little opportunity to follow up his own original ideas. He will now have that chance.

The student should choose his problem, read something about it in this book and others (following up all relevant index entries), and write down in broad outline his plan of campaign, including a list of apparatus and reagents required. He should then discuss this with his supervisor, who will advise on the general feasibility: availability of equipment, probable duration, and any special difficulties or hazards. If difficulties are anticipated it may be wise to carry out some exploratory experiments, to ensure that the essential idea will 'work', before starting the investigation in earnest.

If the problem has been chosen well, the student should need to seek advice only occasionally, but he should keep his records up to date between laboratory sessions so that he can show at any time what progress he has made. Even apparently negative results should be recorded, but any invalidating circumstances or possible mistakes should be mentioned. Some of the investigations will soon lead to a branching point, when an unexplainable observation will result in several tentative

176

hypotheses to be tested in turn. In this situation, adequately methodical note-keeping will be necessary if the student is not to lose sight of some of his ideas.

An attempt has been made to grade the Projects with respect to difficulty (amount of background knowledge, skill, time and resources required), but as there is no knowing exactly how the investigations will proceed, these estimates can only be rough judgments. The student should beware of being too ambitious at first: projects usually take three times as long as expected, and there is perhaps more satisfaction in the successful completion of a simple project than in the abandonment of a tough one.

One of the practical justifications for spending time on projects within the area of electrochemistry is that much interesting work can be done with quite simple resources. The equipment is relatively easily dismantled and reassembled, so it is sufficient for each student to have a storage box, and not necessarily a permanent working space. Some of the Projects involve searches in the library[1] as much as in the laboratory. Some could be undertaken by groups, in collaboration or in parallel. At the end of the session the supervisor may require a written report, or may call upon each student to describe his methods and conclusions to the others, and to answer their critical questions.

The author would be glad to learn of the results obtained by students who have worked on any of the Projects, and to enter into correspondence, through the course supervisor, on any interesting developments (or obstacles) which may arise.

The projects

9.1 Mixed electrolysis products. When $CuSO_4$(aq) is electrolysed, hydrogen may be produced at the cathode. Examine the effect of concentration, pH, current density, temperature, inert salts, 'impurities' etc. Extend the study to zinc sulphate solution. See also *Sch. Sci. Rev.* **50**, 596–8. Discuss 'current efficiency' in the light of your findings.

9.2 Electroplating. Try out some recipes for electroplating, and aim for quality of product. The adhesion of the plating may be tested by pressing on to it (when dry) a piece of adhesive tape ('Sellotape 'etc.), then pelling it off. A poor plating will be pulled off.

Electroforming merely requires longer time. Non-conducting surfaces may be made conducting by graphite (p. 165), a silver mirror (p. 105) or simply glue and a sprinkling of fine iron filings, followed by immersion in copper sulphate solution. Electroformed holly-leaf brooches make acceptable Christmas gifts!

For the copper plating of iron or other reactive metal, try a pyrophosphate bath: prepare $K_4P_2O_7$ by heating dry K_2HPO_4, and make a concentrated solution. Precipitate $Cu_2P_2O_7$ from a solution of a copper(II) salt containing 25 g Cu, then

---

[1] Particularly the suggestions enclosed in square brackets [ ].

redissolve in excess pyrophosphate solution at 40°C. Adjust the pH to 8.5, and plate at 1–4 A dm^{-2} at 40–50°C.

Silver plating is usually done with a cyanide bath, but the following less toxic bath may be tried: in 100 cm^3 solution dissolve 4 g AgNO$_3$, 56 g KI, and 6 g citric acid. Recommended current density is 0.2–1.6 A dm^{-2} (and 0.1–0.3 V) at 26°C.

Iron may be zinc plated for corrosion protection. A recipe for one bath is: ZnSO$_4$.7H$_2$O 360 g; NH$_4$Cl 30 g; NaCO$_2$CH$_3$ (ethanoate) 15 g; glucose 120 g; to 1 dm^3. 1–4 A dm^{-2} at 30–35°C.

9.2a Stripping. Worn or otherwise unwanted plating can sometimes be 'stripped' anodically, if the substrate is of a less reactive metal. The thickness of any plating can be measured coulometrically (see §7.1). For a start, work with galvanized iron.

9.3 Solubility products measured by potentiometry. Use a student potentiometer or a simple metre-bridge potentiometer (see Fig. 4.2 and §4.3). Repeat and extend Expt. 7–2. In this way measure the cell potentials of cells of the type:

$$\text{Metal M} \mid \text{M}^{z+}(\text{aq, 1 M}) \parallel \text{MX(aq, satd.)} \mid \text{M}$$

where M forms a reversible electrode. The solution of the sparingly soluble salt MX is made either by dissolving pure, washed solid MX, or by precipitation from solutions containing excess of one ion or the other. What difference does this make?

Re-read §5.3 and consider the relationship between concentration products and the true (activity) solubility products. Then investigate the effect of loading the solutions of MX and M^{z+} with an inert electrolyte, to make their ionic strengths equal.

9.4 Instability constants measured by potentiometry. This is similar to Project 9.3, but the restricted concentration of the ion being measured arises in this case from a complexing reaction such as the following:

$$\text{Cu(NH}_3)_4^{2+}(\text{aq}) + 4\text{H}_2\text{O} \rightleftharpoons \text{Cu(H}_2\text{O})_4^{2+}(\text{aq}) + 4\text{NH}_3(\text{aq});$$

$$K_{\text{instab}} = \frac{[\text{Cu(H}_2\text{O})_4^{2+}]\,[\text{NH}_3]^4}{[\text{Cu(NH}_3)_4^{2+}]} = 7.1 \times 10^{-14}$$

Instability constants can be calculated if the following are known: (i) the *total* metal concentration (from original composition), (ii) the total ligand (complexing agent); (iii) the *free* aquo-cation concentration (calculated from the cell potential of a concentration cell with the complex in one half).

Possible complexes for this investigation are: Ag(S$_2$O$_3$)$_2^{2-}$, AgI$_3^{2-}$, Zn(NH$_3$)$_2^{2+}$, CuF$_4^{2-}$.

9.5 Stoichiometry of anodic dissolution. Repeat the experiment which has two copper anodes in series, one in acidified solution and the other in alkaline solution

(§2.2 and Nuffield Chemistry Teachers' Guide II (1976), A 16.6). Why are the anode reactions different? Try to deduce the reaction of a copper anode in a solution of sodium chloride and ammonia.

Devise and test similar cases of metal dissolving to different oxidation states in different solutions (Suggestion: Fe in Cl^- and F^- solutions).

9.6 Anodic processes. Pursue the topics introduced in §§8.3 and 8.4. [Consult technical books for further information on anodic dissolution and passivation.] Set up a demonstration of the principles of electrochemical machining, and test steels of different hardness.

Repeat Expt. 8–3 and study the effect of increased current density and treatment duration on the properties of the anodized layer (electrical resistance, resistance to corrosion, etc.). [Can insulated aluminium cables be made by anodizing?]

9.7 Inorganic electrophoresis (analytical). A drop of a dilute mixture of salts is placed on a strip of filter paper soaked in some inert electrolyte, and a high d.c. potential is applied. The cations move towards the negative end, but at different rates. Thus the mixture is separated, and if suitable colour reactions are known, the ions may be identified.

Start by reading the article by Rev. Dr. Michael Casey, *Sch. Sci. Rev.* **45**, 410.

9.8 The simple fuel cell. Set up a fuel cell as in §8.5, in which methanol is oxidized at a platinized nickel anode while dissolved oxygen is reduced at a silver-plated cathode, in potassium hydroxide solution. Measure the ability of the cell to give a steady current. How polarizable is it (how much does the p.d. fall under load)? Can the electrodes be improved by electroplating the catalyst metals on more thickly? Does air-bubbling increase the performance, and if so is it because of the extra oxygen supply or merely because of the stirring? How does the potential vary with methanol concentration, and is the porous partition (to keep the methanol away from the cathode) really necessary?

Aim to construct a battery of fuel cells which will drive a small $1\frac{1}{2}$ V motor.

In September 1972 Dr. Tom Jones, Chemistry Dept., University of Wales Institute of Science and Technology, Cardiff, announced the production of a fuel cell breath test instrument, the Alcolyser. Try to construct an ethanol-measuring fuel cell.

9.9 D.c. conductance measurements. Following on from Expt. 3–1, try to use un-polarizable $Cu/CuSO_4(aq)$ electrodes in the measurement of the d.c. conductance of other electrolytes (H_2SO_4, Na_2SO_4, CH_3COOH etc.), which may be either (i) mixed in with the $CuSO_4$, or (ii) placed in a bridge between anolyte and catholyte. The study might be of (a) the additivity of molar conductivities; or (b) the variation of conductance with total electrolyte concentration.

9.10 Use of radioisotopes in electrochemistry

(a) The use of radioisotopes offers an opportunity of demonstrating the exchange current (§6.3) between a metal and its ion in solution. In principle this is similar to the use of labelled lead(II) chloride to show the dynamic equilibrium between this salt and its saturated solution, as described in the Nuffield Chemistry Teachers' Guide II (1976), A 19.3, which should be performed as an introduction to the technique. The exchange between a metal and its ion would be expected to be much slower, however, and more delicate measurements will be necessary.

A labelled lead electrode may be prepared by making a piece of ordinary lead the cathode in thorium nitrate solution (which contains some ^{212}Pb) for 15–30 minutes at about 200 mA cm^{-2}. This should be used immediately for the exchange experiment, firstly, as a control, in potassium nitrate solution, and then in lead(II) nitrate solution.

A similar experiment may be performed using ^{110m}Ag (from a 'tablet' of labelled $AgNO_3$ obtainable from Philip Harris Biological Ltd). Aim to show that exchange of silver atoms is taking place in both directions. Firstly take the 'background' count of a piece of silver foil a fixed distance in front of a Geiger–Müller tube; then immerse the foil in labelled silver(I) nitrate(V) solution for an hour, rinse and dry, and count again. Secondly prepare labelled silver metal (by electroplating or by chemical reduction) and measure the rate of transfer of radioactive silver into solution. Can you obtain evidence that an equilibrium is being established?

(b) The transport of Ag^+ during electrolysis could be followed by a ^{110m}Ag label; and, by means of the apparatus shown in Fig. 3.12, without the water jacket and modified to allow labelled $AgNO_3$ to be introduced below the graduated tube, it should be possible to measure the transport number of Ag^+ by the moving boundary method.

Note: Special regulations apply to the use of radioisotopes in educational establishments, except for compounds of uranium and thorium (including the lead experiments described above), and an appropriate text should be consulted, e.g., R. A. Faires, *Experiments in Radioactivity*. Methuen Educational, London, 1970.

9.11 Molten salts electrolysis. Experiments on the electrolysis of molten salts are not difficult if low-melting salts or mixtures are used. Chlorides and nitrates are often used, since these are often anhydrous and fusible. (Hydrated salts do not melt in the true sense, but dissolve in their own water of crystallization.) Sulphates are not used. Molten pyrophosphates (e.g. from $NH_4H_2PO_4$) should make good inert (neither oxidizing nor reducing) solvents.

Besides the salts which decompose into their elements on electrolysis (e.g. $PbBr_2$), there are others for which the products are not so readily predictable. For example, what are the electrode reactions in the electrolysis of molten potassium nitrate(V)? Do they depend on the nature of the electrodes? What is the minimum practical decomposition potential? etc. . . . . And what of potassium nitrate(III) (nitrite), perhaps with iron electrodes? In some cases the electrode reaction can be deduced from the stoichiometry, i.e. Faraday's law.

9.12 Conductimetry. A—Soil water. Use the conductivity bridge to investigate the variation of the conductivity of soil water from various locations. Refer to Expt. 3–7 and make measurements of the electrolyte content of soil water.

B—Sea water. Similarly, use conductimetry to investigate the salinity of waters, especially brackish water, or tidal river water. [How does salinity vary with depth in the oceans, and what is the IUPAC definition of 'salinity'?]

C—Pure water. Examine the conductivity of pure distilled water, redistilled water, de-gassed water (to remove CO_2). If an ion-exchange column is available, examine its effectiveness. [Find out the latest value for the conductivity of ultra-pure water, and the ionic concentration which this indicates. How does the self-ionization of water vary with temperature?]

9.13 Conductimetric investigation of stoichiometry. Refer to §7.3 for the discussion of conductimetry. Investigate the stoichiometry of the following reactions by the 'method of continuous variations', that is, by preparing mixtures of the two reactant solutions covering a range of molar proportions. From a graph of conductivity against mole fraction of one reactant, the stoichiometry of the reaction can be deduced.

(i) $Ca(OH)_2(aq) + CO_2(g)$ (CO_2 measured by volume)

(ii) $Ca(OH)_2 + Ca(HCO_3)_2(aq)$ (the latter prepared by saturating $Ca(OH)_2$ soln. with CO_2)

(iii) $CuSO_4(aq) + NaOH(aq)$

(iv) $CuSO_4(aq) + Na_2CO_3(aq)$

(v) $CuSO_4(aq) + NaHCO_3(aq)$

(vi) $Pb(NO_3)_2(aq) + Na_2CO_3(aq)$ ... etc.

9.14 Conductimetry in non-aqueous solvents: I ethanoic acid. Refer to the paper by A. C. Pennington in *Sch. Sci. Rev.* **54**, 56–62 (September 1972). Prepare pure ethanoic acid from the commercial (99%) product and ethanoic anhydride, and measure its conductivity. Mix pure ethanoic acid with small measured amounts of water, and investigate the variation of conductivity of these dilute solutions (of water). Does water behave as a weak or a strong electrolyte?

Similarly investigate the variation of molar conductivity with concentration for: (i) sodium ethanoate; (ii) ammonium ethanoate; (iii) hydrogen chloride; (iv) sulphuric acid; (v) potassium iodide; (vi) aminoethane or other amine.

Repeat the conductimetric titration of sodium ethanoate by hydrogen chloride in ethanoic acid, as described by Pennington, and explain the results. Investigate similar acid–base reactions, or alternatively metathetic (precipitation) titrations (such as the precipitation of copper(II) sulphate from ethanoic acid solutions of ammonium sulphate and copper(II) ethanoate).

9.14a. Extend the investigation to the ethanoic acid–trichloroethanoic acid system. Are the acidic strengths of these mixtures greater or less than you would have predicted?

9.15 Conductimetry in non-aqueous solvents: II sulphuric(VI) acid. Prepare pure sulphuric acid by adding oleum (fuming sulphuric acid) to analytical grade 98% sulphuric acid until the conductance is at a minimum. Measure the molar conductivities of (i) water; (ii) sulphur trioxide; (iii) anhydrous sodium hydrogen sulphate(VI) solutions in pure sulphuric acid. Is there evidence of a 'Grotthus' mechanism (p. 52) of conduction by proton exchange?

Are the conductivities affected by the presence of 'inert' salts?

Would you expect the molar conductivities of salts such as copper(II) sulphate in sulphuric acid to be higher or lower than those of the aqueous solutions?

9.16 A conductimetric hygrometer. In a dry atmosphere, compress a pellet of phosphorus(V) oxide P_2O_5 between platinum foil electrodes and seal into a wide glass tube with a tap at each end. When a moist gas is passed along the tube water will be absorbed chemically and this will cause conduction: $P_2O_5(s) + H_2O(g) \rightarrow 2H_3PO_4(aq)$. Continued passage of d.c. will electrolyse this surface layer of acid solution, destroying the water, and conductance will fall. The current which will maintain a steady conductance is a measure of the moisture content of the gas stream.

Calibrate the instrument using air saturated with water vapour at a known temperature.

[Is a hygrometer (measuring relative humidity) or a barometer the better predictor of the weather?]

9.16a. Alternatively, construct a Soil Moisture Meter for horticultural use, based on the conductimetric principle.

9.17 Calculated 'cell constants'. The relationship between conductance and conductivity (§3.1) is not normally calculable directly from the geometry of the conductivity cell. How different is the cell constant from that calculated from electrode area and separation? [By what means can one cell constant be found from first principles?]

9.18 Electrolytic preparations (inorganic). Investigate one or more of the following electrolytic reactions:

  (i) (following Expt. 6–3). Anodic preparation of peroxodiphosphoric(V) acid. Electrolyse a solution saturated with KH_2PO_4 and 1 M in KOH and KF, with a small Pt cathode and large Pt anode (preferably a Pt dish), at ca. 5°C, at 6 V. Crystals of $K_4P_2O_8$ may be obtained. Estimate iodometrically.

 (ii) (following Expt. 6–4). Investigate the efficiency of the anodic oxidation of V(II) to (III).

(iii) Examine the anodic oxidation of thiosulphate. Does the product depend upon p.d., or upon current density?

(iv) Prepare ammonium amalgam by the electrolysis of ammonium sulphate(VI) solution cooled in ice, with a mercury cathode. (J. H. Reedy, *J. Chem. Educ.* **6**, 1767 (1929.)

(v) Prepare sodium ferrate(VI) from a steel wool anode in concentrated sodium hydroxide solution. See G. C. Britton, *Sch. Sci. Rev.* **57**, 322 (December 1975).

9.19 Electrolytic preparations (organic)

(i) Follow Expt. 6–5 by preparing higher hydrocarbons by the Kolbe method.

(ii) Examine the products of the electrolysis of aqueous ethanol (acidified with sulphuric acid).

(iii) In connection with the proposed free radical mechanism for the Kolbe coupling reactions, investigate whether the electrolysis of ethanoate can initiate the setting of commercial resins (e.g. car repair kits).

(iv) Prepare chlorinated benzene products by electrolysis of a benzene/hydrochloric acid emulsion. Possible means of examining the products include density or refractive index.

9.20 Electrolysis of aqueous sodium chloride solution. Although it is often stated that the anodic product of this electrolysis is chlorine or oxygen, depending on the concentration (see §1.3 and Appendix II), Edwards[2] reports that the electrolysis of neutral sodium chloride solution produces no oxygen even when very dilute, if it is not stirred; but if the alkaline catholyte reaches the anode region, chlorate(I) (hypochlorite) ions are produced, which can be oxidized (1 e^- per ClO^-) to to chlorate(V), chloride and oxygen.

Examine the effect of anolyte pH on oxygen production from dilute sodium chloride; and also the current efficiency of the anodic oxidation of ClO^- to ClO_3^-.

The extent of CO_2 production at carbon anodes is also worthy of study.

9.21 Solid-state cells. Set up and investigate some solid state cells (see Fig. 2.7 and also *J. Electrochem. Soc.* **102**, 208; **106**, 475; **117**, 1; etc.)

Very simple cells of the type: Metal | metal iodide(s) | iodine(s), Pt can be set up by sandwiching iodine between a metal and a small piece of platinum foil, using a clothes peg[3]. Measure the cell potentials. Is direct comparison with the corresponding aqueous cell possible in any example?

9.22 Reversibility of metal electrodes. Use a counter e.m.f. circuit (as Fig. 4.2) to obtain the current–p.d. graph for cells of the type: metal M | M^{n+}(aq) || calomel electrode. Record and plot currents obtained with rising and falling potentials, both sides of the reversible cell potential. Obtain an order of relative reversibility for metals such as Cu, Zn, Ag, Pb, Fe (soft), Fe (steel), Hg, Sn . . .

Also investigate the effect of temperature on reversibility.

[2] Edwards, R. M., *Sch. Sci. Rev.* **52**, 155 (September 1970) and Potter, E. C., *Electrochemistry*, Cleaver-Hume, 1956, p. 342.

[3] Rollino, J. A. and Aronson, S., *J. Chem. Educ.* **49**, 825–6 (1972).

9.23 The isolated anode. Repeat the experiments first performed by Faraday (Exptl. Res. in Electricity, Everyman edn. p. 48 ff) and extend these to aqueous sulphuric acid electrolysed with an ordinary platinum cathode but instead of an anode, a point discharge from a few millimetres above the surface. It is said that hydrogen peroxide is the main product. Aim to determine the current efficiency.

Use a motor driven Van der Graaf generator, and as a preliminary use the electrolysis of potassium iodide solution on paper, to discover the polarity.

9.24 Thermodynamics of a cell reaction. Repeat and extend Expt. 4–3 and, measure $\Delta G^{\ominus}$, $\Delta H^{\ominus}$ and hence $\Delta S^{\ominus}$ for a suitable reaction. $\Delta H^{\ominus}$ can be found by calorimetry or, with care, from the variation of cell potential with temperature (§4.10).

9.25 An oxygen sensing electrode. Following the section in §7.7 on the Mancy Electrode, devise, build and test a cell of the same type. A cylindrical design would probably reduce the problem of making the membrane fit tightly.

As no temperature compensation will be included, the calibration must be performed at the temperature at which the sensor is to be used.

9.26 Concentration cells. (a) Repeat the experiment described by Ogg[4] for determining the formula of the mercury(I) ion. Set up the concentration cell:

$$Hg(l) \,|\, Hg(I)nitrate \;(aq, \; c_1) \,\|\, Hg(I)nitrate \;(aq, \; c_2) \,|\, Hg(l) \quad (c_2 = 10 \; c_1)$$ and compare the measured cell potential with that calculated by the Nernst equation (§5.2) for different values of z, the charge on one Hg(I) ion. (b) Design and perform a similar investigation into the nature of the Cu(I) ion in Cu(I) chloride dissolved in molten $KCl/CaCl_2$.

Historical projects

9.27 The acid-alkali cell and the contact theory. In 1802 Davy, wishing to strengthen the evidence for his theory that galvanic cell action arose from chemical action and not from metallic contact (as claimed by Volta *et al.*), set up the following cell, which gave a substantial current:

$$Pt \,|\, HNO_3(aq, \; about \; 10 \; M) \,|\, KOH(aq, \; about \; 4 \; M) \,|\, Pt$$

(where | represents a porous partition—a porous pot).

He believed that the current was caused by the neutralization, at a distance, of the acid by the alkali. However it is no longer thought that *all* chemical reactions can produce electricity, and it must be noted that a neutralization is not an electron transfer reaction. Had Davy made a mistake?

Repeat Davy's experiment, noting the polarity of the cell, the maximum cell e.m.f., its constancy, and the polarizability of the cell. Attempt to explain the action of the cell, in modern terms. Set up similar cells with different acids.

[4] Ogg, A., *Z. Phys. chem.* **27**, 285–311 (1898); *Chem. Zentralblatt* (1898), 1077–8.

Read about the rival 'chemical' and 'contact' theories in a reference book on the history of chemistry, and summarize the evidence on both sides as seen in, say, 1840. How was the dispute finally resolved? What became of the contact theory?

9.28 Galvanism: is it electricity? In 1800 galvanism was the action of dissimilar metals in contact with each other and with a moist surface, causing a tingling in the tongue, flashes in the eyes, twitches in frogs' legs, etc.; whereas electricity, produced by a frictional machine, manifested itself through sparks, attractions and repulsions, electric shocks, etc. The importance of Volta's Pile was that it enabled galvanic electricity to be produced at sufficiently high potential to prove the identity of the two electricities.

Build a 'pile' (Plate 1) of copper and zinc discs with sodium chloride electrolyte, and measure the potential at which 1 mA can be obtained, as a function of the number of pairs. What is the smallest pile which will produce sparks?—or give a shock?

Also experiment with the electrochemical effects of frictional electricity (see also §9.23). Do you consider that Faraday's summary of the evidence in 1838 (Exptl. Res. §1) adequately settled the question?

If possible, read some original papers (by Nicholson, Cruickshank, Davy, Henry and others) describing the experimental breakthrough in electrochemistry in the second half of 1800 (e.g. *Nicholson's Journal* **4**, 179, 187, 223, 245, 254, 275; and **5**.80). The piles used by these experimenters were always of the form: S–Z–C–S–Z–C– ... S–Z, where S = silver (or copper), Z = zinc, and C = cloth or card. Accounts refer to 'hydrogen produced at the silver end and oxygen at the zinc end': comment.

9.29 Preferential discharge or secondary products? Examine the rival theories put forward to explain the formation of one electrolysis product rather than another, and in particular the evolution of hydrogen and oxygen from certain salt solutions. Chemistry textbooks of the first half of the present century often contained a discussion of both theories.

Review the extensive correspondence in the School Science Review, starting with D. R. Lewis's observation that 'selective discharge' was being taught as a *mechanism*, although there was no evidence for this (**37**, p. 151, November 1955). Pedagogic arguments for the 'secondary products' explanation were advanced by L. H. Angus (**39**, 321, March 1958), and about 12 letters on the subject appeared in the next two volumes (**40** and **41**). Later writers include F. P. Hodgson (**46**, 770) and D. C. Henwood (**48**, 927–8). Was the correspondence valuable? What was the conclusion to the debate? Has it influenced subsequent textbook authors?

9.30 Davy's discovery of the alkali metals. Read Davy's own account of his isolation of the alkali metals, in the Bakerian Lecture of November 1807 (*Phil. Trans.* **98**, 1–44; or *Alembic Club Reprint* no. 6). Devise a demonstration of the electrolysis of solid potassium hydroxide, using a modern power source, and when this has been checked for safety, perform the experiment.

What does Davy mean by the 'battery of the power of 250 of 6 and 4' (middle of section II)? From his reported results, estimate this power.

The Project may be extended to include Davy's electrical decomposition of ammonia (section VIII of the Bakerian Lecture) and the isolation of the alkaline earths (*Phil. Trans.* **98**, 341–6), all in the Alembic Club Reprint no. 6. Why was Davy concerned to show that ammonia contained oxygen?

9.31 Washburn's transport numbers. Read the original paper by E. W. Washburn, *J. Amer. Chem. Soc.* **31**, 322–55 (1909).[5] Repeat the basic experiment using a sugar (estimated by optical activity) as the reference substance; and also use a different reference substance (e.g. H_2O_2 estimated iodimetrically, or an unionized reductant to be titrated versus $KMnO_4$) in an attempt to show that they are, in fact, all equally stationary under electrophoretic conditions.

Write an account of the theory of ionic hydration, and the evidence from these transport numbers and ionic mobilities.

Washburn obtained a value of 0.3 for the hydration number of H^+; is the argument affected by the possibility of a different mechanism for the conductance of H^+ (§3.9)? He also pointed out that the moving boundary method gives 'true' transport numbers: is this so even if the ion which is *not* being observed (e.g. the anion in Expt. 3–6) is substantially hydrated?

Miscellaneous non-practical projects

9.32 Cosmetic electrolysis. Ask a friendly Cosmetic Electrologist to explain the basic principles of the procedure. What is it that actually destroys the hair follicle in the case of (a) d.c. electrolysis, or (b) a.c.? Which is the more reliable and permanent?

Consult a reference book (e.g. A. R. Hinkel and R. W. Lind, *Electrolysis, Thermolysis and the Blend*, Arroway, Los Angeles, 1968) for further details.

9.33 Electric cars. Are electric cars sufficiently developed for wholesale introduction? What are the main advantages over petrol-driven transport? What are the difficulties?

Refer to the article 'Electric Cars' in *Science Journal*, March 1967, and recent articles in periodicals and newspapers. Write to the following for further information: The Electricity Council; Enfield Automotive Co. Ltd., Cowes, I.O.W.; Chloride Ltd. and Westinghouse Electric Inc. (See also Plate 3.)

[5] Most of the literature references cited in this book are available in the Holborn Division of the Science Reference Library, 25 Southampton Buildings, Chancery Lane, London WC2A 1AW; or, in the case of periodicals before 1960, in the Kean St Annexe. A postal photocopy service is offered. Further references: Washburn and Millard, *J. Amer. Chem. Soc.*, **37**, 694 (1915); Taylor and Sawyer, *J. Chem. Soc.*, **1929**, 2095. For criticism of the theoretical foundation, see MacInnes, D. A., *J. Amer. Chem. Soc.*, **43**, 1217 (1921); Longsworth, L. G. *ibid.*, **69**, 1288 (1947); and Hule, C. H. and DeVries, T., *ibid.*, **70**, 2473 (1948).

Consider the relative claims of Planté lead–acid rechargeable cells, Sony zinc powder/air cells (the zinc oxide would be exchanged for fresh zinc at a roadside fuel station), sodium/sulphur cells, lithium/chlorine cells, and fuel cells, e.g. hydrazine/air cells.

9.34 Fuel cells. Obtain an up-to-date picture of fuel cell prospects from periodicals such as *New Scientist* or *Electrical Times*. Also write to the following for information: General Electric Research Laboratories, Schenectady, N.Y.; Allis-Chalmers Manuf. Co., Milwaukee, Wisconsin; Yuasa Co., Tokyo, Japan; and addresses from ref. 10 of Chapter 8.

9.35 Bio-electrochemistry (for students of biology). Consult a recent textbook for an account of the cellular potential—the p.d. which exists across most cell boundaries. Consider the Donnan membrane potential, the Na^+ and K^+ concentrations, and the theories of Hodgkin and Huxley (liquid junction potentials) and DelDuca and Fuscoe (micro fuel cell theory, 1965).[6] The latter, described in *Electrochemical Science* by Bockris and Drazic (Taylor and Francis Ltd.) postulates fuel cell action involving a glucose-rich anodic site within the bio-cell, an oxygen-rich cathodic site on the outside of the cell membrane, diffusion of ions through the membrane (probably cations outwards), and—the most novel proposal— *electronic* conduction from the interior anode to the exterior cathode along a delocalized orbital in a macromolecule.

9.36 Tantrik theories of polarity. Two passages from *Tantra*, by Omar Garrison (Academy Editions, 1972).

(i) (p. 31). *Prana* is cosmic energy. For biological organisms, including man, the most important gross manifestation of *prana* is breathing. . . . When breathing ceases, the body's polarity undergoes radical change: the positive electrical forces of the body, in the form of acid, flood into the negative alkaline of the blood. The body's mechanism becomes static, ceasing to function.

(ii) (p. 70). Pundit Chatterjee's suggestions for combating adverse effects of an urban, industrial environment:
   The polarity of our bodies is directly affected by our physical surroundings, and by the air we breathe. The air of cities and industrialized areas is heavily charged with a positive polarity. . . . The effects include nervous tension, vascular diseases and emotional disorders.
   . . . A solution is to spend time in rural surroundings. Atmospheric ions, which are minute clumps of air molecules having an electric charge, are negative in large open spaces of this kind. And being negative, they can often reverse the damage done by positive ions during sojourn in an urban environment.
   In this connection it is interesting to observe that only recently, researches both in the West and in Soviet Russia, have been seriously studying the effects of atmospheric polarity on human behaviour. To date, their knowledge of this subject is not as extensive as that which has reposed in Tantrik tradition for centuries, but important experiments have been conducted under scientific test conditions.

[6] Del Duca, M. G. and Fuscoe, J. M., *Sci. and Tech.*, **1965**, 56.

At the Batelle Memorial Institution in Columbus, Ohio ... Drs Howard G. Schultz and Richard A. Duffee pointed out that the effect of air ions on human health and behaviour have assumed a new importance in the nuclear, space age.

... Negative ions produce a pleasant feeling of relaxation and drowsiness. Positive ions produce an unpleasant feeling of dizziness and nausea, often accompanied by headache and sore throat.

[In Russian experiments, inhalation of negative ions increased endurance by 46%.]

Questions for discussion or further investigation[7]

1. Extract (i); 'Positive forces, in the form of acid.' Does this point to an identity, or an analogy? Compare with the results of the electrolysis of ordinary water—a fact known since 1800.

2. From the whole of the first passage, decide upon the nearest biochemical equivalent of *prana*. Does the Tantrik term have an exact 'scientific' meaning, or does it include an area outside the scope of conventional scientific enquiry?

3. Extract (ii); Would it be possible, with simple apparatus, to detect the supposed polarity of urban and rural air? Conventional meteorological research points to inversion of polarity before thunderstorms: follow up this line of investigation, and plan a controlled experiment to test the theory of the physiological effect of atmospheric polarity.

Extended essays

9.37 Which, in your view, are the more interesting aspects of electrochemistry: the contributions to theoretical chemistry (equilibrium, reaction feasibility, the nature of solution, etc.) or the technological applications (electrolysis, fuel cells, vehicle propulsion)?

9.38 Is fuel cell research getting anywhere? (There were more electric cars on the streets in 1905 than in 1975.) Which of the following might give the greatest boost to electrochemical research: (i) an increase in 'environmentalist' (anti-air-pollution) campaigning; (ii) a revival of the Space exploration programme; (iii) another rise in world oil prices?

---

[7] *Further reading:* Krueger, A. and Smith, R. 'The physiological significance of positive and negative ionization of the atmosphere'; in *Man's Dependence on the Earthly Atmosphere*. Macmillan, New York, 1962

Appendix I

Standard Reduction Potentials at 298 K.

Elements in standard states unless otherwise indicated, and ions at unit activity in aqueous solution. Arranged alphabetically by symbol of element being reduced. Potentials for basic solutions ($a_{OH^-} = 1$) in heavy type. Some additional potentials appear in Fig. 5.3. Table 5.3 (p. 97) provides an ordered list of reduction potentials while a fuller table, presented in cell notation, appears in the Nuffield Advanced Science *Book of Data* (Penguin, 1972).

Electrode half-reaction	$E_{red}^{\ominus}/V$
$Ag^+ + e^- = Ag$	$+0.799*$
$Ag^{2+} + 2e^- = Ag^+$	$+1.98*$
$AgCl(s) + e^- = Ag + Cl^-$	$+0.22$
$Al^{3+} + 3e^- = Al$	-1.66
$AlO_2^- + 2H_2O + 3e^- = Al + 4OH^-$	$\mathbf{-2.35}$
$As + 3H^+ + 3e^- = AsH_3$	-0.60
$H_3AsO_4 + 2H^+ + 2e^- = H_3AsO_3 + H_2O$	$+0.56$
$Au^{3+} + 3e^- = Au$	$+1.50$
$Ba^{2+} + 2e^- = Ba$	-2.90
$Be^{2+} + 2e^- = Be$	-1.85
$BiO^+ + 2H^+ + 3e^- = Bi + H_2O$	$+0.28$
$Br_2(aq) + 2e^- = 2Br^-$	$+1.09$
$2HBrO(aq) + 2H^+ + 2e^- = Br_2(aq) + 2H_2O$	$+1.57$
$2\,BrO^- + H_2O + 2e^- = Br_2(aq) + 2OH^-$	$\mathbf{+0.43}$
$BrO_3^- + 6H^+ + 5e^- = \frac{1}{2}Br_2(aq) + 3H_2O$	$+1.50$
$BrO_4^- + 2H^+ + 2e^- = BrO_3^- + H_2O$	$+1.76$
$CO_2(g) + 2H^+ + 2e^- = CO(g) + H_2O$	-0.10
$C + 4H^+ + 4e^- = CH_4(g)$	-0.13

$$C_2H_4(g) + 2H^+ + 2e^- = C_2H_6(g) \qquad +0.52$$

$$CH_3OH(aq) + 2H^+ + 2e^- = CH_4(g) + H_2O \qquad -0.59$$

$$HCHO(aq) + 2H^+ + 2e^- = CH_3OH(aq) \qquad -0.19$$

$$HCOOH(aq) + 2H^+ + 2e^- = HCHO(aq) + H_2O \qquad -0.06$$

$$CO_2(g) + 2H^+ + 2e^- = HCOOH(aq) \qquad -0.20$$

$$2CO_2(g) + 2H^+ + 2e^- = H_2C_2O_4(aq) \qquad -0.49$$

$$CNO^- + H_2O + 2e^- = CN^- + 2OH^- \qquad \mathbf{-0.97}$$

$$(CNS)_2 + 2e^- = 2CNS^- \qquad +0.77$$

$$C_6H_4O_2(aq) + 2H^+ + 2e^- = C_6H_4(OH)_2(aq) \qquad +0.70$$

$$Ca^{2+} + 2e^- = Ca \qquad -2.87$$

$$Ca(OH)_2(s) + 2e^- = Ca + 2OH^- \qquad \mathbf{-3.03}$$

$$Cd^{2+} + 2e^- = Cd \qquad -0.40$$

$$Ce^{3+} + 3e^- = Ce \qquad -2.33$$

$$Ce^{4+} + e^- = Ce^{3+} \qquad +1.49$$

$$Cl_2(g) + 2e^- = 2Cl^- \qquad +1.360$$

$$HClO + H^+ + e^- = \tfrac{1}{2}Cl_2 + H_2O \qquad +1.64*$$

$$ClO_3^- + 6H^+ + 5e^- = \tfrac{1}{2}Cl_2 + 3H_2O \qquad +1.47*$$

$$ClO_4^- + 2H^+ + 2e^- = ClO_3^- + H_2O \qquad +1.19$$

$$Co^{2+} + 2e^- = Co \qquad -0.277$$

$$Co^{3+} + e^- = Co^{2+} \qquad +1.82$$

$$Co(OH)_3 + e^- = Co(OH)_2 + OH^- \qquad \mathbf{+0.17}$$

$$Cr^{2+} + 2e^- = Cr \qquad -0.91$$

$$Cr^{3+} + 3e^- = Cr \qquad -0.74$$

$$Cr^{3+} + e^- = Cr^{2+} \qquad -0.41$$

$$\tfrac{1}{2}Cr_2O_7^{2-} + 7H^+ + 3e^- = Cr^{3+} + 7/2H_2O \qquad +1.33*$$

$$Cs^+ + e^- = Cs \qquad -2.92$$

$$Cu^+ + e^- = Cu \qquad +0.521$$

$$\tfrac{1}{2}Cu_2O + \tfrac{1}{2}H_2O + e^- = Cu + OH^- \qquad \mathbf{-0.358}$$

$$Cu^{2+} + 2e^- = Cu \qquad +0.337$$

$$Cu^{2+} + e^- = Cu^+ \qquad +0.15$$

$$Cu(OH)_2 + e^- = \tfrac{1}{2}Cu_2O + OH^- + \tfrac{1}{2}H_2O \qquad \mathbf{-0.080}$$

$$Cu^{2+} + I^- + e^- = CuI \qquad +0.86$$

$$2D^+ + 2e^- = D_2 \qquad -0.003$$

$$F_2 + 2e^- = 2F^- \qquad +2.87$$

*See also Fig. 5.3.

$$F_2 + 2H^+ + 2e^- = 2HF(aq) \qquad +3.06$$
$$F_2O + 2H^+ + 4e^- = H_2O + F^- \qquad +2.15$$
$$Fe^{2+} + 2e^- = Fe \qquad -0.440*$$
$$Fe^{3+} + e^- = Fe^{2+} \qquad +0.771*$$
$$Fe(CN)_6^{3-} + e^- = Fe(CN)_6^{4-} \qquad +0.36$$
$$FeO_4^{2-} + 8H^+ + 3e^- = Fe^{3+} + 4H_2O \qquad +2.2$$
$$FeO_4^{2-} + 2H_2O + 3e^- = FeO_2^- + 4OH^- \qquad \mathbf{+0.9}$$

$$2H^+ + 2e^- = H_2 \qquad 0.000$$
$$2H_2O + 2e^- = H_2 + 2OH^- \qquad \mathbf{-0.828}$$
$$H_2 + 2e^- = 2H^- \qquad -2.25$$
$$\tfrac{1}{2}Hg_2^{2+} + e^- = Hg \qquad +0.789$$
$$Hg^{2+} + 2e^- = Hg \qquad +0.854$$
$$Hg^{2+} + e^- = \tfrac{1}{2}Hg_2^{2+} \qquad +0.920$$
$$\tfrac{1}{2}Hg_2Cl_2(s) + e^- = Hg + Cl^- \qquad +0.27$$

$$I_2(aq \text{ or as } I_3^-) + 2e^- = 2I^- \qquad +0.54$$
$$IO_3^- + 6H^+ + 5e^- = \tfrac{1}{2}I_2 + 3H_2O \qquad +1.20$$

$$K^+ + e^- = K \qquad -2.92$$

$$Li^+ + e^- = Li \qquad -3.03$$

$$Mg^{2+} + 2e^- = Mg \qquad -2.37$$
$$Mg(OH)_2 + 2e^- = Mg + 2OH^- \qquad \mathbf{-2.69}$$
$$Mn^{2+} + 2e^- = Mn \qquad -1.18$$
$$MnO_4^- + 8H^+ + 5e^- = Mn^{2+} + 4H_2O \qquad +1.51*$$

$$N_2H_5^+ + 3H^+ + 2e^- = 2NH_4^+ \qquad +1.27$$
$$N_2H_4 + 2H_2O + 2e^- = 2NH_3(aq) + 2OH^- \qquad \mathbf{+0.1}$$
$$N_2 + 5H^+ + 4e^- = N_2H_5^+ \qquad -0.23$$
$$HN_3(aq) + 3H^+ + 2e^- = NH_4^+ + N_2 \qquad +1.96$$
$$HN_3(aq) + 11H^+ + 8e^- = 3NH_4^+ \qquad +0.69$$
$$\tfrac{1}{2}N_2 + H_2O + 2H^+ + e^- = NH_3OH^+ \qquad -1.89$$
$$\tfrac{3}{2}N_2 + H^+ + e^- = HN_3 \qquad -3.40$$
$$\tfrac{1}{2}N_2 + 4H^+ + 3e^- = NH_4^+ \qquad +0.27$$
$$2HNO_2 + 4H^+ + 4e^- = N_2O + 3H_2O \qquad +1.29$$
$$HNO_2 + H^+ + e^- = NO + H_2O \qquad +1.00$$
$$NO_2 + H^+ + e^- = HNO_2 \qquad +1.07$$

*See also Fig. 5.3.

$$NO_3^- + 2H^+ + e^- = NO_2 + H_2O \qquad +0.81$$

$$NO_3^- + 3H^+ + 2e^- = HNO_2 + H_2O \qquad +0.94$$

$$NO_3^- + H_2O + 2e^- = NO_2^- + 2OH^- \qquad \mathbf{+0.01}$$

$$NO_3^- + 4H^+ + 3e^- = NO + 2H_2O \qquad +0.96$$

$$NO_3^- + 6H^+ + 5e^- = \tfrac{1}{2}N_2 + 3H_2O \qquad +1.24$$

$$NO_3^- + 6H_2O + 8e^- = NH_3(aq) + 9OH^- \qquad \mathbf{-0.13}$$

$$Na^+ + e^- = Na \qquad -2.71$$

$$Ni^{2+} + 2e^- = Ni \qquad -0.250$$

$$NiO_2 + 2H_2O + 2e^- = Ni(OH)_2 + 2OH^- \qquad \mathbf{+0.49}$$

$$H_2O_2(aq) + 2H^+ + 2e^- = 2H_2O \qquad +1.77*$$

$$O_2 + 4H^+ + 4e^- = 2H_2O \qquad +1.229*$$

$$O_2 + 2H_2O + 4e^- = 4OH^- \qquad \mathbf{+0.401}$$

$$O_2 + 2H^+ + 2e^- = H_2O_2 \qquad +0.68$$

$$O_3 + 2H^+ + 2e^- = O_2 + H_2O \qquad +2.07$$

$$P + 3H_2O + 3e^- = PH_3 + 3OH^- \qquad \mathbf{-0.89}$$

$$H_2PO_2^- + e^- = P + 2OH^- \qquad \mathbf{-2.05}$$

$$PO_4^{3-} + 2H_2O + 2e^- = HPO_3^{2-} + 3OH^- \qquad \mathbf{-1.12}$$

$$H_3PO_4 + 2H^+ + 2e^- = H_3PO_3 + H_2O \qquad -0.28$$

$$Pb^{2+} + 2e^- = Pb \qquad -0.126$$

$$Pb^{4+} + 2e^- = Pb^{2+} \qquad +1.69$$

$$PbO_2 + 4H^+ + 2e^- = Pb^{2+} + 2H_2O \qquad +1.46$$

$$PbO_2 + H_2O + 2e^- = PbO + 2OH^- \qquad \mathbf{+0.28}$$

$$PbO_2 + 4H^+ + SO_4^{2-} + 2e^- = PbSO_4(s) + 2H_2O \qquad +1.685$$

$$Ra^{2+} + 2e^- = Ra \qquad -2.92$$

$$Rb^+ + e^- = Rb \qquad -2.92$$

$$S + 2e^- = S^{2-} \qquad \mathbf{-0.48}$$

$$S + 2H^+ + 2e^- = H_2S \qquad +0.14$$

$$2H_2SO_3 + 2H^+ + 4e^- = S_2O_3^{2-} + 3H_2O \qquad +0.40$$

$$2SO_3^{2-} + 3H_2O + 4e^- = S_2O_3^{2-} + 6OH^- \qquad \mathbf{-0.58}$$

$$H_2SO_3 + 4H^+ + 4e^- = S + 3H_2O \qquad +0.47$$

$$SO_4^{2-} + 4H^+ + 2e^- = H_2SO_3 + H_2O \qquad +0.17$$

$$SO_4^{2-} + H_2O + 2e^- = SO_3^{2-} + 2OH^- \qquad \mathbf{-0.93}$$

$$S_4O_6^{2-} + 2e^- = 2S_2O_3^{2-} \qquad +0.09$$

*See also Fig. 5.3.

$$S_2O_8^{2-} + 2e^- = 2SO_4^{2-}$$ $\qquad$ +2.01

$$Sb + 3H^+ + 3e^- = SbH_3(g)$$ $\qquad$ −0.51

$$SbO^+ + 2H^+ + 3e^- = Sb + H_2O$$ $\qquad$ +0.21

$$Sb_2O_5 + 6H^+ + 4e^- = 2SbO^+ + 3H_2O$$ $\qquad$ +0.58

$$Se + 2H^+ + 2e^- = H_2Se(g)$$ $\qquad$ −0.40

$$Se + 2e^- = Se^{2-}$$ $\qquad$ **−0.92**

$$SiO_3^{2-} + 3H_2O + 4e^- = Si + 6OH^-$$ $\qquad$ −1.70

$$Sn^{2+} + 2e^- = Sn$$ $\qquad$ −0.14

$$Sn^{4+} + 2e^- = Sn^{2+}$$ $\qquad$ +0.15

$$Sn(OH)_6^{2-} + 2e^- = SnO(OH)^- + H_2O + 3OH^-$$ $\qquad$ **−0.90**

$$Sr^{2+} + 2e^- = Sr$$ $\qquad$ −2.89

$$Te + 2H^+ + 2e^- = H_2Te(g)$$ $\qquad$ −0.72

$$Te + 2e^- = Te^{2-}$$ $\qquad$ **−1.14**

$$TeO_2 + 4H^+ + 4e^- = Te + 2H_2O$$ $\qquad$ +0.59

$$Th^{4+} + 4e^- = Th$$ $\qquad$ −1.90

$$Ti^{2+} + 2e^- = Ti$$ $\qquad$ −1.63

$$TiO^{2+} + 2H^+ + e^- = Ti^{3+} + H_2O$$ $\qquad$ +0.1

$$TiO^{2+} + 2H^+ + 4e^- = Ti + H_2O$$ $\qquad$ −0.89

$$Tl^{3+} + 2e^- = Tl^+$$ $\qquad$ +1.25

$$U^{3+} + 3e^- = U$$ $\qquad$ −1.80

$$U^{4+} + e^- = U^{3+}$$ $\qquad$ −0.61

$$UO_2^{2+} + 4H^+ + 2e^- = U^{4+} + 2H_2O$$ $\qquad$ +0.62

$$V^{2+} + 2e^- = V$$ $\qquad$ −1.2

$$V^{3+} + e^- = V^{2+}$$ $\qquad$ −0.26

$$VO^{2+} + 2H^+ + e^- = V^{3+} + H_2O$$ $\qquad$ +0.34

$$VO_2^+ + 2H^+ + e^- = VO^{2+} + H_2O$$ $\qquad$ +1.00

$$XeO_3(g) + 6H^+ + 6e^- = Xe + 3H_2O$$ $\qquad$ +1.8

$$H_4XeO_6 + 2H^+ + 2e^- = XeO_3 = 3H_2O$$ $\qquad$ +2.3

$$Zn^{2+} + 2e^- = Zn$$ $\qquad$ −0.763*

*See also Fig. 5.3.

Appendix II

Further information for teachers and course supervisors
(Each note is preceded by the number of the section of the text to which it refers.)

§1.1   For a simple account of the current model for electronic conduction see
        Ayres, A. J. P., *Sch. Sci. Rev.* **51**, 55–60 (Sep. 1969).

§1.2   *Electrophoresis demonstration.* Fig. A.1 shows a modification for individual
        work, and the MnO_4^- migration experiment is also suitable for class work;
        but in each case it is advisable to include a rheostat, initially at about 200 Ω,
        to limit the current on short-circuit. Overheating is one of the problems of
        the glass-slide arrangement.

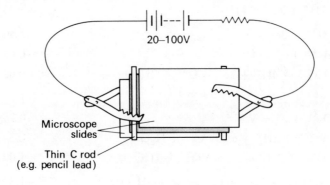

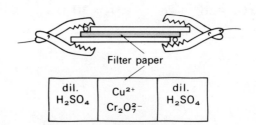

Fig. A.1 Simplified apparatus for electrophoresis on paper

For the U-tube demonstration, a solution of $CuCr_2O_7$ can be made by mixing $CuSO_4$ and $K_2Cr_2O_7$: the dark olive-green solution should be mixed with warm agar solution and allowed to set in the curve of the U-tube; dilute sulphuric acid is then placed in the limbs. Alternatively the solution may be converted to tetra-ammine copper(II) chromate(VI) by the addition of excess aqueous ammonia, and the acid replaced by ammonia plus ammonium sulphate solution, in order to intensify the colour of the migrating copper ions. The demonstration is suitable for overhead projection.

References: Lee, J. H., *Sch. Sci. Rev.* **45**, 679; McDonald, J., *ibid* **46**, 701; Herron, J. D., *J. Chem. Educ.* **46**, 527–8 (1969); *Nuffield Chemistry: Collected Experiments*, E5.9.

§1.3 *Electrolysis of molten lead bromide.* Details in *Revised Nuffield Chemistry: Teachers' Guide 2* (1976) expts. A16, B19 (or *Collected Experiments* E5.5). The arrangement of electrodes in Fig. 1.4 allows more control of the separation distance, but a fume-cupboard is clearly necessary. For class work, closed systems from which the poisonous fumes can be pumped away to be absorbed in sodium hydroxide solution can be devised. Too high a potential gradient causes electrostriction which makes the molten salt draw away from the electrodes.

If lead(II) bromide is not available it can be prepared by precipitation, then washed and well dried. Some PbI_2 may be mixed in, to lower the melting point and to produce the more clearly visible iodine at the anode. But the iodide alone should not be used (as suggested in Nuffield expt. E5.6) for the *quantitative* experiment, because it is insoluble even in boiling water, and cannot therefore be washed off the lead beads before weighing.

The electrolysis of molten salts is the subject of Project 9.11.

Electrolysis of sodium chloride solution. This interesting example will be mentioned several times, and the complications of mixed products may be deferred until §6.4 and Project 9.20. It is often stated that the anodic product is chlorine or oxygen, depending on concentration. Stove, J. D. and Phillips, K. A. in *A Modern Approach to Chemistry*, Heinemann, 1963, give the limits as $>12\%$ NaCl for Cl_2, $<6\%$ for O_2, and a mixture from intermediate concentrations. The six demonstrations in this section are intended to be introductory only.

Carbon electrodes. In some cases up to 50% of the O_2 expected at the anode appears as CO_2.

§2.1 To show that oxidation–reduction reactions are electron transfers (Fig. 2.1): for examples see Winter, R. D., *Sch. Sci. Rev.* **55**, 540–1 (Mar. 1974).

§2.2 *The reaction of a copper anode in different electrolytes*: see *Revised Nuffield Chemistry* (1976) *Teachers' Guide 2*, A16.6. For the quantitative electrolysis of hydrochloric acid see Davis, J. W., *Sch. Sci. Rev.* **39**, 381.

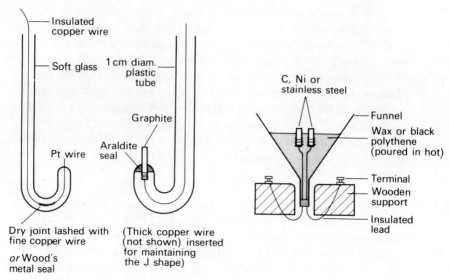

Fig. A.2　Some simple electrodes for gas evolution

Expt. 2-1. Fig. A.2 shows some suggestions for simple improvized cells; numerous other designs have been published, particularly well thought out ones being those described by Reid, J., *Sch. Sci. Rev.* **54**, 538 (Mar. 1973), and Chapman, R. W. *ibid* **56**, 766 (Jun. 1975).

Expt. 2-1.4. If the students are not familiar with calculations using the ideal gas equation (especially those worked in SI units), some examples should be given, initially without the complication of water vapour partial pressure.

§2.6　*The place of hydrogen in the e.c.s.* The 'hydrogen bomb' devised by H. G. Andrew is shown in Fig. A.3: gentle heating of the zinc sulphate hydrate releases some water, which reacts with the lithium hydride, producing hydrogen under pressure, which in turn displaces copper from its sulphate. (An adequate safety screen is recommended.)

　　To demonstrate the reduction of aqueous Cu^{2+} by H_2 at a platinum catalyst, electrolyse some dilute H_2SO_4 for a few minutes, with platinum electrodes, then disconnect the cathode and immediately pour in some $CuSO_4$ solution. This procedure avoids exposing the adsorbed hydrogen to air.

§2.8　For practical work on cells see *Nuffield Chemistry: Collected Experiments* E17.11 ('To investigate the structure of a dry cell') and E17.12 (an improvised lead-acid cell). Up-to-date technical information is available from dry cell manufacturers. See also Andrew, H. G. 'On teaching voltaic cells and electrolysis', *Mod. Sci. Memoirs* no. 41 and *Sch. Sci. Rev.* **41**, 203–11 (1961); and Williams, I. W., 'Batteries old and new', *Educ. Chem.* **6**, 120–6 (1969). For a project on solid-state cells see §9.21.

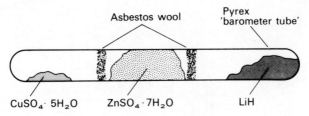

Fig. A.3 The 'hydrogen bomb'

§3.2 *Expt.* 3–1. For the copper electrodes use stiff copper wire, firmly wound round a glass tube, then entering the tube at the lower end through a seal of black polythene melted in a low bunsen flame. The silver–silver chloride electrodes are of silver wire, soldered to copper wire at a point not reached by the solution, and made the anode, against a Pt cathode, in dilute hydrochloric acid for about 10 minutes at about 10 mA, until a brown layer of silver chloride covers the surface.

§3.6 *Expt.* 3–4. The demonstration model shown is after a design by Ridley, E. R., *Sch. Sci. Rev.* **46**, 698. An alternative molar conductivity cell for class use can be constructed by glueing a pair of thin copper-foil strips to the inside of a tall-form beaker or jam-jar. The strips should face each other, reach to the bottom of the vessel, and extend over the top rim, where crocodile clips can be attached. The time spent on a cell with full-height electrodes, in addition to the usual fixed-area conductivity cell, is rewarded with a better understanding of the difference between κ and Λ.

§3.10 *Expt.* 3–6 *Moving boundary.* For the preparation of the Ag/AgCl electrode, see note above, at §3.2. Other electrolytes may be used in this apparatus (as long as $t_+ > t_+$ of $\frac{1}{2}Cd^{2+}$) but the boundary may not be easy to see if both solutions are colourless. 0.2M HCl coloured with methyl orange has been recommended.

An alternative to the cadmium electrode is the 'lithium carbonate electrode', shown in Fig. A.4, which produces Li^+ ion at exactly the rate (how?) required to replace that lost by migration and to partner the Cl^- ion which arrives. The boundary is started by opening the tap, after the p.d. has been applied.

J. L. Latham has published (*Sch. Sci. Rev.* **43**, 204) a problem in the form of a paradox, which may be briefly restated thus: since the moving boundary stays sharp, the ions on either side of it must be moving at exactly the same velocity; yet the ionic mobilities are known to be different (see Table 3.2), that of the ion ahead of the boundary being the greater. How can these conflicting ideas be reconciled? (The answer was subsequently published in *Sch. Sci. Rev.* **44**, 220).

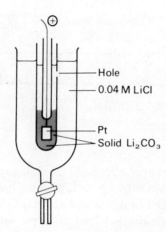

Fig. A.4 The 'lithium carbonate electrode' for the moving boundary experiment

Other references: Baca, G. and Hill, R. D. *J. Chem. Educ.* **47**, 235; Martin, R. *Sch. Sci. Rev.* **39**, 400; MacInnes (see Bibliography), Ch. 4.

Expt. 3–7. For a more robust dip-type pair of conductivity electrodes see Ghee, P. W. and Daniels, D. J., *Sch. Sci. Rev.* **52**, 600 (Mar. 1971).

§4.2   *Salt bridge.* Fig. A.5 shows various forms of salt bridge, containing a concentrated solution of potassium chloride or ammonium nitrate(V), restrained in some way from diffusing into the half-cells being linked. For theory see §5.4.

§4.5   For a discussion of the theoretical position of the standard hydrogen electrode see Biegler, T. and Woods, R., *J. Chem. Educ.* **50**, 604–5 (1973).

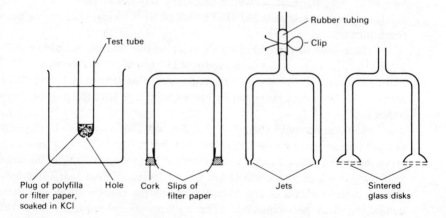

Fig. A.5 Some salt bridges

Platinized electrodes. Kohlrausch in 1875 suggested platinized platinum electrodes as being more reversible and less polarizable than shiny platinum, on account of the very large effective surface area, and high catalytic power, both for $H^+(aq) + e^- \rightleftharpoons \frac{1}{2}H_2(g)$ and for $H_2(g) + \frac{1}{2}O_2(g) \rightarrow H_2O(l)$.

To platinize (or re-platinize) an electrode, first clean it by dipping it in warm 'aqua regia' (a mixture, 2:1 by volume, of concentrated hydrochloric and nitric(V) acids) for a few seconds, then rinse it and use as the negative electrode in a 2% solution of platinum(IV) chloride ('chloroplatinic acid'). It is said that the addition of 0.02% lead(II) ethanoate assists the deposition of platinum in a suitable form. The p.d. should be about 3 V, and the anode can be another platinum wire. After 5 minutes, remove both electrodes to a beaker of very dilute sulphuric(VI) acid and continue electrolysis: the hydrogen evolution helps to clean the platinized electrode, which should then be kept in distilled water when not in use.

Another procedure, involving periodic reversal of the d.c., is described in *Nuffield Advanced Science, Chemistry: Teachers' Guide*, Penguin, 1970, p. 280.

§4.6   *Expt.* 4–2. See Proudfoot, T. E., *Sch. Sci. Rev.* **46**, 185; and, for the technique illustrated, Sutton, C. R. and Collier, K. M., *ibid.* **49**, 810.

§4.7   *Expt.* 4–3. For fuller details see the author's *Chemical Energetics*, Arnold, 1971, p. 35.

§4.9   See also Bailey, D. N. *et al.*, 'On the relationship between cell potential and half-cell reactions', *J. Chem. Educ.* **53**, 77–8 (Feb. 1976).

§4.10   *Expt.* 4–4. A suitable form for the cell is an inner test-tube with a 'Polyfilla' salt-bridge, as in Fig. A.5, containing the $Ag/AgNO_3$ half-cell and a thermometer, inside a larger test-tube with the $Cu/Cu(NO_3)_2$ half-cell. The inner temperature should be that of the water-bath when the measurement is taken. The concentrations specified make the cell potential standard (see §5.1) without the use of expensive 1M $AgNO_3$.

Ch.5   *Square brackets* [ ]. It has not yet been universally agreed whether or not the concentration quotient Q_c and the equilibrium constants K_c and K_p have units. In this book the convention used is that Q_c is a quotient of *pure numbers*, being the numerical values of concentrations in the units mol dm^{-3} and denoted thus [ ]. In other words, [A] denotes $c_A/c^\ominus$ where c_A is the concentration of A and $c^\ominus$ is the standard concentration. If $c^\ominus$ were other than 1 mol dm^{-3}, Q_c (and hence K_c) would take a different value.

The necessity for Q_c to be a pure number is that otherwise ln Q_c would be mathematically incorrect. Similarly, if Q_a and K_a, the quotients of *activities*, are to be pure numbers, it is necessary to define activity a as a pure number thus: $a = f.c/c^{\ominus}$.

§5.2   *Concentration cells*: the tin tree. If a dilute solution of $SnCl_2$ is floated on a concentrated solution, and a rod of tin left to stand in them both, tin crystals grow at the interface, due to concentration cell action: see Britton, G. C., *Sch. Sci. Rev.* **57**, 104 (Sep. 1975).

Expt. 5–2. See *Nuffield Advanced Science: Chemistry, Teachers' Guide*, p. 186 for details of a similar experiment, in which the Fe^{2+}/Fe^{3+} ratio is constant, and $[Ag^+]$ is varied. Also see *ibid* p. 191 for a table of individual ionic activity coefficients.

§5.6   For the effect of complexing agents on reduction potentials see Moody, G. J. and Thomas, J. D. R., 'Energy relations in chemistry—III; Oxidation–reduction', *Sch. Sci. Rev.* **51**, 89–101 (Sep. 1969).

§6.1   Both the *minimum decomposition potential* and the *minimum practical cell overpotential* are open to criticism (§6.2), and their use can only be defended on the pedagogical grounds that they are concepts which arise directly from experience of simple electrolysis, and are an aid, at an early stage, to the understanding of the phenomena; advanced students of electrodics will have no further use for them.

A table of selected m.d.p. values appears in *Nuffield Chemistry: Book of Data*, 1968, p. 139. See also Wood, R. K., *Sch. Sci. Rev.* **38**, 446–7.

§6.4   *Mechanism of hydrogen evolution.* See references in §9.29, especially Hodgson, F. P., *Sch. Sci. Rev.* **46**, 770–1. Although it is unsound to deduce anything about this mechanism from decomposition potentials, evidence *can* be obtained from the variation of overpotential with current density (see Potter, Bibliography). It is likely that the discharge of Na^+ is a step in the production of H_2 from concentrated NaOH solution.

§6.5   *Expt.* 6–4. For details of the electrolytic preparation of ammonium vanadium(II) sulphate(VI) and some reactions of vanadium(II) see Matthew Tracey, *Educ. Chem.* **6**, 24–6 (Jan. 1969); also Jenkins, E. W., *Sch. Sci. Rev.* **50**, 867–8 (1969); and Palmer (Bibliography).

§6.7   *Expt.* 6–5. See also Davis, J. W., *Sch. Sci. Rev.* **43**, 148 (1961).
Organic redox reactions. See Carter, G. J., *Sch. Sci. Rev.* **54**, 545–6 (Mar. 1973) for redox equations. Winter (*op. cit.* at §2.1) suggests a demonstration of the cell: C/MnO_4^-, OH^- : $CH_3CH(OH)CH_3(aq)$, OH^-/C.

§7.2 *Expt. 7–1. Constant current supply.* A circuit is described in Vincent, C. A. and Ward, J. G., 'A simple amperostat for coulometric titration', *J. Chem. Educ.* **46**, 613–4 (Sep. 1969); see also *ibid* **45**, 88 and 736, **46**, 858, **47**, 238.

§7.3 The conductimetric titration of a heavy-metal salt solution by a precipitating agent can be used in an investigation of the stoichiometry of the product; this may be unexpected, e.g. for $Cu^{2+} + OH^-$. See Project 9.13 and McLaughlan, I. T. and MacPherson, J., *Sch. Sci. Rev.* **56**, 546 (Mar. 1975).

§7.4 *Improvised calomel electrodes.* In Fig. 7.3(b) the glass tube is to enable a short piece of platinum to be used, and not to insulate the conductor from the solution (which is unnecessary, since no current will flow at the balance point). An inert wire could be used instead; but if a copper wire is to be used, it could enter the mercury from below, as in a design by Lee, J. H., *Sch. Sci. Rev.* **43**, 734.

§7.5 *Antimony electrode.* For details of construction and calibration of this cheap, robust (but rather temperamental) pH electrode, see Gourd, A. R., *Sch. Sci. Rev.* **55**, 768–9 (Jun. 1974), or *Nuffield Advanced Science: Chemistry Teachers' Guide 2*, 282–4.

§7.6 See Liberti, A. and Mascini, M., 'Study of equilibria in solution by means of anion selective membrane electrodes', *Sch. Sci. Rev.* **52**, 615–9 (Mar. 1971); also Williams, T. R. *et al.*, *J. Chem. Educ.* **47**, 464. For construction of a cell without liquid junction, using a K^+ electrode, see: Rock, P. A., *J. Chem. Educ.* **47**, 683–6 (1970).

§7.7 *Expt. 7–9. Simple polarograph.* Several capillaries should be made and tried: use 0.5 mm bore drawn out to 0.05 mm or less, cut off squarely. They are easily blocked, and are then difficult to clear (try conc. HNO_3). Pure distilled mercury must be used for the dropping electrode, but not necessarily for the anode pool. For further details see: Clarke, J., *Sch. Sci. Rev.* **43**, 410–5 (1962).

'Oxygen electrode'. The Beckman 'Fieldlab' oxygen analyser costs £150 plus. (Beckmann-RIIC Ltd., 4 Bedford Park, Croydon CR9 3LG will supply Bulletin GR-7143 and literature reprints on the applications of the instrument.) Cheaper 'oxygen probes' are available as part of modular environmental meters. Original reference: Mancy, K. H., Okun and Reilley, *J. Electroan. Chem.* **4**, 65–92 (1962).

Answers

1.5 1. (a) $3.77\ \Omega$; (b) $1.26 \times 10^{-2}\ \Omega\ cm^{-1}$; (c) $9.86 \times 10^{-5}\ \Omega\ cm$; (d) $1.014 \times 10^{4}\ \Omega^{-1}\ cm^{-1}$.

4. Pb at cathode in each case; at anode: (i), (ii) $O_2 + CO_2$; (iii) $Pb^{2+}(aq)$.

2.10 1. (a) $Cl_2 + 2e^- \rightarrow 2Cl^-$; $2I^- \rightarrow I_2 + 2e^-$.

(b) $Cl_2 + 2e^- \rightarrow 2Cl^-$; $3I^- \rightarrow I_3^- + 2e^-$.

(c) $Cr_2O_7^{2-} + 14H^- + 6e^- \rightarrow 2Cr^{3+} + 7H_2O$; $3Zn \rightarrow 3Zn^{2+} + 6e^-$.

(d) $Cu^{2+} + I^- + e^- \rightarrow CuI$; $I^- \rightarrow \frac{1}{2}I_2 + e^-$.

2. $96\ 500\ z$ C (mol reaction)$^{-1}$ where $z =$ (a) 2; (b) 2; (c) 6; (d) 1.

3. (a) $2.5\dfrac{t}{s} = \dfrac{2F}{63.5}$; $t = 1.23 \times 10^3$ s.

(b) If the secondary reaction is:

$(CH_3)_2CO + 3I_2 + 4OH^- \rightarrow CH_3CO_2^- + CHI_3 + 3H_2O + 3I^-$.

1 mol CHI_3 requires 3 mol I_2 from the anode reaction:

$6I^- \rightarrow 3I_2 + 6e^-$

$t = \dfrac{6 \times 96\ 500}{2.5 \times 393.7}\ s = 588\ s$

4. 0.01 mol H_2 and 0.005 mol O_2, which occupy $246\ cm^3$ and $123\ cm^3$ if dry. In the third cell, 0.020 mol H^+ produced, equivalent to $40.0\ cm^3$ of 0.50 M NaOH.

5. $RhO_y \rightarrow Rh^{2y+}$; $\dfrac{27 \times 60 \times 0.10}{96\ 500 \times 2y} = \dfrac{80 \times 10^{-3}}{186}$; $y \simeq 2$, i.e. RhO_2.

6. Reactions a, c and d could drive simple galvanic cells; b could not (but see §9.27).

7. (a) i $-$, ii $-$, iii $Q(NO_3)_2 + NO$ or NO_2; (b) i $-$, ii $Q + RSO_4$, iii $Q + RSO_4$ (and some H_2 unless $[Q^{2+}] \gg [H^+]$); (c) $\ominus\ P|P^{2+}(aq)|Q^{2+}(aq)|Q\ \oplus$.

3.12 2. (a) 1.27 cm^{-1}; (b) 0.00121 Ω^{-1} cm^{-1}; (c) 121 Ω^{-1} cm^2 mol^{-1}.

3. 20.0 mol m^{-3} KCl, 0.2768 Ω^{-1} m^{-1}; 0.555 kg m^{-3}; (a) 127 m^{-1}; (b) 0.121 Ω^{-1} m^{-1}; (c) 0.0121 Ω^{-1} m^2 mol^{-1}.

4. Amt. $\frac{1}{2}$BaSO$_4$ $= \dfrac{(4.63 - 1.21) \times 10^{-6}}{63.6 + 79.8}$ mol cm^{-3} $= 2.44 \times 10^{-5}$ mol dm$^{-3} \equiv 2.85$ mg dm^{-3}.

5. $\kappa \simeq 0.012\ 65$ Ω^{-1} m^{-1}; cell const. $= 20$ cm$/2^2\pi$ cm$^2 = 159$ m^{-1}; $I = 6.37$ mA.

6. Approx. $128, 91, 432, 395$ Ω^{-1} cm^2 mol^{-1}.

$c/$(mol dm^{-3})	Λ/Λ^0	K	
(a) 0.10 CH$_3$COOH	0.0127	1.85×10^{-5}	} mean 1.8×10^{-5}
0.001 CH$_3$COOH	0.124	1.75×10^{-5}	
(b) 0.5 CH$_3$CO$_2$Na	0.644	5.86×10^{-1}	equilibrium
0.05 CH$_3$CO$_2$Na	0.846	2.32×10^{-1}	law not
0.005 CH$_3$CO$_2$Na	0.943	0.78×10^{-1}	obeyed

7. (a) 1.038 mmol e$^-$ passed, 0.483 mmol Ag$^+$ migrated, $\therefore$ $t_+ = 0.466$.
(b) $t_- = 0.534$, $\therefore$ $\Lambda(\text{NO}_3^-) = 66$, $\Lambda(\text{Ag}^+) = 58$, $\Lambda(\text{Na}^+) = 48$, $\Lambda(\frac{1}{2}\text{Ba}^{2+}) = 60$ Ω^{-1} cm^2 mol^{-1}.

8. 13.5 cm^3 NaOH soln.; 0.0273 mol dm^{-3} HCl.

4.13 1. Pt$|$U^{3+}(aq), U^{4+}(aq)$\|$Zn^{2+}(aq)$|$Zn(s); $E_{\text{cell}} = -0.15$ V.
Pb, PbSO$_4$(s)$|$H$_2$SO$_4$(aq)$|$PbO$_2$(s), Pb–Sb; $E_{\text{cell}} = +2.0$ V.

2. (i) -0.337 V; (ii) $+0.18$ or 0.19 V; (iii) $+2.07$ V; (iv) $+0.89$ V.

3. (a) Br$_2$ + H$_2$S $\to$ S + 2HBr(aq); $z = 2$.
(b) H$_2$ + 2Ag$^+$(aq) $\to$ 2Ag + 2H$^+$(aq); $z = 2$.
(c) 3Ti + 3H$_2$O + 4In^{3+}(aq) $\to$ 3TiO^{2+}(aq) + 4In + 6H$^+$(aq); $z = 12$.
(d) Cu + Fe(CN)$_6^{3-}$(aq) + 2CN$^-$(aq) $\to$ Cu(CN)$_2^-$(aq) + Fe(CN)$_6^{4-}$(aq); $z = 1$.
(e) 4HN$_3$ + 2H$^+$(aq) + 3H$_2$O $\to$ NO$_3^-$(aq) + 3NH$_4^+$(aq) + 4N$_2$; $z = 8$.

4. (a) Sn$|$Sn^{2+}(aq)$\|$Pb^{2+}(aq)$|$Pb; $E_{\text{cell}}^\ominus = +0.0098$ V.
(b) Cu$|$Cu^{2+}(aq)$\|$NO$_3^-$(aq), H$^+$(aq)$|$NO(g), Pt; $E_{\text{cell}}^\ominus = +0.622$ V.
(c) el$_L$, O$_2$(g)$|$H$_2$O$_2$(aq)$\|$H$_2$O$_2$(aq), H$^+$(aq)$|$el$_R$; $E^\ominus = +1.23$ V if $z = 1$ (where el$_L$ is an inert electrode which catalyzes the oxidation of H$_2$O$_2$ to O$_2$, and el$_R$ preferentially catalyzes the reduction of H$_2$O$_2$).

5. (a) little change; (b) an increase, for given current, due to fall in over-potential and internal resistance.

204   *Answers*

6. Incorrect—see §§4.6, 4.7.

7. (a) Spontaneous; (b) Ag -ve; 47 mV; (c) (i) 10 kJ absorbed from surroundings; (ii) $w = 0.80$ kJ, $\Delta G = -7$ kJ; heat $q = \Delta H - w = +10 + 7 = 17$ kJ (absorbed).

5.10 1. (a) $Cu|Cu^{2+}(aq)\|Fe^{3+}(aq), Fe^{2+}(aq)|Pt$.

(b) (i) no change; (ii) increase; (iii) decrease; (iv) increase.

2. (a) $[Ag^+] = 1.7 \times 10^{-7}$ mol dm^{-3}; (b) $[Ag^+] = 2.7 \times 10^{-13}$ and $E_{cell} = +0.74$ V.

3. (i) $\ominus$ $Pt|Sn^{2+}(aq), Sn^{4+}(aq)\|Cu^{2+}(aq)|Cu$ $\oplus$; $E_{cell}^\ominus = +0.19$ V.
   (ii) $\ominus$ $Sn|Sn^{2+}(aq)\|Sn^{4+}(aq), Sn^{2+}(aq)|Pt$ $\oplus$; $E_{cell}^\ominus = +0.29$ V.

(b) $[Cu^{2+}] = [Sn^{2+}] = y; [Sn^{4+}] = (2-y); \dfrac{0.059}{2} \lg \dfrac{2-y}{y^2} = +0.19; y = 8.5 \times 10^{-4}$ mol dm^{-3}.

5. 8.0×10^3; 6.3×10^7; 1.2×10^{46}.

6. Ni deposits first, at -0.279 V; Co at -0.306 V, when $[Ni^{2+}] = 0.012$ M (hardly a sufficient degree of separation).

7. At 0.01 M, Ag would be deposited at $+0.681$ V, and Hg (from Hg^{2+}) at $+0.795$ V; but reduction to Hg_2^{2+} is preferred, and goes virtually to completion. Then Ag is deposited until $[Ag^+]$ falls to 0.0067 M when, at $+0.671$ V, Hg is deposited from the Hg_2^{2+}.

6.9 1.

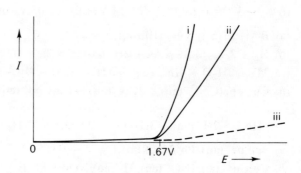

2. (i) zero; (ii) Cl_2, Br_2, I_2 zero; O_2 0.46 or 0.47 V.

5. (i) Mainly Cu with some H_2; (ii) mainly H_2; (iii) Cu + H_2; (iv) Cu only; (v) Zn; (vi) Zn + H_2; (vii) H_2.

6. $\dfrac{2.55 \text{ g} \times 2 \times 96\ 500 \text{ C mol}^{-1}}{2.5 \text{ A} \times 3600 \text{ s} \times 58.7 \text{ g mol}^{-1}} = 93.5\%$

7. $1.23/2.60 = 47.3\%$. $\eta_H = 0.69 + 0.12 \lg 0.02 = 0.49$ V; $\eta_0 = 1.05$ $+ 0.15 \lg 0.02 = 0.80$ V; $= 1.29$ V; max. efficiency $= 1.23/2.52 = 49\%$.

8. $a = -(\ln A)/\beta$, $b = (\ln 10)/\beta$.

9. When $[Br_2] = 0.01$, $E_{ox}(Br^-) = -1.03$; $\therefore \lg [I^-]^2 = \dfrac{2}{0.059}(1.03 - 0.54)$ $[I^-] = 5 \times 10^{-9}$ mol dm^{-3}.

10. Ag: $pH = \dfrac{0.43 - (0.70 - 0.47)}{0.059} = 3.4$;

$\qquad$ Cd: $pH = \dfrac{1.63 - (1.98 - 0.47)}{0.059} = 2.0$

11. When $Br_2 = 10^{-18}$ M, $E_{ox}(Br^-) = -1.09 + 0.03 \lg 18 = -0.55$ V.

12. (i) $Na^+(aq, 6 \text{ M}) + e^- \to Na(s)$; $E_{red} = -2.71 + 0.059 \lg 6 = -2.66$ V (at 298 K).

(ii) $2.66 - 1.83 = 0.83$ V $= -0.059 \lg a_{Na}$; $a_{Na} = 10^{-14}$.

But 0.2 mass % Na corresponds to mole fraction 0.0175. Therefore the amalgam is not a simple solution, but contains a *compound* of sodium and mercury.

(iii) At pH 13: $H_2O + e^- \to OH^- + \frac{1}{2}H_2$; $E_{red} = -0.77$ V (see Fig. 5.3). $\therefore$ Overpotential $= 1.83 - 0.77 = 1.06$ V (note: concentration polarization is zero).

(iv) H_2 current $= 0.003 \times$ total current; $\therefore$ c.d. for H_2 process $= 0.003 \times 0.3 = 0.001$ A cm^{-2}. From Table 6.1, η at 10^{-3} A cm^{-2} for H_2 from NaOH (aq) at Hg $= 1.15$ V. The value is lower at $T > 298$ K, as would be expected.

13. (i) $RCH=CH_2 + 2H_2O \to RCH(OH)CH_2OH + 2H^+ + 2e^-$.

(ii) $RCH=CH_2 + 4H^+ + 4e^- \to RCH_2CH_3$.

(iii) $C_{10}H_8 + 7H_2O \to C_6H_4C_2O_3 + 2CO_2 + 18H^+ + 18e^-$.

(iv) $C_6H_5CH_3 + 7OH^- \to C_6H_5CO_2^- + 5H_2O + 6e^-$

(v) $CH_2O + 4OH^- \to CO_2 + 3H_2O + 4e^-$.

(vi) $CH_3CH_2OH \to CH_3CHO + 2H^+ + 2e^-$.

(vii) $=C(OH).C(OH)= \to 2 =CO + 2H^+ + 2e^-$.

14. Cathodic reduction of ketones: probable first step $R_2CO + e^- \to R_2\dot{C}O^-$. If these radical-ions are in sufficient concentration (high current density) they dimerize thus: $2R_2\dot{C}O^- \to R_2C\!-\!O^- \qquad R_2COH$
$\qquad\qquad\qquad\qquad\qquad\qquad | \quad \xrightarrow{2H^+} \quad |$
$\qquad\qquad\qquad\qquad\qquad R_2C\!-\!O^- \qquad R_2COH$

If the radical-ions are in low concentration (low current density) they are further reduced: $R_2\dot{C}O^- + 2H^+ + e^- \to R_2CHOH$

7.9   1. Volume of Ni $= \dfrac{4.0 \times 10^{-3} \text{ mol} \times 58.7 \text{ g mol}^{-1}}{8.9 \text{ g cm}^{-3}} = 26.4 \times 10^{-3} \text{ cm}^{-3}$;

∴ thickness $= 0.132$ mm.

2. $4.90 \ (\text{cm}^3 \ O_2) \ (\text{dm}^3 \ \text{water})^{-1} \ \text{min}^{-1}$.

3. 1–d, 2–c, 3–a, 4–b, 5–e.

4. a.

5. $1.31 \times 10^{-8} \text{ mol dm}^{-3}$.

6. $1.8 \times 10^{-8} \text{ mol dm}^{-3}$.

9. 0.20 M H_3PO_4. Along line A the reaction is: $H_3PO_4 + OH^- \rightleftharpoons H_2PO_4^-$ $+ H_2O$, and the pH is controlled by the buffer action of this reaction. At B the reaction is complete, and the second reaction commences, and continues along C: $H_2PO_4^- + OH^- \rightleftharpoons HPO_4^{2-} + H_2O$. At D this is complete, and along E the reaction is: $HPO_4^{2-} + OH^- \rightleftharpoons PO_4^{3-} + H_2O$. The final end-point F is very indistinct.

(ii) The reverse reactions show a curve roughly the inverse of the one given, but the points of inflexion are not equally spaced, being at 6.7, 10 and 20 cm^3 H_3PO_4.

10. (4).

11. (c) the cathode; and (d) the anode.

12. $1.27 \times 10^{-3} \%$ or 12.7 p.p.m.

Bibliography

Standard reference works, suggestions for further reading, and source material. A bibliography for Chapter 8 appears at the end of that chapter. References to the science education journals are given in Appendix II.

General

Bockris, J. O'M. (ed.). *Electrochemistry of a Cleaner Environment.* Plenum, 1972.

Bockris, J. O'M., Bonciocat, N. and Gutmann, F. *An Introduction to Electrochemical Science.* Wykeham, 1974.

Bockris, J. O'M. and Drazic, D. *Electrochemical Science.* Taylor and Francis, 1972.

MacInnes, D. A. *The Principles of Electrochemistry.* Dover Books, 1961.

Milazzo, G. *Electrochemistry.* Elsevier, 1963.

Potter, E. C. *Electrochemistry.* Cleaver-Hume, 1956.

Robinson, R. A. and Stokes, R. H. *Electrolyte Solutions.* Butterworths, 1970.

Special topics

Allen, M. J. *Organic Electrode Processes.* Chapman and Hall, 1958.

Bates, R. G. *Determination of pH.* Interscience, 1973.

Davies, C. W. *Principles of Electrolysis.* R.I.C., 1960.

Hladik, J. (ed.). *The Physics of Electrolytes* (2 vols). Academic Press, 1972. (For solid-state electrolytes.)

Janz, G. J. and Ives, D. J. G. *Reference Electrodes.* Academic Press, 1961.

Latimer, W. M. *Oxidation Potentials.* Prentice Hall, 1952.

Palmer, W. G. *Experimental Inorganic Chemistry.* Cambridge University Press, 1954.

Sharpe, A. G. *Principles of Oxidation and Reduction.* R.I.C., 1960.

Vinal, G. W. *Primary Batteries. Storage Batteries.* Chapman and Hall, 1951, 1955.

Historical

Alembic Club Reprints (published by E. and S. Livingstone): Davy, *Decomposition of the Fixed Alkalis*; Kolbe, *Electrolysis of Organic Compounds*, and Arrhenius.

Glasstone, S. *The Electrochemistry of Solutions.* Methuen, 1930 (for references to early research).

Faraday, M. *Experimental Researches in Electricity.* Complete in 2 vols, Dover, 1966. Everyman edn. (abridged), Dent, 1914, reprinted 1951.

Williams, L. P. *Michael Faraday.* Chapman and Hall, 1965.

Index